Analysis of Variance *William C. Guenther*

Professor of Statistics, University of Wyoming

Prentice-Hall, Inc., Englewood Cliffs, N. J.

To Norma, Eda, Clark, and Paul
William C. Guenther   ANALYSIS OF VARIANCE

PRENTICE-HALL INTERNATIONAL, INC., *London*
PRENTICE-HALL OF AUSTRALIA, PTY., LTD., *Sydney*
PRENTICE-HALL OF CANADA, LTD., *Toronto*
PRENTICE-HALL FRANCE, S.A.R.L., *Paris*
PRENTICE-HALL OF INDIA PRIVATE LIMITED, *New Delhi*
PRENTICE-HALL OF JAPAN, INC., *Tokyo*
PRENTICE-HALL DE MEXICO, S.A., *Mexico City*

© 1964 by PRENTICE-HALL, INC., Englewood Cliffs, N.J.

Library of Congress Catalog Card No. 64-10664
Printed in the United States of America
C

Preface

The material in this book was developed from a set of class notes prepared for an elementary course in analysis of variance. It was written primarily for students who are not well prepared in either statistics or mathematics. An attempt has been made to present as many necessary concepts as possible without resorting to the use of advanced mathematics.

Although some of the formulas may appear to be quite formidable, the mathematics needed does not involve anything beyond that found in a modest college algebra course. Perseverance and a mature attitude are apt to be greater assets than a large collection of sophisticated mathematical techniques. Minimum prerequisites for the course should probably be (a) one semester of college mathematics and (b) a reasonably good one-semester (pre-calculus) statistics course covering statistical inference.

Since some experience with statistical inference is assumed, Chapter 1 is intended to be mainly a review. Consequently, the treatment of many of the topics included there is fairly brief. The discussion of the various statistical tests gradually leads to some simple analysis of variance situations.

Numerical examples are frequent in Chapter 2. Since many of the formulas and techniques presented there require minor modifications in order to fit the situations described in later chapters, the number of numerical illustrations decreases as one proceeds through the book.

Needless to say, a desk calculator is indispensable to solve the numerical problems. These machines are well adapted to do the many arithmetic operations that are required in each analysis.

Although no attempt has been made to produce an exhaustive bibliography of the field, references that students may find helpful are listed at the end of the chapters.

I am indebted to Sir Ronald A. Fisher, F.R.S., Cambridge, and to Dr. Frank Yates, F.R.S., Rothamsted, also to Messrs. Oliver & Boyd Ltd., Edinburgh, for permission to reprint Table No. III from their book *Statistical Tables for Biological, Agricultural and Medical Research*.

William C. Guenther

Contents

1

REVIEW OF STATISTICAL INFERENCE

2

THE ONE-WAY CLASSIFICATION

v

3

RANDOMIZED BLOCKS

4

LATIN SQUARES

5

FACTORIAL EXPERIMENTS

6

ANALYSIS OF COVARIANCE

APPENDIX

1

Review of Statistical Inference

1-1 INTRODUCTION

That portion of statistics concerned with drawing conclusions and making decisions is sometimes called statistical inference. Although most of the readers already have some knowledge of this subject, a brief review may be helpful. No attempt will be made to give an extensive coverage. However, important ideas needed to understand the language of analysis of variance will be discussed in detail.

1-2 AN EXAMPLE

Many ideas and terms that we shall encounter arise naturally in the discussion of an example. Suppose that we suspect that a coin, when properly tossed, has the same chance of showing a head as a tail. We wish to "prove" this so we toss the coin 100 times and observe 47 heads. Of course, this proves nothing, but suppose we had agreed in advance that if less than 40 or more than 60 heads appeared, we would accept this as evidence that our assumption was incorrect.

Let us consider the possible outcomes if we were to make such a decision rule. Suppose first that our hypothesis about the coin is correct. Assuming that the binomial distribution with $p = 1/2$ is appropriate for computing the probabilities associated with the possible outcomes, we find in tables of the binomial distribution that

$$\text{Pr (number of heads less than 40)}$$
$$+ \text{Pr (number of heads greater than 60)} = .035.$$

The correctness of the assumption or the use of the table need not concern us here. Of importance are the consequences of using the agreed-upon decision rule. If this experiment were repeated many times, then about 35 out of every 1000 such experiments would lead to rejection of the hypothesis even though it were true. We would err if we did so, since we would be rejecting a hypothesis that is true. This kind of mistake is called a Type I error. The probability of committing a Type I error is called the level of significance.

It may be that our method of throwing is such that only .45 of the time a head will occur. By using binomial tables with $p = .45$, we find that

$$\text{Pr (number of heads between 40 and 60 inclusive)} = .865.$$

This means the probability is .865 that the agreed-upon decision rule will lead us to conclude our hypothesis about the coin is correct when actually the probability of a head appearing on each throw is .45. In this situation another kind of mistake is made; that is, the hypothesis is accepted when it is not true. This is called a Type II error.

The various possibilities are summarized in Table 1.1.

Table 1.1 DECISION.

	Accept	Reject
Hypothesis true	Correct decision	Type I error
Hypothesis false	Type II error	Correct decision

Naturally, we do not want to make either kind of error. Unfortunately, in most practical situations, the possibility of doing so cannot be avoided. Usually the size of the Type I error is chosen by the experimenter, quite often as .05 or .01, and he then seeks to minimize the Type II error. Increasing the sample size is an effective device for reducing the Type II error. This is in accord with one's intuition since it is reasonable to conclude that better decisions can be made if more information is available.

1-3 SOME DEFINITIONS

Before proceeding further, some important terms will be defined and discussed. Most of these are basic to the vocabulary of a statistician.

population   (a) A set or collection of observations is called a population. For example, the ages of all people living within a given city constitute a population. With time, patience, and cooperation, we could eventually write down all these ages. When this is possible, the term finite is used to characterize the population. In many situations, particularly those encountered in analysis of variance, the set of observations is infinite. In the coin-tossing experiment we would probably regard the population as being the infinite set of outcomes from all conceivable tosses made with the coin in its present condition. Obviously, it is physically impossible to collect this set of observations.

sample   (b) A sample is a subset or a part of a population. The outcomes obtained from 100 tosses of a coin constitute a sample from the population of all possible outcomes.

parameter   (c) A parameter is a quantity that could be computed from a population if the entire population were available. Such quantities as the mean μ and the standard deviation σ are parameters. In the coin example, p could be computed if the results of every possible toss were available. Thus μ, σ, and p are parameters. As one might guess, it is often impossible to compute a parameter.

statistic   (d) A statistic is a quantity computed from a sample. Examples are $\bar{x}$, the sample mean, and s, the sample standard deviation. Likewise $\sqrt{n}\,(\bar{x}-\mu)/\sigma$ is a statistic if μ and σ are known. Since it is often impossible to obtain the value of parameter, statistics are used as substitutes; that is, not knowing μ, we often use $\bar{x}$ in its place.

model   (e) When used in a statistical sense, the term model usually refers to a mathematical statement used in studying the results of an experiment or predicting the behavior of future repetitions of the experiment. In Section 1-2 the model, which may be expressed mathematically as

$$f(x) = \binom{100}{x} p^x (1-p)^{100-x}, \qquad x = 0,\ 1,\ 2,\ \ldots,\ 100,$$

is often called the binomial distribution. In choosing a model to fit a particular situation, the statistician may make use of the conditions under which the experiment is performed, experience, or intelligent guessing. For example, the binomial is appropriate if an experiment is repeated a fixed number of times under the conditions that (i) there are only two categories, say success and failure, (ii) the probability of a success remains constant from experiment to experiment, and (iii) each experiment is independent of all the others. In the coin-tossing example, these conditions are reasonably satisfied. Often one obtains good results by using a model even though all the conditions used in its derivation are not exactly satisfied.

hypothesis (f) The Merriam-Webster Dictionary defines hypothesis as "a tentative theory or supposition provisionally adapted to explain certain facts and to guide in the investigation of others." When used in a statistical sense, a hypothesis is an assumption about the form of a population or its parameters. In the example of Section 1-2, the hypothesis is "the coin is unbiased" or, equivalently, $p = 1/2$. In the literature H_0 is used as the abbreviation for hypothesis. Frequently used is the term "null hypothesis," which means literally a hypothesis of no differences.

null hypothesis (g) If the experimental evidence at hand indicates that the null hypothesis is not true, then the conclusion we accept may be called the alternate hypothesis. For example, the appearance of 72 heads in the coin example is strong support for the belief that $p \neq 1/2$. Using H_1 to stand for alternate hypothesis, we wish to choose between

$$H_0: p = 1/2$$

and

$$H_1: p \neq 1/2 .$$

It is not always easy to select H_0 and H_1 for a particular situation, but they should both be specified before the experiment is conducted.

test (h) A test is a rule or procedure used for deciding whether to accept or reject the hypothesis. The test of Section 1-2 is as follows: reject if the number of heads is less than 40 or more than 60. Much of the literature of mathematical statistics is devoted to obtaining best tests for comparing particular H_0's against particular H_1's, the selection usually being made on the basis of minimum Type II error. We shall consider a number of examples, and choose in each situation tests regarded as best.

critical region (i) The critical region is the set of outcomes for the experiment which leads to the rejection of the hypothesis. In the coin example 0, 1, 2, ..., 39, 61, 62, ..., 100 heads comprise the critical region.

Type I error (j) A Type I error is committed when a true hypothesis is rejected.

Type II error (k) When a false hypothesis is accepted, a Type II error is made.

level of significance (l) The probability of committing a Type I error is called the level of significance. This probability will be designated by the Greek letter α. As we have previously observed, α is chosen in advance with .05 and .01 being the most common choices.

power of test (m) The probability of rejecting the hypothesis is called the power of the test. If we let β be the probability of committing a Type II error, then the power is $1 - \beta$. In the coin example, we observed that for the chosen test $\alpha = .035$ and, if $p = .45$, the power is .135. If the power were computed for every p between 0 and 1 and the results plotted on a graph, then we would obtain a picture like Figure 1.1. Note that if H_0 is true, then the power is equal to α.

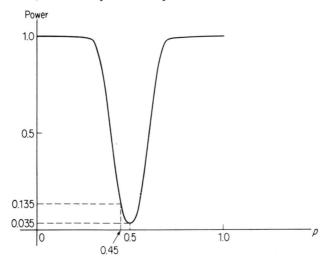

Fig. 1.1 Power curve for H_0: $p = .5$, H_1: $p \neq .5$, $n = 100$.

An ideal power curve would have an ordinate 1 for all values of the parameter except those corresponding to H_0. Naturally, it is impossible to achieve such a result in practice. Usually the power can be increased to any desired level by making samples sufficiently large. Often an experimenter desires a specified value of power for some value of the parameter and must find the sample size that achieves this result. We will illustrate this by example in a later section.

The importance of the power of the test cannot be over-emphasized. If false hypotheses are rejected with low probability, the test may be worth very little. Usually power calculations are quite difficult and are avoided in elementary courses. For most of the tests to be reviewed in this chapter, we will not make an attempt to evaluate power. However, when we get to our main area of interest, analysis of variance, the topic will be pursued further.

random sample (n) If the population is finite, then a sample chosen in a manner which gives every sample of the same size an equal chance of being selected is called a random sample. Most introductory texts in statistics explain how a table of random numbers can be used to draw a random sample from a finite population. When dealing with infinite populations, the concept of a random sample is more difficult. In this case a sample is random if each observation in the sample (a) comes from the same population and (b) is drawn independently of all the other observations. The term "independently" implies that the result obtained from any one drawing in no way influences the result obtained from any of the other drawings. In the coin-tossing experiment, both (a) and (b) seem to be realistic assumptions. Here, as with other infinite populations, we cannot prove that these assumptions are true, but we can usually perform the experiment in a manner which makes them seem reasonable.

unbiased estimate (o) Another term we shall use in later chapters is unbiased estimate. We have already observed that statistics can be used to estimate parameters. One desirable characteristic of a statistic used for this purpose is unbiasedness. If the average value of a statistic is equal to a parameter, then the statistic is said to be an unbiased estimate of the parameter. The sample mean $\bar{x}$ and the sample variance

$$s^2 = \sum_{i=1}^{n} (x_i - \bar{x})^2 / (n-1)$$

are unbiased estimates of the population mean μ and population variance σ^2. In other words, if we were to write down every possible sample of size n which could be selected from a population, compute $\bar{x}$ and s^2 for each sample, and then find the average of the $\bar{x}$'s and s^2's, we would get μ and σ^2, respectively. Obviously, we cannot enumerate every sample when the population is infinite, but the remarks concerning the unbiasedness of $\bar{x}$ and s^2 are still true.

Other definitions of terms and symbols will be made as they are needed. At this point a further example may be helpful.

1-4 ANOTHER EXAMPLE

Suppose that it is hypothesized that in a certain city the average height for adult males is 68 inches. To check the supposition, we select a random sample of 100 men and find that the sample mean $\bar{x} = 68.9$ inches. We agree in advance to accept the hypothesis if $\bar{x}$ is close to 68; otherwise, we will reject it. To simplify the situation, assume that the population standard deviation σ is known and is equal to 2.5 inches.

First, we must decide what we mean by " close." Suppose we clarify the issue by selecting the level of significance to be $\alpha = .05$. Now we are able to determine the critical region. To do this we recall some facts from elementary statistics. These are:

(a) The mean of the population of all possible sample means for samples of size 100 is the same as the mean of the original population. In statistical symbols $\mu_{\bar{x}} = \mu_x$.

(b) The standard deviation of the population of sample means is the standard deviation of the original population divided by the square root of the sample size. In symbols

$$\sigma_{\bar{x}} = \frac{\sigma_x}{\sqrt{n}} = \frac{2.5}{\sqrt{100}} = .25.$$

(c) The distribution of sample means is approximately normal for samples coming from most real-life populations. If the original population is normal, then the distribution of sample means is exactly normal.

If we reject the hypothesis when

$$\bar{x} > 68 + 1.96\sigma_{\bar{x}} = 68.49 \text{ or } \bar{x} < 68 - 1.96\sigma_{\bar{x}} = 67.51, \quad (1.1)$$

then the desired level of significance is achieved. These values of $\bar{x}$ constitute the critical region. Figure 1.2 illustrates these facts. Since $\bar{x} = 68.9$ falls within the critical region, we would conclude that the hypothesis is false.

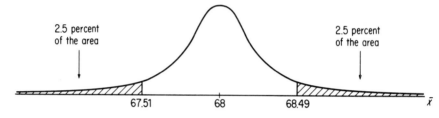

Fig. 1.2 Distribution of sample means, $\mu=68$, $\sigma x=2.5$, $n=100$, showing critical region.

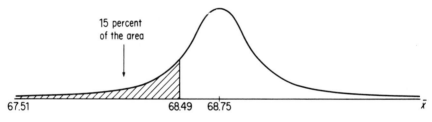

Fig. 1.3 Distribution of sample means, $\mu=68.75$, $\sigma x=2.5$, $n=100$, showing probability of Type II error.

Next we will suppose that $\mu = 68.75$, not 68, and compute the Type II error. It is necessary to find the area of the shaded region in Figure 1.3. We have

$$\beta = \Pr(67.51 < \bar{x} < 68.49)$$

$$= \Pr\left(\frac{67.51 - 68.75}{.25} < \frac{\bar{x} - 68.75}{.25} < \frac{68.49 - 68.75}{.25}\right)$$

$$= \Pr(-4.96 < Z < -1.04) = .15.$$

Here Z is the standardized normal variable. Appendix Table 1 may be used to evaluate probabilities associated with Z.

Similarly, if any other value of μ is selected, the corresponding β

(and hence power) can be computed. If all these points are plotted to form one curve, then the result is Figure 1.4. This is the power curve we get when we use the test specified by Equation (1.1) to choose between

$$H_0: \quad \mu = 68$$

and

$$H_1: \quad \mu \neq 68$$

with $\alpha = .05$ and $n = 100$.

Several characteristics of power curves are worth noting. First, the curves in Figures 1.1 and 1.4 are U-shaped. Some tests such as the ones to be encountered in analysis of variance yield S-shaped power curves. Second, if n is increased while α is left unchanged, then both the curves under discussion are higher at every point that belongs to H_1.

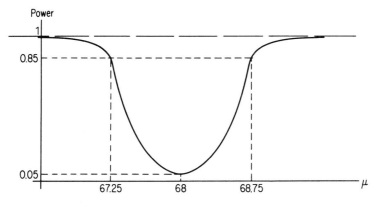

Fig. 1.4 Power curve for H_0: $\mu = 68$, H_1: $\mu \neq 68$, with $\alpha = .05$, $\sigma_{\bar{x}} = 2.5$, $n = 100$.

EXERCISE

1.1 Compute the power of the test whose critical region is given by Equation (1.1) for $\mu = 67.00$, 67.25, 67.50, 67.75, 68.00, 68.25, 68.50, 68.75, 69.00, and draw a smooth curve through the points obtained. Repeat the calculations if $n = 50$ instead of 100 and draw the curve on the same set of axes so that the two may be compared. Observe that changing n gives a different critical region for $\bar{x}$.

1-5 AN OUTLINE

Many elementary texts advocate that the study should follow an outline when testing a statistical hypothesis. This is good procedure and is strongly recommended. Such an outline should include the following steps:

---

1. State the hypothesis and its alternate. For the preceding example, we would write

$$H_0: \mu = 68$$
$$H_1: \mu \neq 68.$$

2. Choose a value of α. $\alpha = .05$

3. List the assumptions. (i) Random sampling and (ii) known standard deviation were assumed.

4. Select a statistic whose behavior is known if the assumptions are satisfied. Our choice was $\bar{x}$, or equivalently $\sqrt{n}\,(\bar{x}-\mu)/\sigma$, which is known to have a normal distribution. Sometimes several statistics can be used to test the same hypothesis. Usually, it is best to select the one with the greatest power. Since mathematical statisticians have devoted a great deal of effort in this direction, it is advantageous to make use of their results. Most elementary textbooks list the best tests to use in standard situations. Know the assumptions under which the statistic is derived and inquire into the reasonableness of these assumptions. In some cases it may prove helpful to know the consequences of using the statistic when one or more assumptions are violated.

   It is apparent that Steps 3 and 4 are accomplished simultaneously; that is, in listing the assumptions we have a statistic in mind and in choosing the statistic we need to know the conditions under which it is derived.

5. Find the critical region. For the standard situations it is usually a straightforward problem to find this region. Typically, it is known immediately upon entry into the proper table. In the previous example $Z = \sqrt{n}(\bar{x}-\mu)/\sigma$ lies in the region if $Z > 1.96$ or $Z < -1.96$. This type of critical region is called "two-sided"; many times a "one-sided" region is appropriate.

6. Compute the statistic. In the example of Section 1-4, $\bar{x} = 68.9$, $n = 100$, $\sigma_x = 2.5$, $\mu = 68$ if H_0 is true. Thus $Z = 10(68.9 - 68)/2.5 = 3.6$.

7. Draw conclusions. If the statistic falls within the critical region, reject the hypothesis. Otherwise accept it.

1-6 A ONE-SIDED CASE

Often we will want to reject a hypothesis only in one direction (that is, if the statistic is large or small, but not both). For example, if we were considering the adoption of a new type fertilizer, it may be that we would want to discard the old brand only if significantly higher results were obtained from using the new. Suppose that the mean yield using the old brand is $\mu = \mu_0 = 50$ bushels per acre. If the test were to be conducted using mean yields, then the situation for the new fertilizer could be summarized as

$$H_0 : \mu \leqq 50$$
$$H_1 : \mu > 50.$$

In this case, only large values of $\bar{x}$ contradict H_0 and lead to rejection. Thus only large values of $\bar{x}$ supply justification for switching brands.

Let us pursue the example further following the steps of the proposed outline.

---

1. $H_0 : \mu \leqq 50$
   $H_1 : \mu > 50.$
2. Choose $\alpha = .05$.
3. Assume (i) a random sample of yields using a new fertilizer is available, (ii) the standard deviation of yields using the new fertilizer is the same as that obtained using the old, which is known to be 8 bushels per acre, and (iii) the distribution of yields is normal.
4. The standard statistic to use in this situation is

$$Z = \sqrt{n}(\bar{x} - \mu)/\sigma,$$

   which is known to have a normal distribution with mean zero and unit variance.
5. Since only large values of $\bar{x}$, and hence large Z, contradict this hypothesis, we seek a value of Z, say Z_0 such that $\Pr (Z > Z_0) = .05$. From the normal table we find $Z_0 = 1.645$. Consequently, if Z turns out to be greater than 1.645, we reject the hypothesis.
6. Suppose that for $n = 25$ acres the average yield using the

new fertilizer is $\bar{x} = 54$. Then

$$Z = \frac{5(54-50)}{8} = 2.5.$$

7. Since Z falls in the critical region, H_0 is rejected. Thus we conclude that the new fertilizer is better.

Power calculations for this test are relatively simple. The critical region $Z > 1.645$ is the same as $5(\bar{x}-50)/8 > 1.645$ and $\bar{x} > 50 + 8(1.645)/5$. To get points on the power curve we need to evaluate

$$\text{Pr}\,[\bar{x} > 50 + 8(1.645)/5]$$

for different values of μ. If $\bar{x}$ is normally distributed with mean μ and standard deviation 8, then $5(\bar{x}-\mu)/8$ is normally distributed with mean zero and unit standard deviation. Thus we have

$$\begin{aligned}
\text{Power} &= \text{Pr}\left[\bar{x} > 50 + \frac{8(1.645)}{5}\right] \\
&= \text{Pr}\left[\bar{x} - \mu > 50 - \mu + \frac{8(1.645)}{5}\right] \\
&= \text{Pr}\left[\frac{5(\bar{x}-\mu)}{8} > \frac{5(50-\mu)}{8} + 1.645\right] \\
&= \text{Pr}\left[Z > \frac{5(50-\mu)}{8} + 1.645\right].
\end{aligned} \qquad (1.2)$$

Consider any other value of μ, say $\mu = 51$. We get

$$\text{Pr}\left[Z > \frac{5(50-51)}{8} + 1.645\right] = \text{Pr}\,[Z > 1.020] = .154.$$

Observe that we have choosen $\mu = 50$ from the range of values $\mu \leqq 50$. Any other choice of μ in this one-sided interval makes Z larger and increases the probability of rejection. If H_0 is rejected using $\mu = 50$ in Z, then it is rejected using any $\mu \leqq 50$.

If $\mu = 50$, then Equation (1.2) reduces to $\text{Pr}\,[Z > 1.645] = .05$. If $\mu < 50$, then (1.2) yields a value less than .05. [†]

EXERCISE

1.2 Evaluate the power from Equation (1.2) for $\mu = 49$, 50, 51, 52, 53, 54 and draw the curve. Repeat the calculations for $n = 50$, making the appropriate changes. Draw the curve on the same set of axes so that the two may be compared.

---

† According to the previous definition, the meaning of significance level is ambiguous. If we are going to permit the parameter to assume more than one value under H_0, the type I error should be regarded as the maximum value of the power when H_0 is true.

1·7 SELECTING THE HYPOTHESIS AND THE ALTERNATE

In testing hypotheses we are sometimes confronted with a difficult choice in selecting the hypothesis and the alternate. A few general suggestions may be helpful.

1. The choice should be made before the experiment is conducted. A hypothesis that is suggested by the data is apt to be "proven" when actually the data warrants no such conclusion.

2. When a single parameter θ is involved and the situation is of the type

$$H_0: \quad \theta = \theta_0$$
$$H_1: \quad \theta \neq \theta_0,$$

   usually a two-tailed critical region is appropriate.

3. When only large or only small (but not both) values of the parameter are unsatisfactory, then either

   $$H_0: \quad \theta \leqq \theta_0 \qquad \text{or} \qquad H_0: \quad \theta \geqq \theta_0$$
   $$H_1: \quad \theta > \theta_0 \qquad\qquad\qquad H_1: \quad \theta < \theta_0$$

   may be used in the analysis. Usually a one-tailed critical region is indicated with large values of the statistic being critical in the first case, small values in the second case.

4. A desirable procedure, when we can afford to use it, consists of setting up as the hypothesis to be tested the conclusion which we hope the data will disprove. When H_0 is rejected with assurance, we can feel fairly certain that H_1 is true. On the other hand, when H_0 is accepted, we may not have any great degree of confidence in its truth. All we may be willing to admit is that the data indicates H_0 is not too unreasonable.

5. In considering the adoption of a new process or a new method that involves time or expense, we usually prefer to have the product proven. For example, when buying a new car, we require that the salesman prove the new car is better rather than no worse than our old one. This leads to a choice of the type

   $$H_0: \quad \mu \leqq \mu_0 \quad \text{(the new car is no better)}$$
   $$H_1: \quad \mu > \mu_0 \quad \text{(the new car is better)}.$$

We will not buy unless H_0 is disproved with a high degree of confidence.

6. If a new product is cheaper than the one we are are now using, then perhaps we may prefer to reverse our position and use the new product unless it is proven that it is terrible. This leads to a choice of the type

$$H_0: \quad \mu \geq \mu_0 \quad \text{(the new is at least as good as the old)}$$
$$H_1: \quad \mu < \mu_0 \quad \text{(the new is worse than the old)}.$$

Unless H_0 is disproved with a high degree of confidence, we will switch to the new product.

7. There is no general formula that works for all cases. Blindly following rules is no substitute for reasoning.

This section may be reread with profit when some of the exercises appearing later in the chapter are encountered.

1-8 SOME NOTATION

Since we will be using Z, t, X^2, and F, and tables of these variables, it seems desirable to establish some notation.

As we have done previously, we will denote the standard normal variable by Z. Then Z_p designates a particular value of Z such that $\Pr[Z < Z_p] = p$. Due to the symmetry of the normal distribution, we also have $\quad \Pr[Z > Z_{1-p}] = p.$

We will use t_ν and X_ν^2 to designate t and chi-square variables with ν degrees of freedom. The quantities $t_{p;\,\nu}$ and $X_{p;\,\nu}^2$ are defined by

$$\Pr[t_\nu < t_{p;\,\nu}] = p$$

and

$$\Pr[X_\nu^2 < X_{p;\,\nu}^2] = p \ .$$

Due to the symmetry of the t-distribution,

$$\Pr[t_\nu > t_{1-p;\,\nu}] = p \ .$$

Since F has two parameters, two subscripts will be necessary. Thus $F_{\nu_1,\,\nu_2}$ denotes an F variable with ν_1, and ν_2 degrees of freedom. Also, $F_{p;\,\nu_1,\,\nu_2}$ is a particular value of F such that

$$\Pr[F_{\nu 1,\,\nu 2} < F_{p;\,\nu 1,\,\nu 2}] = p.$$

1-9 TESTS INVOLVING ONE MEAN

For this type of problem, the situation regarding the hypothesis and the alternate can usually be written in one of three ways:

(1) $H_0 : \mu = \mu_0$ (2) $H_0 : \mu \geq \mu_0$ (3) $H_0 : \mu \leq \mu_0$

     $H_1 : \mu \neq \mu_0$ $H_1 : \mu < \mu_0$ $H_1 : \mu > \mu_0$.

If we assume that (a) the sample is randomly selected, (b) the observations are drawn from a normal distribution, and (c) the standard deviation σ is known, then the best statistic to use is

$$Z = \frac{\sqrt{n}(\bar{x} - \mu_0)}{\sigma} . \tag{1.3}$$

The variable Z is normally distributed with mean zero and unit standard deviation. In the more typical situation, we can assume (a) and (b), but not (c). Then the best statistic to use is

$$t_{n-1} = \frac{\sqrt{n}(\bar{x} - \mu_0)}{s} \tag{1.4}$$

which has a t distribution with $n-1$ degrees of freedom. Here

$$s^2 = \frac{\sum\limits_{i=1}^{n}(x_i - \bar{x})^2}{n-1}$$

with $x_1, x_2, \ldots, x_n$ denoting the sample values.

In situation (1) both large and small values of $\bar{x}$ refute the hypothesis. Both Z and t_{n-1} are large when $\bar{x}$ is large and small when $\bar{x}$ is small. Thus we seek a value from the tables such that

$$\Pr[Z < Z_{\alpha/2}] = \alpha/2 \quad \text{or} \quad \Pr[t_{n-1} < t_{\alpha/2;\, n-1}] = \alpha/2 .$$

Due to the symmetry of both the Z and t distributions, the critical regions are

$$Z < Z_{\alpha/2}, \; Z > -Z_{\alpha/2}$$

and

$$t_{n-1} < t_{\alpha/2;\, n-1}, \; t_{n-1} > -t_{\alpha/2;\, n-1} .$$

In situation (2) only small values of $\bar{x}$, and hence small values of Z and t_{n-1}, contradict H_0. Now we need Z_α and $t_{\alpha;\, n-1}$ and the critical regions are $Z < Z_\alpha$ and $t_{n-1} < i_{\alpha;\, n-1}$, respectively. Finally for (3), only large values of Z and t_{n-1} lead to rejection. Thus the critical regions are $Z > Z_{1-\alpha}$ and $t_{n-1} > t_{1-\alpha;\, n-1}$, respectively.

Assumption (a) is much more critical than (b). Experimental evidence seems to indicate that mild departures from normality do not seriously affect these tests. Usually it increases the Type I error to some figure slightly above α. If n is large, then assumption (b) is unnecessary.

EXERCISES

1.3 Incoming freshman are given entrance examinations in a number of fields including English. Over a period of years it has been found that the average score in the English examination is 67. An instructor in English I looks up the grades for his class of 25 and finds that they average 70 with $s = 7.5$. He then claims his class is better than average. Is he justified?

1.4 Suppose that you are hopelessly enslaved by the cigarette manufacturers. Even though you are aware of the fact that you may contract lung cancer, it is impossible for you to quit. Suppose it has definitely been established by scientists that if cigarettes average 30 milligrams or more of nicotine, lung cancer is certain to develop in the user. You are willing to take your chances if the average is less than 30 milligrams, so you test 100 brand A cigarettes and find $\bar{x} = 26$, $s = 8$. What decision should you make concerning brand A? Which type of error would you rather make?

1.5 A fisherman decides that he needs a line that will test more than 10 pounds if he is to catch the size fish he desires. He tests 100 pieces of brand M line and finds $\bar{x} = 10.4$ pounds with $s = .8$ pounds. What can he conclude?

1.6 A tomato cannery prints "weight 16 ounces" on its label. The plant supervisor selects 10 cans at random and weighs them. He finds $\bar{x} = 15.8$, $s = .5$. What is he apt to conclude? Note that he is likely to adopt a somewhat different viewpoint from the investigators in the two previous exercises.

1-10   TESTS INVOLVING ONE VARIANCE

As in the previous paragraph, the situation regarding the hypothesis and the alternate can usually be written in one of three ways:

$$(1)\ H_0 : \sigma^2 = \sigma_0^2 \quad (2)\ H_0 : \sigma^2 \geq \sigma_0^2 \quad (3)\ H_0 : \sigma^2 \leq \sigma_0^2$$
$$H_1 : \sigma^2 \neq \sigma_0^2 \qquad H_1 : \sigma^2 < \sigma_0^2 \qquad H_1 : \sigma^2 > \sigma_0^2.$$

Let $x_1, \cdots, x_n$ be a random sample from a normal population with variance σ_0^2. Then it can be shown that

$$\chi_{n-1}^2 = \frac{(n-1)s^2}{\sigma_0^2} = \frac{\sum\limits_{i=1}^{n} (x_i - \bar{x})^2}{\sigma_0^2} \tag{1.5}$$

has a chi-square distribution with $n-1$ degrees of freedom and that this is a good statistic to use for the three situations. Thus the assumptions are the same as for the t-statistic. The variance is specified by the hypothesis and hence it is not necessary to list under assumptions that $\sigma^2 = \sigma_0^2$ is known.

Values of s^2 that differ greatly in either direction from σ_0^2 contradict H_0 in case (1). The critical region usually chosen is $\chi_{n-1}^2 < \chi_{\alpha/2;\, n-1}^2$ and $\chi_{n-1}^2 > \chi_{1-\alpha/2;\, n-1}^2$. In situation (2) only small values of s^2, and hence small values of χ_{n-1}^2, refute the hypothesis. The critical region that we select is $\chi_{n-1}^2 < \chi_{\alpha;\, n-1}^2$. Finally, in situation (3) the critical region is $\chi_{n-1}^2 > \chi_{1-\alpha;\, n-1}^2$.

Variablity problems arise in a number of applications. In choosing material for a highway surface, for example, they are likely to be considered since it may be more expensive to repair small sections frequently than to repair the entire road periodically. If this were the only consideration, low variability in useful life would be highly desirable. Suppose that it has been decided that the highway material is too variable if, for ten-foot sections, the elapsed times (from construction until repairs are required) have a standard deviation of 2 months or more. A sample of 20 sections are tested, and it is found that $s = 1.2$ months. Should this material be used? A good choice regarding H_0 and H_1 would be

$$H_0: \ \sigma^2 \geq 4$$

$$H_1: \ \sigma^2 < 4.$$

Thus if H_0 is rejected with a high degree of confidence, we can feel reasonably sure that H_1 represents the true state of affairs and that the material meets the variability requirements. Note that H_0 represents what we would like to disprove. If we choose $\alpha = .05$, then we reject H_0 if $(n-1)s^2/\sigma_0^2 < 10.1$, a number easily found in the chi-square table with 19 degrees of freedom. Since $(n-1)s^2/\sigma_0^2 = (19)(1.44)/4 = 6.84$, which is less than 10.1, H_0 is rejected. Of course, the assumptions of random sampling and normality are necessary.

In the example chosen the hypothesis assumes that the material is no good, a viewpoint to which we cling until proven wrong. If H_0 and H_1 are interchanged, then we assume that the material is satisfactory. Only very poor results will convince us otherwise. Which way we are to look at the problem may depend upon considerations other than those given here. When working with a problem of this type, the seven-step outline should be followed.

EXERCISES

1.7 The English instructor in Exercise 1.3 finds out that the variance of English scores over the years has been 25. He then claims that his class is more variable than the population as a whole. Is he justified if $\alpha = .05$?

1.8 It is desirable to have a small variance in the burning time of a fuse for a hand grenade. With large variance, too many will burn too short or too long a time, either of which could be fatal to the user. Suppose it is determined that if $\sigma \geq .5$ seconds, the grenade will not be safe. If $\alpha = .005$ and $s = .25$ for a sample of 25 fuses, what conclusions can be drawn? Which kind of mistake do you especially want to avoid?

1-11   TESTS INVOLVING TWO VARIANCES

Suppose that we have two normal populations with unknown variances σ_1^2 and σ_2^2. The usual hypothesis of interest states that the two variances are equal. Thus the position regarding the hypothesis and the alternate may be written

$$(1) \quad H_0: \sigma_1^2 = \sigma_2^2$$
$$H_1: \sigma_1^2 \neq \sigma_2^2.$$

Occasionally, we encounter one-sided problems so that we may wish to choose between

$$(2) \; H_0: \sigma_1^2 \geq \sigma_2^2 \quad \text{or} \quad (3) \; H_0: \sigma_1^2 \leq \sigma_2^2$$
$$H_1: \sigma_1^2 < \sigma_2^2 \qquad\qquad H_1: \sigma_1^2 > \sigma_2^2.$$

Let $x_{11}, x_{21}, x_{31}, \cdots, x_{n_11}$, and $x_{12}, x_{22}, x_{32}, \cdots, x_{n_22}$ denote samples from the first and second populations respectively. We assume (a) both samples are randomly drawn, and (b) the two populations are normal. The population variances σ_1^2 and σ_2^2 are not known, but the sample variances

$$s_1^2 = \frac{\sum_{i=1}^{n_1} (x_{i1} - \bar{x}_1)^2}{n_1 - 1} \quad \text{and} \quad s_2^2 = \frac{\sum_{i=1}^{n_2} (x_{i2} - \bar{x}_2)^2}{n_2 - 1}$$

may be computed. If the two samples are drawn randomly, it is known that

$$F_{n_1-1, \, n_2-1} = \frac{s_1^2}{s_2^2} \qquad\qquad (1.6)$$

and that this is the appropriate statistic to use in testing all three hypotheses.

Both large and small values of $F_{n_1-1,\ n_2-1}$ contradict H_0 in Case (1). Hence the critical region usually selected is

$$F_{n_1-1,\ n_2-1} < F_{\alpha/2;\ n_1-1,\ n_2-1} \text{ and } F_{n_1-1,\ n_2-1} > F_{1-\alpha/2;\ n_1-1,\ n_2-1}.$$

In Case (2) H_0 is rejected when s_1^2 is small by comparison to s_2^2. Thus the critical region is

$$F_{n_1-1,\ n_2-1} < F_{\alpha;\ n_1-1,\ n_2-1}.$$

Finally, the critical region for situation (3) is

$$F_{n_1-1,\ n_2-1} > F_{1-\alpha;\ n_1-1,\ n_2-1}.$$

The statistic encountered in analysis of variance has an F distribution. We will find that a one-sided critical region is dictated by both our intuition and mathematical considerations. Such a region is pictured in Figure 1.5. Consequently Appendix Table 4 gives only the right-hand

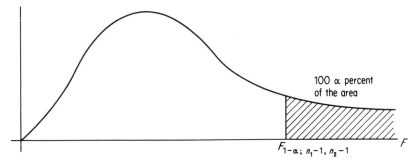

Fig. 1.5 Typical F curve showing the one-sided region encountered in analysis of variance.

percentage points. However, every right-hand percentage point can be converted into a left-hand percentage point since it is known that

$$F_{1-p;\ \nu_2,\ \nu_1} = \frac{1}{F_{p;\ \nu_1,\ \nu_2}}. \tag{1.7}$$

To illustrate this computation, we obtain $F_{.95;\ 6,12} = 3.00$ from the table. Hence $F_{.05;\ 12,6} = 1/3.00 = .33$. Tables found in references [1] and [2] give the left-hand points directly. Since these tables require a number of pages to reproduce and are not essential to our main purpose, we have not included them.

EXERCISES

1.9 It is known that two brands of tires have an average life of 25,000 miles. However, there may be some difference in the variability of mileage attained from the two brands. An experiment is conducted in which 16 tires of each brand are used. They are run under similar conditions until they wear out. It is found that the two sample standard deviations are $s_1 = 4{,}200$ miles, $s_2 = 2{,}800$ miles. If $\alpha = .05$, what are your conclusions?

1.10 In turning out machined parts, small variability is often a desirable characteristic. Machine A is somewhat more expensive than machine B. Both can be used to turn out the same part. The manufacturer would like to buy machine B unless machine A is significantly better, that is, has lower variability. After 100 parts are turned out on each machine, it is found that $s_A^2 = .0004$ and $s_B^2 = .0006$. What decision should be made?

1-12 BARTLETT'S TEST FOR MORE THAN TWO VARIANCES

In analysis of variance problems we will find that it is necessary to assume that a number of population variances are equal. If we have reason to doubt that this is the case, we may first want to test the hypothesis

$$H_0: \sigma_1^2 = \sigma_2^2 = \ldots = \sigma_r^2$$

H_1: at least two variances are different.

Under the assumptions that (a) r random samples are drawn from r populations and (b) the r populations are normal, the statistic

$$\frac{2.3026}{C}\left[(N-r)\ \log\ s_p^2 - \sum_{j=1}^{r} (n_j-1)\ \log\ s_j^2\right] \qquad (1.8)$$

is approximately distributed as chi-square with $r-1$ degrees of freedom if H_0 is true. Here $s_1^2, s_2^2, \ldots, s_r^2$ are the r sample variances. The sample sizes are $n_1, n_2, \ldots, n_r$ with

$$\sum_{j=1}^{r} n_j = N.$$

Also

$$s_p^2 = \frac{\sum_{j=1}^{r} (n_j-1)\ s_j^2}{N-r}$$

and
$$C = 1 + \frac{1}{3(r-1)} \left[\sum_{j=1}^{r} \frac{1}{n_j - 1} - \frac{1}{N-r} \right].$$

The more the s_j^2 differ from one another, the larger this statistic becomes. If the s_j^2 are all nearly the same, then the statistic is small. Hence H_0 is rejected only for large values.

To illustrate the use of the test, suppose that $r = 3$ and $n_1 = 5$, $s_1^2 = 205$, $n_2 = 8$, $s_2^2 = 157$, $n_3 = 10$, $s_3^2 = 416$. Then $N = 23$,

$$s_p^2 = \frac{4(205) + 7(157) + 9(416)}{20} = 283.15,$$

and

$$C = 1 + \frac{1}{6} \left[\frac{1}{4} + \frac{1}{7} + \frac{1}{9} - \frac{1}{20} \right] = 1.0757.$$

Next

$$(n_1 - 1) \ \log \ s_1^2 = 4 \ \log \ 205 = 4(2.31175) = 9.24700,$$
$$(n_2 - 1) \ \log \ s_2^2 = 7 \ \log \ 157 = 7(2.19590) = 15.37130,$$
$$(n_3 - 1) \ \log \ s_3^2 = 9 \ \log \ 416 = 9(2.61909) = 23.57181,$$

so that $\displaystyle\sum_{j=1}^{3} (n_j - 1) \ \log \ s_j^2 = 48.19011$

and $(N - r) \ \log \ s_p^2 = 20 \ \log \ 283.15 = 20(2.44739) = 48.94780$. Hence the value of the statistic is

$$\frac{2.3026}{1.0757} \left[48.94780 - 48.19011 \right] = 1.62.$$

Entering the chi-square table with two degrees of freedom, we find that this is considerably smaller than 5.99, the critical value if $\alpha = .05$. Thus we accept the hypothesis of equal variances.

EXERCISE

1.11 Suppose that we have four random samples drawn from four normal populations. If $s_1^2 = 190$, $n_1 = 12$, $s_2^2 = 527$, $n_2 = 8$, $s_3^2 = 66.2$, $n_3 = 11$, $s_4^2 = 873$, $n_4 = 16$, use Bartlett's test to investigate this homogeneity of the variances.

1-13 COCHRAN'S TEST FOR HOMOGENEITY OF VARIANCES

If $n_1 = n_2 = \cdots = n_r = n$, that is, all r samples are of equal size, then Cochran's test provides an easy method for testing the hypothesis of equal variances. Appendix Table 5 gives the upper .05 and .01 points of the

statistic
$$R_{n,r} = \frac{\text{largest } s_j^2}{s_1^2 + s_2^2 + \ \ldots \ + s_r^2} \qquad (1.9)$$

if the null hypothesis is true. We reject H_0 if $R_{n,r} > R_{1-\alpha;\,n,r}$. The assumptions are the same as for Bartlett's test.

As an example, suppose that $s_1^2 = 140$, $s_2^2 = 200$, $s_3^2 = 660$, $n = 10$. Then

$$R_{10,3} = \frac{660}{140 + 200 + 660} = .66$$

In the table we find $R_{0.99;\,10,3} = .6912$ and $R_{0.95;\,10,3} = .6167$. Thus the hypothesis of equal variance is rejected if $\alpha = .05$ but not if $\alpha = .01$.

EXERCISE
1.12 Suppose $s_1^2 = 190$, $s_2^2 = 527$, $s_3^2 = 66.2$, $s_4^2 = 873$, $n = 8$. Use Cochran's test to investigate the hypothesis of equal variances.

1-14 TESTS CONCERNING TWO POPULATION MEANS USING TWO RANDOM SAMPLES

A number of problems of considerable interest arise when we consider hypotheses about the means of two populations. If we let μ_1 and μ_2 denote the two means, then the most commonly formulated hypotheses are

(1) $H_0: \mu_1 = \mu_2$ (2) $H_0: \mu_1 \geq \mu_2$ (3) $H_0: \mu_1 \leq \mu_2$
     $H_1: \mu_1 \neq \mu_2$ $H_1: \mu_1 < \mu_2$ $H_1: \mu_1 > \mu_2$.

Let $x_{11}, x_{21}, \ldots, x_{n_1 1}$ and $x_{12}, x_{22}, \ldots, x_{n_2 2}$ be random samples drawn from the first and second populations respectively. Denote the sample means by $\bar{x}_1$ and $\bar{x}_2$.

If the variances are known, then the statistic to use is

$$Z = \frac{\bar{x}_1 - \bar{x}_2 - (\mu_1 - \mu_2)}{\sqrt{\dfrac{\sigma_1^2}{n_1} + \dfrac{\sigma_2^2}{n_2}}} . \qquad (1.10)$$

When the two populations are normal, Z has the standard normal distribution. With moderate sample sizes, Z may be interpreted as a standard normal variable even though the populations are non-normal.

If the two populations are normal with the same variance, then it may be shown that

$$t_{n_1 + n_2 - 2} = \frac{\bar{x}_1 - \bar{x}_2 - (\mu_1 - \mu_2)}{s_p \sqrt{\dfrac{1}{n_1} + \dfrac{1}{n_2}}} \qquad (1.11)$$

where

$$s_p^2 = \frac{(n_1 - 1) s_1^2 + (n_2 - 1) s_2^2}{n_1 + n_2 - 2}$$

is a good statistic to use for testing hypotheses about $\mu_1 - \mu_2$.

For each of the three situations regarding H_0 and H_1 mentioned above, we use $\mu_1 - \mu_2 = 0$. For the first case both large and small values of $\bar{x}_1 - \bar{x}_2$, and hence $t_{n_1 + n_2 - 2}$, contradict the hypothesis. In (2) only small values of the statistic lead to rejection while in (3) only large values fall in the critical region.

If the variances are unknown and not equal, only approximate solutions are available for testing hypotheses about the two means using two random samples. A statistic that can be used in this case is

$$t_\nu' = \frac{\bar{x}_1 - \bar{x}_2 - (\mu_1 - \mu_2)}{\sqrt{\dfrac{s_1^2}{n_1} + \dfrac{s_2^2}{n_2}}} \tag{1.12}$$

which is approximately distributed as t_ν, where

$$\nu = \frac{\left(\dfrac{s_1^2}{n_1} + \dfrac{s_2^2}{n_2}\right)^2}{\dfrac{\left(\dfrac{s_1^2}{n_1}\right)^2}{n_1 - 1} + \dfrac{\left(\dfrac{s_2^2}{n_2}\right)^2}{n_2 - 1}} - 2,$$

if the two populations are normal. Since the degrees of freedom will usually not be an integer, interpolation in the t-table may be necessary. As a general rule, using the nearest integer will suffice. Note that if $n_1 = n_2$, Equations (1.11) and (1.12) reduce to the same number. However, the degrees of freedom associated with the two quantities are different.

Experimental evidence seems to indicate that mild departures from the assumptions of normality and equal variances do not seriously influence conclusions drawn from (1.11) provided the sample sizes are equal or nearly so. Under these circumstances it is quite likely that the Type I error will be slightly larger than the α chosen by the experimenter.

EXERCISES

1.13 Two types of wheat are being compared for yield. Thirty-two acres of each kind are planted and are exposed to fairly uniform growing conditions. The results are: variety A, average yield 32 bushels per acre, sample variance 5.9; variety B, average yield 35.7 bushels per acre, sample variance 11.2. Analyze the results.

1.14 A company is trying to decide which of two types of tires to buy for their trucks. They would like to adopt brand G unless there is some evidence that F is better. An experiment is conducted in which 16 tires of each brand are used. They are run under similar conditions until they wear out. The results are:

$$\text{Brand } F: \quad \bar{x}_1 = 26{,}000 \text{ miles, } s_1 = 4{,}200 \text{ miles}$$
$$\text{Brand } G: \quad \bar{x}_2 = 25{,}000 \text{ miles, } s_2 = 2{,}800 \text{ miles}$$

What conclusions may be drawn?

1.15 A psychologist thinks that dogs who drink vinegar are more intelligent than those which do not. For his experiment he has 20 dogs which are assigned at random to two groups. One group is fed vinegar for part of its diet for 30 days while the other group has the same diet minus the vinegar. At the end of this period, all 20 dogs are subjected to an intelligence test, and the following scores are obtained:

Vinegar:
115,   91,   99, 105, 96, 101, 104, 106,   99, 119
No vinegar:
86, 109, 109, 104, 82,   94, 106,   87, 110, 103,

Does vinegar affect intelligence?

1·15 PAIRED OBSERVATIONS AND TESTS CONCERNING TWO POPULATION MEANS

There are many situations in which we may wish to compare two treatments yet find that observations occur in pairs. Thus, instead of having two random samples, we have one random sample of pairs. The two observations of a pair are related to each other. When this happens, the procedures of the previous paragraph no longer apply. A typical problem of this type is one that involves before-and-after data. For example, suppose 20 adults are given a strenuous physical training program. Their weights are recorded before they begin and after they complete the course. We desire to know if the program produces a significant change in the average weight of individuals. Obviously, the measurements are related. That is, if an individual weighs 200 pounds before beginning, he will probably weigh about 200 pounds at the end. Similarly, a person who begins at 100 pounds will not differ too greatly from this after completing the course. The final weight depends to a large extent upon the initial weight. Thus our testing procedure must be changed to meet this situation.

Another important reason for pairing observations is to eliminate effects in which there is no interest. Suppose that two teaching methods are to be compared by using 50 students divided into two equal classes. One way to conduct the experiment is to assign randomly 25 students to each class and then compare average scores when the experiment is concluded. If one group happens to get better students, the results may not give a fair comparison of the two methods. A better procedure would be to pair the students according to ability (as measured by some test or IQ) and assign one of each pair to each class. Any conclusions reached are then based upon differences of paired scores, which we hope measure the effects due to different teaching methods. When extraneous effects are eliminated, the resulting scores upon which the test is based are less variable. If the data from the teaching experiment measures both ability and difference in methods, the variance will be larger since each score has two sources of variation instead of one. Decreasing the variability of the observations increases the accuracy of the conclusions by reducing the probability of a Type II error.

In the teaching method example, there is an advantage in having available pairs of different ability. The conclusions drawn are then applicable to a larger class of individuals than would be the case if pairs of about the same ability had been used for the experiment. In general, it is advantageous to choose pairs so that the units within a pair are similar and there are wide differences from pair to pair.

Suppose that the experiment yields n pairs of measurements

$$(x_{11}, \ x_{12}), \ (x_{21}, \ x_{22}), \ \cdots, \ (x_{n1}, \ x_{n2}) \ .$$

From each pair a difference can be computed. Denote these by

$$d_1, \ d_2, \ \cdots, \ d_n \quad \text{where} \quad d_i = x_{i1} - x_{i2}, \ i = 1, \ 2, \ \cdots, \ n.$$

Let

$$\bar{d} = \frac{\sum\limits_{i=1}^{n} d_i}{n} \quad \text{and} \quad s_d^2 = \frac{\sum\limits_{i=1}^{n} (d_i - \bar{d})^2}{n-1} \ .$$

If it is assumed that the d_i form a random sample from a normal population with mean $\mu_d = \mu_1 - \mu_2$, then

$$t_{n-1} = \frac{\bar{d} - \mu_d}{s_d} \ \sqrt{n} \tag{1.13}$$

is the best statistic to use for each of the three cases listed at the beginning of Section 1-14. The case most often encountered is

$$H_0: \quad \mu_d = 0$$
$$H_1: \quad \mu_d \neq 0.$$

We note that the paired observations test has only $n-1$ degrees of freedom for $2n$ observations. If the data are not paired, then the degrees of freedom for the t-test is $2(n-1)$, twice the previous number. This is a big loss if pairing is not necessary. However, if the paired units are quite similar or highly related, the smaller variance more than compensates for the loss of degrees of freedom.

EXERCISES

1.16 Ten men are fed a new diet for two months. We would like to know if the diet has any effect upon weight. The men were weighed at the beginning and at the conclusion of the experiment. The observations were

Man

	1	2	3	4	5	6	7	8	9	10
Before	210	163	135	171	197	185	123	164	145	227
After	195	158	138	164	203	181	120	152	144	208

What can we conclude?

1.17 Two hybrid seed corn companies both claim that their product is superior. Three scientists from universities are hired to settle the dispute. They plant one acre of each kind in eight different localities where soil and climate conditions vary. When the corn is harvested, they record (yields in bushels)

Locality

	1	2	3	4	5	6	7	8
Long ear	114	86	93	75	102	89	64	95
Fat kernel	107	94	86	70	90	82	73	81

What should the professors say in their report?

1-16 THE ANALYSIS OF VARIANCE

In the two preceding paragraphs, we have discussed procedures for testing hypotheses about two population means. In particular we stated

that
$$H_0: \mu_1 = \mu_2$$
$$H_1: \mu_1 \neq \mu_2 \qquad (1.14)$$

was perhaps the most important case. Suppose we have more than two, say r, populations. In many applications we need a statistical procedure for testing

$$H_0: \mu_1 = \mu_2 = \cdots = \mu_r$$
$$H_1: \text{at least two means are not equal.}$$

In other words, we seek an extension of the previously described methods. This leads us to a body of statistics called the analysis of variance. Chapter 2 can be regarded as an extension of the t-test for (1.14) when two random samples are available. Chapter 3 extends the procedure for paired or related measurements. The choice of title for this branch of statistics arises from a process of partitioning sums of squares into components in order to estimate variability due to different sources. This partitioning process will be demonstrated in the chapters that follow.

We have mentioned some types of problems that are encountered in the study of analysis of variance and, in addition, have formulated a preliminary definition of the subject. However, analysis of variance is more comprehensive than we have previously inferred. Consequently, it now seems necessary to give a more complete definition for analysis of variance.

We will use the notation, "The x_i are independently $N(\mu, \sigma^2)$," to mean that $x_1, x_2, \cdots, x_n$ is a random sample from a population that is normal with mean μ and variance σ^2.

In order to use the t-test to investigate hypotheses about a population mean, we assume that the x_i are independently $N(\mu, \sigma^2)$ with μ being specified by the hypothesis and σ^2 being unknown. An alternate way to write the assumptions is as follows:

$$x_i = \mu + e_i, \qquad i = 1, 2, \cdots, n$$
$$e_i \text{ are independently } N(0, \sigma^2). \qquad (1.15)$$

Actually this implies nothing that is new. The e's and the x's have the same variance since the two variables differ by a constant. Secondly, since $e_i = x_i - \mu$ and the average value of x_i is μ, the average value of e_i must be 0. This follows immediately from a basic theorem of elementary statistics which states:

If a constant is added to each of a set of values, the mean of the set is increased by that constant.

Here the constant is $-\mu$ so that the mean of the set is decreased by an amount μ.

To test hypotheses about two means in Section 1-14, it is necessary to assume that the x_{ij} are independently

$$N(\mu_j, \sigma^2), \qquad i=1, 2, \cdots, n_j, \qquad j=1, 2.$$

An equivalent formulation is

$$x_{ij} = \mu_j + e_{ij}, \qquad i=1, 2, \cdots, n_j, \qquad j=1, 2,$$
$$e_{ij} \text{ are independently } N(0, \sigma^2). \tag{1.16}$$

Note that we can write

$$x_{ij} = \mu + (\mu_j - \mu) + e_{ij}$$
$$= \mu + \beta_j + e_{ij}.$$

Thus

$$n_1\beta_1 + n_2\beta_2 = n_1(\mu_1 - \mu) + n_2(\mu_2 - \mu) = n_1\mu_1 + n_2\mu_2 - (n_1 + n_2)\mu$$

which has the value 0 if we let

$$\mu = \frac{n_1\mu_1 + n_2\mu_2}{n_1 + n_2}.$$

Let us agree to define μ this way. (The choice is not obvious and arises from mathematical considerations.) Then (1.16) can be rewritten

$$x_{ij} = \mu + \beta_j + e_{ij}, \qquad i=1, 2, \cdots, n_j, \; j=1, 2$$
$$e_{ij} \text{ are independently } N(0, \sigma^2). \tag{1.17}$$

In the paired situation we assume that the d_i are independently $N(\mu_1 - \mu_2, \sigma_d^2)$. This could be written

$$d_i = \mu_1 - \mu_2 + e_i, \qquad i=1, 2, \cdots, n$$
$$e_i \text{ are independently } N(0, \sigma_d^2). \tag{1.18}$$

This does not require that the population from which $x_{11}, x_{21}, \cdots, x_{n1}$ is drawn to have the same variance as the population yielding $x_{12}, x_{22}, \cdots, x_{n2}$.

The assumptions concerning the form of the observations in each of the above situations (1.15), (1.17), and (1.18) are special cases of a more general formulation. Let $y_1, y_2, \cdots, y_n$ be observations from an experiment. Assume that

$$y_i = w_{1i}a_1 + w_{2i}a_2 + \cdots + w_{pi}a_p + e_i$$
$$e_i \text{ are independently } N(0, \sigma^2) \tag{1.19}$$

where w_{1i}, w_{2i}, $\cdots$, w_{pi} are either 0 or 1 and a_1, a_2, $\cdots$, a_p are unknown quantities. We now define analysis of variance as a collection of statistical methods used to study observations which satisfy assumptions (1.19). This is essentially the definition given by Scheffé [3].

For the observations of the form $x_i = \mu + e_i$ an identification is simple. We have $y_i = x_i$, $i = 1, 2, \cdots, n$, $w_{1i} = 1$ and all other w's are zero, $a_1 = \mu$, and the e_i are correctly identified. In the next case where $x_{ij} = \mu + \beta_j + e_{ij}$, $i = 1, 2, \cdots, n_j$, $j = 1, 2$, we have

$$y_1 = x_{11}, \quad y_2 = x_{21}, \quad \cdots, \quad y_{n_1} = x_{n_11}, \quad y_{n_1+1} = x_{12}, \quad \cdots, \quad y_N = x_{n_22}$$
$$a_1 = \mu, \quad a_2 = \beta_1, \quad a_3 = \beta_2,$$
$$w_{i1} = 1, \quad i = 1, 2, \cdots, N, \quad N = n_1 + n_2,$$
$$w_{i2} = 1, \quad i = 1, 2, \cdots, n_1, \quad w_{i2} = 0, \quad i = n_1 + 1, \cdots, n_1 + n_2,$$
$$w_{i3} = 0, \quad i = 1, 2, \cdots, n_1, \quad w_{i3} = 1, \quad i = n_1 + 1, \cdots, n_1 + n_2,$$
$$e_1 = e_{11}, \quad e_2 = e_{21}, \quad \cdots, \quad e_N = e_{n_22}.$$

Finally, when

$$d_i = \mu_1 - \mu_2 + e_i, \quad i = 1, 2, \cdots, n,$$

we have

$$y_i = d_i, \quad i = 1, 2, \cdots, n,$$
$$a_1 = \mu_1, \quad a_2 = -\mu_2,$$
$$w_{i1} = 1, \quad i = 1, 2, \cdots, n,$$
$$w_{i2} = 1, \quad i = 1, 2, \cdots, n,$$

and the e_i are already correctly identified. Thus according to our definition these t-tests are included in analysis of variance.

EXERCISE

1.18 Suppose that we have observations x_{ij}, $i = 1, 2, \cdots, n$, $j = 1, 2$. If $x_{ij} = \mu + \alpha_i + \beta_j + e_{ij}$, make an identification with the y's, w's, a's and e's of Equation (1.19).

REFERENCES

[1] Dixon, W.J., and F.J. Massey, *Introduction to Statistical Analysis* (2nd ed.; New York: McGraw-Hill Book Co., Inc., 1957).

[2] Graybill, Franklin A., *An Introduction to Linear Statistical Models* (New York: McGraw-Hill Book Co., Inc., 1961), Volume 1.

[3] Scheffé. Henry, *The Analysis of Variance* (New York: John Wiley & Sons, Inc. 1959).

2

The One-Way Classification

2-1 INTRODUCTION

We have discussed the method that is most frequently used to test the equality of two‑population means when the data are composed of two random samples. The first objective of this chapter will be to extend the procedure so that the equality of r, $r \geq 2$, population means can be tested using r independent random samples. Thus the hypothesis and alternate are

$$H_0: \quad \mu_1 = \mu_2 = \ldots = \mu_r$$
$$H_1: \quad \text{at least two means are not equal}$$

where μ_j, $j = 1,2, \ldots, r$ is the mean of the jth population.

It is not difficult to imagine many situations where it may be of interest to compare a number of means. For example, 6 varieties of wheat instead of 2 are available, and it is to be determined whether or not the average yield from each variety is the same; a company is testing 3 brands of tires and wants to know if the average life of each brand is the same; 5 teaching methods instead of 2 are being investigated for their effectiveness; an experimenter wishes to compare the influence upon growth of 4 different types of hog diets.

31

In the analysis of this type of experiment, we often wish to do more than choose between H_0 and H_1. Sometimes H_0 is not the main hypothesis of interest. Later in this chapter we will discuss some other types of hypotheses that may be tested with only a few more calculations. A problem might arise that may be formulated as follows: How large should the samples be to insure a given power when H_0 is incorrect by a specified amount? In the event H_0 is rejected, we may desire to know what can be inferred about the relative sizes of the means. These are some of the topics that will be pursued.

In designing an experiment for a one-way classification, units are assigned at random to any one of the r treatments under investigation. For this reason, the one-way classification is sometimes referred to as a completely randomized design.

2-2 NOTATION

Before discussing the assumptions and the test procedure, we will illustrate how the data can be arranged once it is collected and give some notation that will be needed.

Table 2.1 SUMMARY OF RESULTS FOR THE ONE-WAY CLASSIFICATION

	Treatments					
	1	2	3	$\cdots$	r	
Observations	x_{11}	x_{12}	x_{13}		x_{1r}	
	x_{21}	x_{22}	x_{23}		x_{2r}	
	.	.	.		.	
	.	.	.		.	
	.	.	.		.	
	x_{n_11}		x_{n_33}			
		x_{n_22}			$x_{n_r r}$	
TOTALS	$T_{.1}$	$T_{.2}$	$T_{.3}$		$T_{.r}$	$T_{..}$
Means	$\bar{x}_{.1}$	$\bar{x}_{.2}$	$\bar{x}_{.3}$		$\bar{x}_{.r}$	$\bar{x}_{..}$
Variances	s_1^2	s_2^2	s_3^2		s_r^2	s^2

The observations can be arranged as in Table 2.1. The first column represents a random sample of size n_1 from the population that has received treatment 1; the second column, a random sample of size n_2 from the population that has received treatment 2; the jth column, a random sample from the population that has received treatment j. The symbols are defined as follows:

The ith observation receiving treatment j $= x_{ij}$, $\quad i = 1, 2, \ldots, n_j, \quad j = 1, 2 \ldots, r$

Total of the jth column $= T_{.j} = \sum_{i=1}^{n_j} x_{ij}$

Mean of the jth column $= \bar{x}_{.j} = \dfrac{T_{.j}}{n_j} = \dfrac{\sum\limits_{i=1}^{n_j} x_{ij}}{n_j}$

Variance of the jth column $= s_j^2 = \dfrac{\sum\limits_{i=1}^{n_j} (x_{ij} - \bar{x}_{.j})^2}{n_j - 1}$

Total of all observations $= T_{..} = \sum\limits_{j=1}^{r} T_{.j} = \sum\limits_{j=1}^{r} \sum\limits_{i=1}^{n_j} x_{ij}$

Mean of all observations $= \bar{x}_{..} = \dfrac{T_{..}}{N}, \quad N = \sum\limits_{j=1}^{r} n_i$

Variance of all N observations regarded as a single sample $= s^2 = \dfrac{\sum\limits_{j=1}^{r} \sum\limits_{i=1}^{n_j} (x_{ij} - \bar{x}_{..})^2}{N - 1}$.

Finally, we will let μ_j and σ_j^2, $j = 1, 2, \cdots, r$, denote the mean and variance of population j.

The double-summation notation may present an obstacle to those who encounter it for the first time. In the next section some remarks and theorems are presented which may help to overcome this difficulty.

A numerical example of Table 2.1 is next considered. Suppose that

Table 2.2 A COMPLETELY RANDOMIZED EXPERIMENT—A NUMERICAL EXAMPLE

	Treatment (variety)			
	1	2	3	
Yields in bushels per acre	36 33 48	57 53 43 54 48	50 41 47 42	
TOTALS	$T_{.1} = 117$	$T_{.2} = 255$	$T_{.3} = 180$	$T_{..} = 552$
Means	$\bar{x}_{.1} = 39$	$\bar{x}_{.2} = 51$	$\bar{x}_{.3} = 45$	$\bar{x}_{..} = 46$
Sample sizes	$n_1 = 3$	$n_2 = 5$	$n_3 = 4$	$N = 12$
Variances	$s_1^2 = 63$	$s_2^2 = 30.5$	$s_3^2 = 18$	$s^2 = 52.6$

a completely randomized arrangement is used to study yields of wheat for $r = 3$ varieties. A fifteen-acre field was divided into one-acre plots, and each variety of wheat was planted on 5 plots. Three acres were flooded out. The results from the other twelve are presented in Table 2.2.

2-3 MORE ON DOUBLE SUMMATION

To evaluate the double summation

$$\sum_{j=1}^{r} \sum_{i=1}^{n_j} x_{ij}$$

from either Table 2.1 or 2.2, first add the recorded values in each column to get column totals and then add the column totals. Symbolically, we have

$$\sum_{j=1}^{r} \sum_{i=1}^{n_j} x_{ij} = \sum_{j=1}^{r} \left(\sum_{i=1}^{n_j} x_{ij}\right) = \sum_{j=1}^{r} T_{.j} = T_{..} \; .$$

In other words

$$\sum_{j=1}^{r} \sum_{i=1}^{n_j} x_{ij} = \sum_{j=1}^{r} \left(\sum_{i=1}^{n_j} x_{ij}\right)$$
$$= \sum_{j=1}^{r} (x_{1j} + x_{2j} + x_{3j} + \cdots + x_{n_j j})$$
$$= (x_{11} + x_{21} + x_{31} + \cdots + x_{n_1 1}) + (x_{12} + x_{22} + x_{32} + \cdots x_{n_2 2})$$
$$+ \cdots + (x_{1r} + x_{2r} + x_{3r} + \cdots + x_{n_r r})$$

so that the double sum is a convenient abbreviation form to use.

Until one gains facility in the use of summation signs, it is good practice to write out the sum completely. For example,

$$\sum_{j=1}^{2} \sum_{i=1}^{3} x_{ij} = \sum_{j=1}^{2} (x_{1j} + x_{2j} + x_{3j})$$
$$= (x_{11} + x_{21} + x_{31}) + (x_{12} + x_{22} + x_{32}).$$

Here we note

$$\sum_{i=1}^{3} \sum_{j=1}^{2} x_{ij} = \sum_{i=1}^{3} (x_{i1} + x_{i2}) = (x_{11} + x_{12}) + (x_{21} + x_{22}) + (x_{31} + x_{32})$$
$$= \sum_{j=1}^{2} \sum_{i=1}^{3} x_{ij}.$$

This example illustrates

THEOREM I: $\displaystyle \sum_{j=1}^{b} \sum_{i=1}^{a} x_{ij} = \sum_{i=1}^{a} \sum_{j=1}^{b} x_{ij}.$

That is, if the limits on the summation signs are constants, the order of the summation may be changed. This is not possible with

$$\sum_{j=1}^{r} \sum_{i=1}^{n_j} x_{ij}$$

where the inside limit n_j contains the outside index of summation. Most of the double sums to be encountered in this and later chapters have limits that are constants. Thus if $n_1 = n_2 = \cdots = n_r = n$, then

$$\sum_{j=1}^{r} \sum_{i=1}^{n} x_{ij} = \sum_{i=1}^{n} \sum_{j=1}^{r} x_{ij}.$$

Next consider

$$\sum_{j=1}^{r} \sum_{i=1}^{n_j} y_j x_{ij}.$$

This equals

$$\sum_{j=1}^{r} (y_j x_{1j} + y_j x_{2j} + \cdots + y_j x_{n_j j}) = \sum_{j=1}^{r} y_j (x_{1j} + x_{2j} + \cdots + y_{n_j j}) = \sum_{j=1}^{r} y_j \sum_{i=1}^{n_j} x_{ij}.$$

This proves

THEOREM II: $$\sum_{j=1}^{r} \sum_{i=1}^{n_j} y_j x_{ij} = \sum_{j=1}^{r} y_j \sum_{i=1}^{n_j} x_{ij}.$$

Hence if part of a product which is being summed involves only the outside index of summation, this part can be factored out of the inside summation sign. As a corollary we can state

$$\sum_{j=1}^{r} \sum_{i=1}^{n_j} C x_{ij} = C \sum_{j=1}^{r} \sum_{i=1}^{n_j} x_{ij}$$

since C will appear in every term of the sum and can be factored out.

Another useful fact is

THEOREM III: $$\sum_{j=1}^{r} \sum_{i=1}^{n_j} (x_{ij} + y_{ij}) = \sum_{j=1}^{r} \sum_{i=1}^{n_j} x_{ij} + \sum_{j=1}^{r} \sum_{i=1}^{n_j} y_{ij}.$$

This is easily proved by writing out the left-hand side of the equation and then grouping the x's together and the y's together. Theorem III is easily extended in the obvious way. For example

$$\sum_{j=1}^{r} \sum_{i=1}^{n_j} (x_{ij} + y_{ij} + z_{ij}) = \sum_{j=1}^{r} \sum_{i=1}^{n_j} x_{ij} + \sum_{j=1}^{r} \sum_{i=1}^{n_j} y_{ij} + \sum_{j=1}^{r} \sum_{i=1}^{n_j} z_{ij},$$

etc.

Occasionally, we will want to use

THEOREM IV: $$\sum_{j=1}^{r} \sum_{i=1}^{n_j} C = NC.$$

Since every term is the sum of exactly the same number, C, and the sum contains N terms, the result follows.

EXERCISES

2.1   Write out the proof for Theorem III.

2.2   Show that $\displaystyle\sum_{j=1}^{r}\sum_{i=1}^{n_j}(x_{ij}-\bar{x}_{.j})=0.$

2.3   Show that $\displaystyle\sum_{j=1}^{r}\sum_{i=1}^{n_j}(\bar{x}_{.j}-\bar{x}_{..})(x_{ij}-\bar{x}_{.j})=0.$

2-4 THE FIXED-EFFECTS MODEL FOR THE ONE-WAY CLASSIFICATION

In order to derive a test which will serve as a basis for choosing between H_0 and H_1, certain assumptions are necessary. These are (a) the r columns represent r random samples from r different populations, (b) each of the r populations is normal, and (c) each of the r populations has the same variance. In order words, the x_{ij} are independently $N(\mu_j, \sigma^2)$.

Consider the identity $x_{ij}=\mu+(\mu_j-\mu)+(x_{ij}-\mu_j)$.

Let $\beta_j=\mu_j-\mu$ and

$$\mu=\sum_{j=1}^{r} n_j\mu_j/N,$$

where

$$N=\sum_{j=1}^{r} n_j,$$

so that

$$\sum_{j=1}^{r} n_j\beta_j=\sum_{j=1}^{r} n_j(\mu_j-\mu)=\sum_{j=1}^{r} n_j\mu_j-\sum_{j=1}^{r} n_j\mu=N\mu-N\mu=0.$$

Also define $e_{ij}=x_{ij}-\mu_j$ which has mean 0 since the mean of x_{ij} is μ_j. Both the e_{ij} and x_{ij} have the same variance σ^2 since they differ by a constant. Finally the e_{ij} are normally distributed since the x_{ij} came from a normal distribution. Thus the assumptions (a), (b), and (c) may be written

$$x_{ij}=\mu+\beta_j+e_{ij}, \qquad i=1, 2, \ldots, n_j, \qquad j=1,2, \ldots, r$$

e_{ij} are independently $N(0, \sigma^2)$ (2.1)

$\displaystyle\sum_{j=1}^{r} n_j\beta_j=0$ (which reduces to $\displaystyle\sum_{j=1}^{r}\beta_j=0$ if all $n_j=n$).

Until the reader becomes familiar with this formulation (2.1), it is advisable that he list the assumptions both ways when doing a problem.

Now the hypothesis and the alternate may be written

$$H_0 : \beta_j = 0, \ j = 1, 2, \ldots, r$$
$$H_1 : \text{not all } \beta_j \text{ are zero.}$$

Each β_j is a measure of the deviation of the jth population mean from the average of all r population means. If all r means are equal, then every β_j is zero.

In the model specified by (2.1), the β_j are considered to be a set of r fixed quantities. We have interest only in the r populations that are under investigation, and any conclusions that we reach are valid only for the r populations. This is in contrast to the situation for another model to be discussed later in the chapter where the r populations are considered to be a random sample from a larger group of populations. Various names are used to identify these two models, but we shall usually refer to the former as the fixed-effects model and to the latter as the random-effects model. This is the identification used by Scheffé [5]. The fixed-effects model is sometimes called Model I, the random-effects, Model II. In most applied problems where a one-way classification is used, Model I is the appropriate choice.

In concluding the discussion of the fixed-effects model, we will mention some advantages in choosing each of the r sample sizes equal. First, it has been demonstrated that consequences of unequal variances are not serious if each $n_j = n$; that is, the F ratio is not sensitive to this type of departure from the assumptions when the samples are of equal size. Second, this choice of sample size minimizes the probability of committing a Type II error. Third, if H_0 is rejected, some further tests may be desirable, and some of these are not available unless the sample sizes are equal.

2-5 PARTITIONING THE SUM OF SQUARES

Consider the quantity $(N-1)s^2$. It may be written

$$\sum_{j=1}^{r} \sum_{i=1}^{n_j} (x_{ij} - \bar{x}_{..})^2 = \sum_{j=1}^{r} \sum_{i=1}^{n_j} [\,(x_{ij} - \bar{x}_{.j}) + (\bar{x}_{.j} - \bar{x}_{..})\,]^2$$

$$= \sum_{j=1}^{r} \sum_{i=1}^{n_j} [\,(x_{ij} - \bar{x}_{.j})^2 + 2(x_{ij} - \bar{x}_{.j})(\bar{x}_{.j} - \bar{x}_{..}) + (\bar{x}_{.j} - \bar{x}_{..})^2\,],$$

Using Theorem III of Section 2.3, this can be written as the sum of three separate sums:

$$\sum_{j=1}^{r} \sum_{i=1}^{n_j} (x_{ij} - \bar{x}_{.j})^2 + \sum_{j=1}^{r} \sum_{i=1}^{n_j} 2(x_{ij} - \bar{x}_{.j})(\bar{x}_{.j} - \bar{x}_{..})$$

$$+ \sum_{j=1}^{r} \sum_{i=1}^{n_j} (\bar{x}_{.j} - \bar{x}_{..})^2.$$

Using Theorem II and its corollary we have

$$\sum_{j=1}^{r} \sum_{i=1}^{n_j} 2(x_{ij} - \bar{x}_{.j})(\bar{x}_{.j} - \bar{x}_{..}) = 2 \sum_{j=1}^{r} (\bar{x}_{.j} - \bar{x}_{..}) \sum_{i=1}^{n_j} (x_{ij} - \bar{x}_{.j}).$$

In Exercise 2.2 we demonstrated that

$$\sum_{i=1}^{n_j} (x_{ij} - \bar{x}_{.j}) = 0$$

or in other words, that the sum of the deviations from the mean is zero. Hence the middle term has the value zero, leaving two sums of squares. The second of these is

$$\sum_{j=1}^{r} \sum_{i=1}^{n_j} (\bar{x}_{.j} - \bar{x}_{..})^2 = \sum_{j=1}^{r} n_j (\bar{x}_{.j} - \bar{x}_{..})^2.$$

The results can be summarized by the identity

$$\sum_{j=1}^{r} \sum_{i=1}^{n_j} (x_{ij} - \bar{x}_{..})^2 = \sum_{j=1}^{r} \sum_{i=1}^{n_j} (x_{ij} - \bar{x}_{.j})^2 + \sum_{j=1}^{r} n_j (\bar{x}_{.j} - \bar{x}_{..})^2. \tag{2.2}$$

To save writing, let

$$\sum_{j=1}^{r} \sum_{i=1}^{n_j} (x_{ij} - \bar{x}_{..})^2 = SS_T,$$

which we will call total sum of squares,

$$\sum_{j=1}^{r} \sum_{i=1}^{n_j} (x_{ij} - \bar{x}_{.j})^2 = SS_W,$$

which we will call within-sample or within-groups sum of squares, and

$$\sum_{j=1}^{r} n_j (\bar{x}_{.j} - \bar{x}_{..})^2 = SS_A,$$

which will be known as among-samples or among-groups sum of squares. Thus the Identity (2.2) may be written

$$SS_T = SS_A + SS_W. \tag{2.3}$$

Let us take a closer look at the individual terms of the identity. First, $SS_T = (N-1)s^2$ is a measure of the overall variation of the N observations. The more variable the observations, the larger SS_T becomes. Next SS_A, except for the weighing factor n_j, looks like the numerator of the variance of sample means. At any rate it is not difficult to see that this term reflects the variability of the r sample means. If they are nearly alike, it is small. If they differ greatly, it is large. Finally,

$$SS_W = \sum_{j=1}^{r} \sum_{i=1}^{n_j} (x_{ij} - \bar{x}_{.j})^2 = \sum_{j=1}^{r} (n_j - 1) s_j^2$$

is a measure of the variation within the individual samples. It is the sum of the variances within each column weighted by 1 less than the number of observations. If there is little variation within each column, the term is small. Great variation within the columns makes this sum of squares large.

2-6 TESTING THE HYPOTHESIS OF EQUAL MEANS

Consider

$$SS_W = \sum_{j=1}^{r} (n_j - 1) s_j^2.$$

We have observed that the average value of s_j^2 is σ^2; that is, the sample variance is an unbiased estimate of the population variance. According to the Assumptions (2.1), all r populations have the same variance. This leads to the conclusion that the average value of

$$(n_1 - 1) s_1^2 + (n_2 - 1) s_2^2 + \ldots + (n_r - 1) s_r^2$$

is

$$(n_1 - 1) \sigma^2 + (n_2 - 1) \sigma^2 + \ldots + (n_r - 1) \sigma^2$$
$$= [(n_1 + n_2 + \ldots + n_r) - r] \sigma^2 = (N - r) \sigma^2$$

so that $SS_W/(N-r)$ has an average value of σ^2 and is an unbiased estimate of σ^2. It can also be shown that the average value of SS_A is

$$(r - 1) \sigma^2 + \sum_{j=1}^{r} n_j (\mu_j - \mu)^2$$

where

$$\mu = \sum_{j=1}^{r} n_j \mu_j / N.$$

Thus the average value of $SS_A/(r-1)$ is

$$\sigma^2 + \frac{\sum_{j=1}^{r} n_j (\mu_j - \mu)^2}{r - 1}. \qquad (2.4)$$

Now if $\mu_1 = \mu_2 = \cdots = \mu_r = \mu$ so that H_0 is true, the sum appearing in (2.4) will be zero. If this is the case, $SS_A/(r-1)$ and $SS_W/(N-r)$ should have compatible values since they both estimate σ^2. Let us seek some way of comparing these two estimates.   Past experience with tests concerning variances might suggest a type of F test.   Indeed, it can be shown mathematically that

$$F_{r-1, N-r} = \frac{\frac{SS_A}{r-1}}{\frac{SS_W}{N-r}}$$

if H_0 is true.   If the means are not equal, then the average value of $SS_A/(r-1)$ is increased.   This would tend to produce a larger value of F.   Hence we would conclude that only large values of F contradict the hypothesis.   Mathematical statisticians have justified this choice of critical region.   The hypothesis of equal means is rejected if

$$F_{r-1, N-r} > F_{1-\alpha;\, r-1,\, N-r}.$$

For the data of Table 2.2, we have

$$SS_A = 3(39-46)^2 + 5(51-46)^2 + 4(45-46)^2 = 276,$$
$$SS_W = 2(63) + 4(30.5) + 3(18) = 302.$$

$$F_{2,\, 9} = \frac{\frac{276}{2}}{\frac{302}{9}} = 4.11.$$

From the table we obtain $F_{.95;\, 2,9} = 4.26$.   Since 4.11 is less than 4.26, the hypothesis of equal means is accepted at the 5 percent level of significance.

2-7 COMPUTING FORMULAS

Using the formulas that define SS_T, SS_A, and SS_W is not the best method for computing these numbers.   In the example from Table 2.2, they worked out nicely since all squared quantities were integers.   Since this is not always the case, we will rewrite them in a form more adaptable to computation.   We have

$$SS_T = \sum_{j=1}^{r} \sum_{i=1}^{n_j} (x_{ij} - \bar{x}_{..})^2$$

$$= \sum_{j=1}^{r} \sum_{i=1}^{n_j} (x_{ij}^2 - 2\bar{x}_{..} x_{ij} + \bar{x}_{..}^2)$$

$$= \sum_{j=1}^{r} \sum_{i=1}^{n_j} x_{ij}^2 + \sum_{j=1}^{r} \sum_{i=1}^{n_j} (-2\bar{x}_{..} x_{ij}) + \sum_{j=1}^{r} \sum_{i=1}^{n_j} \bar{x}_{..}^2$$

$$= \sum_{j=1}^{r} \sum_{i=1}^{n_j} x_{ij}^2 - 2\bar{x}_{..} \sum_{j=1}^{r} \sum_{i=1}^{n_j} x_{ij} + N\bar{x}_{..}^2.$$

But

$$\sum_{j=1}^{r} \sum_{i=1}^{n_j} x_{ij} = N\bar{x}_{..}$$

so that the last two terms yield

$$-2\bar{x}_{..}(N\bar{x}_{..}) + N\bar{x}_{..}^2 = -N\bar{x}_{..}^2 = -N\left(\frac{T_{..}}{N}\right)^2 = -\frac{T_{..}^2}{N}.$$

Thus

$$SS_T = \sum_{j=1}^{r} \sum_{i=1}^{n_j} x_{ij}^2 - \frac{T_{..}^2}{N}. \tag{2.5}$$

Next consider

$$SS_A = \sum_{j=1}^{r} \sum_{i=1}^{n_j} (\bar{x}_{.j} - \bar{x}_{..})^2 = \sum_{j=1}^{r} n_j (\bar{x}_{.j} - \bar{x}_{..})^2$$

$$= \sum_{j=1}^{r} n_j (\bar{x}_{.j}^2 - 2\bar{x}_{.j}\bar{x}_{..} + \bar{x}_{..}^2)$$

$$= \sum_{j=1}^{r} (n_j \bar{x}_{.j}^2 - 2n_j \bar{x}_{.j}\bar{x}_{..} + n_j \bar{x}_{..}^2)$$

$$= \sum_{j=1}^{r} n_j \bar{x}_{.j}^2 + \sum_{j=1}^{r}(-2\bar{x}_{..} n_j \bar{x}_{.j}) + \sum_{j=1}^{r} n_j \bar{x}_{..}^2$$

$$= \sum_{j=1}^{r} n_j \left(\frac{T_{.j}}{n_j}\right)^2 - 2\bar{x}_{..} \sum_{j=1}^{r} n_j \bar{x}_{.j} + \bar{x}_{..}^2 \sum_{j=1}^{r} n_j.$$

The first term is

$$\sum_{j=1}^{r} \frac{T_{.j}^2}{n_j}.$$

The last two terms may be written

$$-2\frac{T_{..}}{N} \sum_{j=1}^{r} n_j \frac{T_{.j}}{n_j} + \left(\frac{T_{..}}{N}\right)^2 N = -2\frac{T_{..}}{N} \sum_{j=1}^{r} T_{.j} + \frac{T_{..}^2}{N}$$

$$= -2\frac{T_{..}}{N} T_{..} + \frac{T_{..}^2}{N} = -\frac{T_{..}^2}{N}.$$

Hence

$$SS_A = \sum_{j=1}^{r} \frac{T_{.j}^2}{n_j} - \frac{T_{..}^2}{N}. \tag{2.6}$$

Finally, by subtraction we get

$$SS_W = SS_T - SS_A \ . \tag{2.7}$$

To illustrate the formulas using the data of Table 2.2, we write

$$SS_T = 36^2 + 33^2 + 48^2 + 57^2 + 53^2 + 43^2 + 54^2 + 48^2 + 50^2$$
$$+ 41^2 + 47^2 + 42^2 - \frac{(552)^2}{12}$$
$$= 25{,}970 - 25{,}392 = 578, \tag{2.8}$$
$$SS_A = \frac{(117)^2}{3} + \frac{(255)^2}{5} + \frac{(180)^2}{4} - \frac{(552)^2}{12}$$
$$= 25{,}668 - 25{,}392 = 276,$$
$$SS_W = 578 - 276 = 302.$$

EXERCISE

2.4 Prove

$$SS_W = \sum_{j=1}^{r} \sum_{i=1}^{n_j} x_{ij}^2 - \sum_{j=1}^{r} \frac{T_{.j}^2}{n_j}$$

by starting from the definition of SS_W.

2-8 THE ANALYSIS OF VARIANCE TABLE

It is customary to summarize the results in a table. The form we will use for the one-way classification is given in Table 2.3.

Table 2.3 ANALYSIS OF VARIANCE FOR THE ONE-WAY CLASSIFICATION

Source of Variation	SS	d.f.	MS	EMS	F
Among groups	SS_A	$r-1$	$SS_A/(r-1) = MS_A$	$\sigma^2 + \sum_{j=1}^{r} \frac{n_j(\mu_j - \mu)^2}{r-1}$	$\dfrac{MS_A}{MS_W}$
Within groups	SS_W	$N-r$	$SS_W/(N-r) = MS_W$	σ^2	
TOTAL	SS_T	$N-1$			

The expected mean square (abbreviated *EMS*) column deserves further comment. It has been pointed out that the average value of

$$\left[\frac{SS_W}{N-r} = MS_W \right] = \sigma^2$$

and the average value of

$$\left[\frac{SS_A}{r-1} = MS_A \right] = \sigma^2 + \frac{\sum_{j=1}^{r} n_j (\mu_j - \mu)^2}{r-1} \ .$$

These are called expected mean squares and will always be included in a column of the analysis of variance table. For the special case $n_1 = n_2 = \cdots = n_r = n$, we note that

$$\sum_{j=1}^{r} \frac{n_j(\mu_j - \mu)^2}{r-1} = n \frac{\sum_{j=1}^{r}(\mu_j - \mu)^2}{r-1}.$$

In more complicated situations to be presented later, a glance at the EMS column will indicate which mean squares should be compared in an F ratio to test hypotheses of interest. In Table 2.3, both EMS's have the value σ^2 if the hypothesis of equal means is true. As we already know

$$F_{r-1,\,N-r} = \frac{MS_A}{MS_W}$$

is the proper ratio to use.

The results from the data to Table 2.2 are presented in Table 2.4. We accepted the hypothesis of equal means since 4.11 is not a significantly large F.

Table 2.4 ANALYSIS OF VARIANCE FOR TABLE 2.2

Source of Variation	SS	d.f.	MS	EMS	F
Among groups	276	2	138	$\sigma^2 + \frac{1}{2}\sum_{j=1}^{3} n_j(\mu_j - \mu)^2$	4.11
Within groups	302	9	33.56	σ^2	
TOTAL	578	11			

Quite often the notations 4.11* and 4.11** are used to indicate that 4.11 is significant at the 5 and 1 percent level respectively. Of course, in the Table 2.2 example it is not significant at either level.

2-9 THE OUTLINE REORGANIZED

Since the outline that is advocated in Section 1-5 is not particularly suited to analysis of variance problems, some changes seem to be in order. A more reasonable sequence of steps is:

1. State the hypotheses and the alternates. Thus far we have considered examples involving only one test. Quite often, as we shall see later, more than one hypothesis will be of interest. This step should be completed before the data are examined. In general, it is not a valid statistical procedure to use data to test hypotheses that the data themselves suggest.

2. Choose the levels of significance. As Step 1 implies, if several hypotheses are to be tested, a significance level for each hypothesis will have to be chosen.

3. List the assumptions. It is advisable to write them out in words as we did at the beginning of Section 2-4. Then follow this with a statement such as "the equivalent symbolic formulation is" and then give the assumptions in the form of Equation (2.1). Since others who are not familar with analysis of variance might read the write-up, it may be helpful to express the assumptions both ways even after you have mastered the symbolic form.

4. Make an analysis of variance table filling in the *EMS* column. Then it should be apparent which calculations are required.

5. Do the calculations and fill in the missing spaces in the table. Even though all computations are performed on a calculator, it is advisable to summarize the sums of squares calculations as was done with Equation (2.8).

6. Consult the *F* table to determine which ratios, if any, are significant. Mark those that exceed the critical value.

7. Draw the conclusions. Either accept or reject each hypothesis.

8. If hypotheses are rejected, we may still want to investigate further and use the *T*-method or the *S*-method described later in the chapter.

EXERCISES

2.5 A professor is trying to select a good textbook for his elementary course in statistics from 4 different ones which are available. He has 47 students, whom he distributes at random to four different groups, placing 12 in three of the groups and 11 in the fourth group. The assignment of textbooks to groups is also done at random. After the course is over, all students who are still enrolled take the same examination. The results are:

Textbook	A	B	C	D
	68	41	54	44
	68	47	44	51
	69	54	51	69
Final	60	65	56	59
exami-	73	32	47	59
nation	64	73	61	55
grades	71	44	59	66
	67	48	49	
	75	64	41	
		54	61	
			73	

Assuming that differences attributed to using a number of textbooks are the only variables that need be considered, what conclusions can be drawn? Follow the first seven steps of the outline given in Section 2-9.

2.6   Worms are classified into three groups by a structural characteristic (small, medium, or large ventral flap in the region of the vulva). Three random samples of 11 are taken from each group and the length of each worm is measured. These data are recorded in the table. Test the hypothesis that the mean length of each group is the same.

Worm Groups		
No. 1	No. 2	No. 3
8.9	12.2	9.5
9.7	12.0	8.0
11.5	11.5	8.3
8.2	8.7	10.0
10.5	10.5	9.5
10.8	9.0	10.0
11.0	10.5	11.3
8.0	13.0	10.5
9.9	13.0	8.0
11.0	11.0	8.0
11.0	11.1	9.2

2.7   A psychologist has devised an examination in such a way that the final score achieved depends almost entirely upon the ability to follow instructions. It is then administered to 40 available students, who have been divided into four groups at random. The instructions are given in the following ways:

To group I—written and brief,
To group II—oral and brief,
To group III—written and detailed,
To group IV—oral and detailed.

The scores yield $SS_T = 870$, $SS_A = 150$. What conclusions are likely to be drawn?

2.8   Given the two random samples

Sample 1:   7, 2, 11, 4, 1,
Sample 2:   10, 6, 5, 13, 6.

Use both t and F to test the hypothesis of equal means. Show that in this example, $t^2 = F$.

2-10 EQUIVALENCE OF THE F AND t TESTS WHEN $r=2$

When we have only 2 random samples,

$$SS_W = (n_1 - 1) s_1^2 + (n_2 - 1) s_2^2$$

and

$$SS_A = n_1 (\bar{x}_{.1} - \bar{x}_{..})^2 + n_2 (\bar{x}_{.2} - \bar{x}_{..})^2.$$

If we use the fact that

$$\bar{x}_{..} = \frac{n_1 \bar{x}_{.1} + n_2 \bar{x}_{.2}}{n_1 + n_2},$$

then

$$(\bar{x}_{.1} - \bar{x}_{..})^2 = \frac{n_2^2 (\bar{x}_{.1} - \bar{x}_{.2})^2}{(n_1 + n_2)^2}$$

and

$$(\bar{x}_{.2} - \bar{x}_{..})^2 = \frac{n_1^2 (\bar{x}_{.1} - \bar{x}_{.2})^2}{(n_1 + n_2)^2}.$$

Thus

$$\begin{aligned} SS_A &= \frac{n_1 n_2^2 (\bar{x}_{.1} - \bar{x}_{.2})^2 + n_2 n_1^2 (\bar{x}_{.1} - \bar{x}_{.2})^2}{(n_1 + n_2)^2} \\ &= \frac{(n_1 + n_2)(n_1 n_2)(\bar{x}_{.1} - \bar{x}_{.2})^2}{(n_1 + n_2)^2} \\ &= \frac{n_1 n_2 (\bar{x}_{.1} - \bar{x}_{.2})^2}{n_1 + n_2} = \frac{(\bar{x}_{.1} - \bar{x}_{.2})^2}{\dfrac{1}{n_1} + \dfrac{1}{n_2}}. \end{aligned}$$

Hence

$$F_{1,\, n_1 + n_2 - 2} = \frac{\dfrac{SS_A}{1}}{\dfrac{SS_W}{n_1 + n_2 - 2}}$$

$$= \frac{(\bar{x}_{.1} - \bar{x}_{.2})^2}{\dfrac{(n_1 - 1) s_1^2 + (n_2 - 1) s_2^2}{n_1 + n_2 - 2} \left(\dfrac{1}{n_1} + \dfrac{1}{n_2} \right)} = t^2_{n_1 + n_2 - 2}.$$

This is exactly the square of the statistic given by Equation (1.11) when $\mu_1 = \mu_2$. In other words, the same quantity is computed in each case.

We have yet to compare the critical regions for the two tests. If $n_1 = 7$, $n_2 = 5$, $n_1 + n_2 - 2 = 10$, $\alpha = .05$, the t test rejects the hypothesis when $t_{10} < -2.23$ or $t_{10} > 2.23$. The F test rejects when $F_{1,\,10} > 4.96$. Observe that $4.96 = (2.23)^2$. It can be shown mathematically that if t has a t_ν distribution, then t^2 has an $F_{1,\,\nu}$ distribution. The upper one-tail critical region for the F test corresponds exactly to the two-tail critical region for the t test with the same significance level. Numerical verification can be made for other entries from the two tables.

Thus it makes no difference whether the two-tailed t test or the one-tailed F test is used in this situation. They produce exactly the same result. This justifies the previous remark that the F test may be regarded as an extension of the t test.

2-11 THE POWER OF THE F TEST

In Chapter 1 we defined power and considered several simple examples of power curves. We emphasized the importance of the concept and pointed out that, in general, power calculations are quite complex. Fortunately, Pearson and Hartley [4] have prepared a set of curves that simplify the problem considerably for F tests arising from standard analysis of variance models. These curves are reproduced in Table 6 of the Appendix.

In order to use the graphs, certain information is required. First, we must use ν_1, the degrees of freedom of the numerator, to find the correct page. This number is found in the upper left-hand corner and runs from 1 through 8. Second, we need ν_2, the degrees of freedom of the denominator. On all eight graphs there are curves corresponding to $\nu_2 = 6, 7, 8,$ 9, 10, 12, 15, 20, 30, 60, ∞. For other values of ν_2, interpolation is necessary. Third, we need to have α, the significance level of the experiment. The curves on the left side of the graph are for $\alpha = .05$; those on the right, for $\alpha = .01$. No other values of α are considered. Fourth, a parameter ϕ, which is used to enter the horizontal scale, must be computed. This parameter has the value

$$\phi = \frac{\sqrt{\dfrac{1}{r}\sum_{j=1}^{r}\beta_j^2}}{\dfrac{\sigma}{\sqrt{n}}} = \frac{\sqrt{\dfrac{n}{r}\sum_{j=1}^{r}\beta_j^2}}{\sigma} \tag{2.9}$$

for the one-way classification with equal sample sizes. When other models are discussed in later chapters, the appropriate formulas for ϕ will be given. These four quantities are used to locate a point on one of the graphs. The value on the vertical scale corresponding to the point is the power. We now turn our attention to some examples.

Suppose that the psychologist in Exercise 2.7 would like to know the probability of rejecting the hypothesis if three-treatment effects (or treatment means) are equal and the fourth exceeds the others by σ. Then the β_j's can be replaced by β, β, β, $\beta+\sigma$. Since

$$\sum_{j=1}^{4} \beta_j = 0,$$

we have

$$\beta+\beta+\beta+\beta+\sigma=0, \quad \beta=-\frac{\sigma}{4}$$

and

$$\beta+\sigma=-\frac{\sigma}{4}+\sigma=\frac{3}{4}\sigma.$$

Thus

$$\sum_{j=1}^{4} \beta_j^2 = \left(-\frac{\sigma}{4}\right)^2 + \left(-\frac{\sigma}{4}\right)^2 + \left(-\frac{\sigma}{4}\right)^2 + \left(\frac{3\sigma}{4}\right)^2 = \frac{3\sigma^2}{4}$$

so that (since $n=10$)

$$\phi=\frac{\sqrt{\dfrac{10}{4}\left(\dfrac{3\sigma^2}{4}\right)}}{\sigma}=\sqrt{\frac{30}{16}}=\frac{\sqrt{30}}{4}=\frac{5.477}{4}=1.37.$$

For this example $\nu_1=3$, $\nu_2=36$. Turning to the graph we find

Power $=.58$ if $\alpha=.05$

Power $=.32$ if $\alpha=.01$.

Since interpolation is necessary on both ϕ and ν_2, others may read answers differing from these by .01 or .02.

The psychologist may want to know how large to choose n so that the power is at least .95 when the β_j's are as given above and $\alpha=.05$. This involves some trial-and-error and is complicated by the difficulty of interpolating between 60 and ∞ degrees of freedom. However, we can get an approximate answer. The graph shows that for $\nu_2=60$, $\phi=2.14$ gives a power of .95. When 10 is replaced by n, we obtain $\phi=\sqrt{3n}/4$. If we choose n so that ϕ is at least 2.14 and $\nu_2=4n-4$ is 60 or more, then we can be sure that the power is at least .95. Solving $2.14=\sqrt{3n}/4$ for n yields $n=[(2.14)(4)]^2/3=24.3$. In other words, if $n=25$, then $\nu_2=96$ and $\phi=2.165$, and the power is slightly more than .95. Thus, if we use 100 students, the probability is more than .95 that the hypothesis of equal means is rejected when one mean exceeds the other three by one standard deviation.

Next suppose that the psychologist seeks information about the power if the largest difference among the means (and hence the β_j's) is σ.

Many choices of the β_j's yield a maximum difference of σ. By using a little calculus it can be shown that

$$\sum_{j=1}^{4}\beta_j^2$$

(and hence ϕ) is minimized by selecting the β_j's as $-\sigma/2$, $\sigma/2$, 0, 0. Since the power increases with ϕ, any other choice of the β_j's such that they have a maximum difference of σ will give a larger power. We have

$$\sum_{j=1}^{4}\beta_j^2=\left(-\frac{\sigma}{2}\right)^2+\left(\frac{\sigma}{2}\right)^2+0+0=\frac{\sigma^2}{2},$$

$$\phi=\frac{\sqrt{\frac{10}{4}\left(\frac{\sigma^2}{2}\right)}}{\sigma}=\sqrt{\frac{10}{8}}=\sqrt{\frac{5}{4}}=\frac{\sqrt{5}}{2}=\frac{2.236}{2}=1.12.$$

Turning to the graph, we find for $\alpha=.05$, a power of approximately .40. The psychologist can state that the probability is at least .40 of rejecting the hypothesis of equal means when, in fact, a maximum difference of σ is present. In general, if the largest difference among the means is $a\sigma$, the smallest power is found using for the β_j's $-a\sigma/2$, $a\sigma/2$, and all others 0. In this case

$$\sum_{j=1}^{r}\beta_j^2=\left(-\frac{a\sigma}{2}\right)^2+\left(\frac{a\sigma}{2}\right)^2=\frac{a^2\sigma^2}{2},$$

$$\phi=\frac{\sqrt{\frac{n}{r}\left(\frac{a^2\sigma^2}{2}\right)}}{\sigma}=a\sqrt{\frac{n}{2r}}.$$

It is unfortunate that ϕ as given by Equation (2.9) depends upon the unknown parameter σ. In the examples we avoided the difficulty that this presents by choosing the β_j's as multiples of σ. If we are interested in obtaining the power for a set of β_j's not expressed this way, we could replace σ by an estimate. However, this is a rather unsatisfactory procedure since relatively small errors in the estimate can introduce a large error into the power calculations.

Power calculations should be made before the experiment is performed so that this information may be used in organizing the experiment. This is consistent with good statistical procedure, which dictates advance planning. Unfortunately, investigators frequently collect data first and then discover that a large part of their effort has been wasted.

EXERCISE

2.9 Taking $\alpha=.05$, find the probability of rejecting the hypothesis of equal means for Exercise 2.6 when two means are equal and the third exceeds these two by 1.25σ. How large should n be if this probability is to be raised to .95? If the largest difference among three means is 1.25σ, find the least value for the power.

2-12 HYPOTHESES INVOLVING LINEAR COMBINATIONS OF THE POPULATION MEANS

In previous sections we have been concerned with testing the hypothesis of equal means. We may be interested in formulating other hypotheses before conducting the experiment, particularly if we are reasonably certain that all means are not equal. For example, in Exercise 2.7, we may hypothesize

$$H_0': \quad \frac{\mu_1 + \mu_2}{2} = \frac{\mu_3 + \mu_4}{2}$$

$$H_1': \quad \frac{\mu_1 + \mu_2}{2} \neq \frac{\mu_3 + \mu_4}{2}$$

if we feel that it makes no difference whether the instructions are brief or detailed. If we are inclined to believe that written and oral instructions produce about the same results, then it is reasonable to test

$$H_0'': \quad \frac{\mu_1 + \mu_3}{2} = \frac{\mu_2 + \mu_4}{2}$$

$$H_1'': \quad \frac{\mu_1 + \mu_3}{2} \neq \frac{\mu_2 + \mu_4}{2}.$$

Observe that H_0' and H_0'' may be rewritten

$$H_0': \quad \mu_1 + \mu_2 - \mu_3 - \mu_4 = 0$$

and

$$H_0'': \quad \mu_1 - \mu_2 + \mu_3 - \mu_4 = 0.$$

The left-hand sides of each of these equations are of the form

$$L = c_1\mu_1 + c_2\mu_2 + \ldots + c_r\mu_r \qquad (2.10)$$

where the c_j's are constants. This is called a linear combination of the treatment means. When

$$\sum_{j=1}^{r} c_j = 0,$$

then (2.10) is called a contrast. Further, if

$$L_1 = c_{11}\mu_1 + c_{21}\mu_2 + \cdots + c_{r1}\mu_r$$

and

$$L_2 = c_{12}\mu_2 + c_{22}\mu_2 + \cdots + c_{r2}\mu_r$$

are contrasts such that

$$c_{11}c_{12} + c_{21}c_{22} + \cdots + c_{r1}c_{r2} = 0,$$

then L_1 and L_2 are called orthogonal contrasts. It is easy to verify that $\mu_1 + \mu_2 - \mu_3 - \mu_4$ and $\mu_1 - \mu_2 + \mu_3 - \mu_4$ are orthogonal contrasts.

We might expect that

$$\hat{L} = c_1 \bar{x}_{.1} + c_2 \bar{x}_{.2} + \cdots + c_r \bar{x}_{.r} \tag{2.11}$$

would be the statistic to use to test hypotheses about L. It can be shown that either

$$t_{N-r} = \frac{\hat{L} - L_0}{\sqrt{MS_W} \sqrt{\sum_{j=1}^{r} \frac{c_j^2}{n_j}}} \tag{2.12}$$

or

$$F_{1,\,N-r} = \frac{(\hat{L} - L_0)^2}{MS_W \sum_{j=1}^{r} \frac{c_j^2}{n_j}} \tag{2.13}$$

are the proper statistics when choosing between

$$H_0^*: \quad L = L_0$$
$$H_1^*: \quad L \neq L_0.$$

As before, a two-sided critical region is used with the t test. The critical region for the F test is again the right-hand tail.

In the most frequently occurring situation, all n_j are equal to n, L is a contrast, and the hypothesis specifies that L is 0. For this case we may rewrite (2.13). After multiplying both numerator and denominator by n^2, it becomes

$$F_{1,\,N-r} = \frac{\left[\sum_{j=1}^{r} c_j T_{.j} \right]^2}{MS_W \left[n \sum_{j=1}^{r} c_j^2 \right]}. \tag{2.14}$$

The quantity

$$D^2 = \frac{\left[\sum_{j=1}^{r} c_j T_{.j} \right]^2}{n \sum_{j=1}^{r} c_j^2}$$

may be regarded as a sum of squares with which is associated 1 degree of freedom. Recall that the degrees of freedom for SS_A is $r - 1$. A set of D^2's, say

$$D_1^2, \ D_2^2, \cdots, \ D_{r-1}^2,$$

such that

$$SS_A = D_1^2 + D_2^2 + \cdots + D_{r-1}^2, \qquad (2.15)$$

are sometimes sought by experimenters partly because (2.15) provides a computational check. If L_1, L_2, $\cdots$, L_{r-1} are $r-1$ mutually orthogonal contrasts which are all equal to zero by hypothesis, then the D^2's associated with these L's exhibit property (2.15).

We now turn to an example to clarify some of these concepts. Suppose that a teacher wishes to compare the relative merits of the following combinations of teaching aids:

> Treatment 1 :   textbook only
> Treatment 2 :   textbook and class notes
> Treatment 3 :   textbook and lab manual
> Treatment 4 :   textbook, lab manual, and class notes.

Suspecting that the hypothesis of equal means will be rejected, he feels that the following additional hypotheses are worth testing

$$\begin{aligned} H_0' &: \quad \mu_1 = \mu_2 \text{ or } \mu_1 - \mu_2 = 0 \\ H_1' &: \quad \mu_1 \neq \mu_2 \\[8pt] H_0'' &: \quad \mu_3 = \mu_4 \text{ or } \mu_3 - \mu_4 = 0 \\ H_1'' &: \quad \mu_3 \neq \mu_4 \end{aligned} \qquad (2.16)$$

and

$$\begin{aligned} H_0''' &: \quad \frac{\mu_1 + \mu_2}{2} = \frac{\mu_3 + \mu_4}{2} \text{ or } \mu_1 + \mu_2 - \mu_3 - \mu_4 = 0 \\[8pt] H_1''' &: \quad \frac{\mu_1 + \mu_2}{2} \neq \frac{\mu_3 + \mu_4}{2}. \end{aligned}$$

The first hypothesis infers that notes add nothing additional if used with a textbook. The second says that notes add nothing additional if used with a textbook and lab manual. The third states that the average result without a lab manual is the same as the average result using one. In order to test these hypotheses, 100 students are assigned randomly to 4 classes of 25 each, and the study is conducted using final examination grades. We note that $L_1 = \mu_1 - \mu_2$, $L_2 = \mu_3 - \mu_4$, and $L_3 = \mu_1 + \mu_2 - \mu_3 - \mu_4$ are mutually orthogonal contrasts. The D^2's are

$$\begin{aligned} D_1^2 &= \frac{(T_{.1} - T_{.2})^2}{25\,(2)} \\[8pt] D_2^2 &= \frac{(T_{.3} - T_{.4})^2}{25\,(2)} \\[8pt] D_3^2 &= \frac{(T_{.1} + T_{.2} - T_{.3} - T_{.4})^2}{25\,(4)}. \end{aligned} \qquad (2.17)$$

The results are summarized in Table 2.5.

Table 2.5 ANALYSIS OF VARIANCE

Source	SS	d.f.	MS	EMS	F
Among Groups—	SS_A	3	MS_A	$\sigma^2 + \dfrac{25}{3}\sum\limits_{j=1}^{4}(\mu_j - \mu)^2$	MS_A/MS_W
notes *vs.* none (without manual)	D_1^2	1	D_1^2		D_1^2 / MS_W
notes *vs.* none (with manual)	D_2^2	1	D_2^2		D_2^2 / MS_W
manual *vs.* none	D_3^2	1	D_3^2		D_3^2 / MS_W
Within groups—	SS_W	96	MS_W	σ^2	
TOTAL	SS_T	99			

The *EMS*'s opposite D_1^2 D_1^2 and D_3^2 have been left blank. It can be shown that

$$\text{average value of } D_1^2 = \sigma^2 + k_1(\mu_1 - \mu_2)^2 = \sigma^2 + k_1(\beta_1 - \beta_2)^2$$
$$\text{average value of } D_2^2 = \sigma^2 + k_2(\mu_3 - \mu_4)^2 = \sigma^2 + k_2(\beta_3 - \beta_4)^2$$
$$\text{average value of } D_3^2 = \sigma^2 + k_3(\mu_1 + \mu_2 - \mu_3 - \mu_4)^2$$
$$= \sigma^2 + k_3(\beta_1 + \beta_2 - \beta_3 - \beta_4)^2$$

where k_1, k_2 and k_3 are constants that play no roll in the analysis.

Several comments concerning this example seem to be worthwhile. First, as we have emphasized before, all hypotheses should be formulated before conducting the experiment. Second, select hypotheses of interest. Whether they involve mutually orthogonal contrasts is of minor importance. Contrasts are apt to arise frequently with a one-way classfication, but more than likely they will not be mutually orthogonal. Third, if all means are equal, then all contrasts are equal and vice versa. Fourth, when several hypotheses are tested at one time, the problem of determining the significance level for the experiment as a whole becomes very complicated. This last point merits further discussion.

In the example summarized by Table 2.5, three *F*-ratios are required. A little reflection makes it apparent that even though the chance of rejecting a true hypothesis is some small number α on each test, the probability of rejecting at least one true hypothesis when several tests are conducted becomes considerably larger than α. In other words, if we conduct enough tests, we will very likely reject one or more hypotheses even though they are all true. This undesirable state of affairs has been the subject of a number of articles appearing in the journals.

Even though a number of tests are conducted, the sum of the significance levels is an upper bound to the probability of rejecting one or more hypotheses when all are true. If H_0', H_0'' and H_0''' of Equation (2.16) are the only hypotheses of interest in the textbook-notes-manual problem and if we select $\alpha = .025$ for each of the three tests, then we can be sure that the probability of rejecting one or more of these is less than .075 when all are true.

EXERCISES

2.10 (a) Verify that $\mu_1 - \mu_2$, $\mu_3 - \mu_4$ and $\mu_1 + \mu_2 - \mu_3 - \mu_4$ are mutually orthogonal contrasts.

(b) Verify by direct algebra that $D_1^2 + D_2^2 + D_3^2 = SS_A$ for the D^2's defined by Equation (2.17).

2.11 A study of the effect of herbicides upon wheat yields is conducted. The treatments are :

Treatment 1 :   nothing
Treatment 2 :   first type of herbicide in powdered form
Treatment 3 :   second type of herbicide in powdered form
Treatment 4 :   first type of herbicide in pellet form
Treatment 5 :   second type of herbicide in pellet form.

Each treatment is randomly assigned to 10 plots of ground, and then the yields are recorded for each of the 50 plots. The treatment totals are

$$T_{.1} = 50, \ T_{.2} = 70, \ T_{.3} = 100, \ T_{.4} = 60, \ T_{.5} = 120,$$

and the total sum of squares is 565. Find a reasonable set of 4 mutually orthogonal contrasts (more than one such set is possible), and test to determine whether or not each is equal to zero. Select as one hypothesis of interest : the average for Treatment 1 equals the average of the other four treatments. Write out the complete analysis and list your conclusions.

2·13 TUKEY'S METHOD FOR MULTIPLE COMPARISONS

We have observed that when several hypotheses are tested, each with specified significance level, the probability of rejecting one or more of them is a difficult number to obtain. In other words, we do not know the significance level of experiment as a whole even though all hypotheses are formulated before the experiment is conducted. Usually the null hypothesis is tested in analysis of variance type experiments with no special concern being given to other hypotheses. If the null hypothesis is rejected, then it is reasonable to look for contrasts which are responsible. It is desirable to have a procedure (a) that permits selection of the contrasts after the data are available and (b) with which a known level of significance is associated. One such procedure has been devised by Tukey. Following the notation of Scheffé [5], this will be called the T-method.

Let L (2.10) be a contrast estimated by $\hat{L}$ (2.11) and all r samples be of size n. Tukey has shown that the probability is $1-\alpha$ that

$$\hat{L}-T\sqrt{MS_W}\left(\frac{1}{2}\sum_{j=1}^{r}\mid c_j\mid\right)\leq L\leq\hat{L}+T\sqrt{MS_W}\left(\frac{1}{2}\sum_{j=1}^{r}\mid c_j\mid\right)\quad(2.18)$$

holds simultaneously for every possible contrast that may be constructed. Here

$$T=\frac{1}{\sqrt{n}}\,q_{1-\alpha;\,r,\,N-r}$$

where $q_{1-\alpha;\,r,\,N-r}$ is tabulated in Table 7 in the Appendix and is the point exceeded $100\,\alpha$ percent of the time in the distribution of the studentized range. (If $y_1,\,\cdots,\,y_n$ are independently $N(\mu,\,\sigma^2)$ and s^2 is an unbiased estimate of σ^2 based upon ν degrees of freedom, then

$$q_{n,\,\nu}=\frac{\text{largest }y-\text{smallest }y}{s}$$

is called the studentized range.)

The T-method was originally designed for contrasts comparing two means (i.e., $L=\mu_1-\mu_2$). It is seldom used in practice except for this special case. For this situation

$$\frac{1}{2}\sum_{j=1}^{r}\mid c_j\mid=\frac{1}{2}(\mid 1\mid+\mid-1\mid)=1$$

and the probability is $1-\alpha$ that the intervals

$$\bar{x}_{.j}-\bar{x}_{.j'}-T\sqrt{MS_W}\leq\mu_j-\mu_{j'}\leq\bar{x}_{.j}-\bar{x}_{.j'}+T\sqrt{MS_W}\quad(2.19)$$

capture all $r(r-1)/2$ differences of the type $\mu_j-\mu_{j'}$ where j and j' refer to any two columns. Usually we will want to know which of the intervals given by (2.19) do not include zero. For example, suppose calculations yield results such as

$$-3.2\leq\mu_1-\mu_2\leq 7.8$$
$$4.7\leq\mu_1-\mu_3\leq 10.5.$$

Since the interval for $\mu_1-\mu_2$ includes zero, this offers no evidence to support the contention that these two means are different. The second interval does not include zero, and therefore we infer that $\mu_1>\mu_3$ or that Treatment 1 is superior to Treatment 3. When the interval computed for a contrast L does not include zero, then L is said to be significantly different from zero.

Suppose that $\bar{x}_{.j}$ is larger than $\bar{x}_{.j'}$. Then the interval (2.19) will not include zero if

$$\bar{x}_{.j} - \bar{x}_{.j'} > T\sqrt{MS_W}$$

or

$$\bar{x}_{.j} - \bar{x}_{.j'} > q_{1-\alpha;\, r,\, N-r}\sqrt{\frac{MS_W}{n}}. \tag{2.20}$$

Thus, in order to discuss which means differ from which others, compute all sample mean differences and compare these differences with the right-hand side of Inequality (2.20).

To illustrate this procedure with a numerical example, we will use the data of Exercise 2.11. Here $r = 5$, $n = 10$, $N - r = 45$, $MS_W = 5$. If we let $\alpha = .05$, then $q_{.95;\, 5,\, 45} = 4.03$ by interpolating between 45 and 60 in the degrees-of-freedom column. Differences of sample means will be compared to

$$q_{.95;\, 5,\, 45}\sqrt{\frac{MS_W}{n}} = 4.03\sqrt{\frac{5}{10}} = 2.85.$$

The five sample means are

$$\bar{x}_{.1} = 5,\ \bar{x}_{.2} = 7,\ \bar{x}_{.3} = 10,\ \bar{x}_{.4} = 6,\ \bar{x}_{.5} = 12$$

so that there are $5(4)/2 = 10$ differences. These can be arranged systematically as in Table 2.6. The differences above the dotted line exceed 2.85. The conclusions are that Treatments 5 and 3 are significantly better than

Table 2.6 Differences $\bar{x}_{.j} - \bar{x}_{.j'}$

	$\bar{x}_{.j}$	$\bar{x}_{.j} - \bar{x}_{.1}$	$\bar{x}_{.j} - \bar{x}_{.4}$	$\bar{x}_{.j} - \bar{x}_{.2}$	$\bar{x}_{.j} - \bar{x}_{.3}$
$\bar{x}_{.5}$	12	7	6	5	2
$\bar{x}_{.3}$	10	5	4	3	
$\bar{x}_{.2}$	7	2	1		
$\bar{x}_{.4}$	6	1			
$\bar{x}_{.1}$	5				

Treatments 1, 4 or 2. There may be no significant difference between 5 and 3 since the interval for $\mu_5 - \mu_3$ covers the value 0. In the language of the experiment, the results indicate that the second type of herbicide is superior in either powder or pellet form. The probability that we have made one or more incorrect statements is .05.

To illustrate the computation of an interval for a more complex contrast, say $L = \mu_2 + \mu_3 - \mu_4 - \mu_5$, we will use the same data. Here

$$\frac{1}{2}\sum_{j=1}^{5} |c_j| = \frac{1}{2}[1+1+1+1] = 2$$

$$T\sqrt{MS_W}\left(\frac{1}{2}\sum_{j=1}^{5} |c_j|\right) = 4.03\sqrt{\frac{5}{10}}(2) = 5.70$$

$$\hat{L} = 7 + 10 - 6 - 12 = -1$$

so that (2.18) gives

$$-1 - 5.70 \leq \mu_2 + \mu_3 - \mu_4 - \mu_5 \leq -1 + 5.70,$$
$$-6.70 \quad \mu_2 + \mu_3 - \mu_4 - \mu_5 \leq 4.70.$$

We conclude $\hat{L}$ is not significantly different from zero.

2-14 SCHEFFE'S METHOD FOR MULTIPLE COMPARISONS

Another procedure for handling multiple comparisons has been devised by Scheffé and will be called the S-method. It can be applied in a number of situations where the T-method is not applicable (for example, when the sample sizes are not equal) and more is known about the behavior of the S-method.

Scheffé has proven that the probability is $1 - \alpha$ that all imaginable contrasts will be captured by the set of intervals given by

$$\hat{L} - S\hat{\sigma}_{\hat{L}} \leq L \leq \hat{L} + S\hat{\sigma}_{\hat{L}} \tag{2.21}$$

where

$$S^2 = (r - 1)\ F_{1-\alpha;\ r-1,\ N-r}$$

and

$$\hat{\sigma}_{\hat{L}}^2 = MS_W \sum_{j=1}^{r} \frac{c_j^2}{n_j}.$$

Thus again, the probability is α that one or more false conclusions will be made.

Let us use the numerical data of Exercise 2.11 once more. We have

$$S^2 = 4F_{.95;\ 4,\ 45} = 4(2.59) = 10.36$$
$$S = 3.22.$$

For contrasts consisting of differences of two means

$$\hat{\sigma}_{\hat{L}}^2 = 5\left(\frac{1+1}{10}\right) = 1$$

so that $S\hat{\sigma}_{\hat{L}} = 3.22$. Thus differences of sample means are compared to 3.22 as opposed to 2.85 for the T-method. Hence, in Table 2.6,

$$\bar{x}_{.3} - \bar{x}_{.2} = 3$$

is not significant by the S-method. For simple contrasts of this type, the T-method gives shorter intervals and consequently finds more differences significant.

For the contrast $L = \mu_2 + \mu_3 - \mu_4 - \mu_5$ we get

$$\hat{\sigma}_{\hat{L}}^2 = 5\left(\frac{1+1+1+1}{10}\right) = 2$$

and $S\hat{\sigma}_{\hat{L}} = 3.22(1.41) = 4.54$.

Equation (2.21) gives

$$-1 - 4.54 \leqq \mu_2 + \mu_3 - \mu_4 - \mu_5 \leqq -1 + 4.54,$$
$$-5.54 \leqq \mu_2 + \mu_3 - \mu_4 - \mu_5 \leqq 3.54,$$

a shorter interval than that provided by the T-method. For the more complex contrasts, the S-method generally gives shorter intervals than the T-method.

An interesting feature of the S-method is that one or more of the intervals given by (2.21) will not cover zero whenever the F-test rejects the hypothesis of equal means. Thus we are able to draw more conclusions than merely that all treatments are not the same. An additional advantage associated with this method is that it is known to be affected very little if the assumptions of normality and equal variances are not satisfied.

Suppose that we decide before conducting the experiment that the only contrast of interest is $L = \mu_2 + \mu_3 - \mu_4 - \mu_5$. Then we can get an interval for L based upon the ordinary t-distribution. The probability is $1 - \alpha$ that L is covered by

$$\hat{L} - t_{1-\alpha/2;\, N-r}\, \hat{\sigma}_{\hat{L}} < L < \hat{L} + t_{1-\alpha/2;\, N-r}\, \hat{\sigma}_{\hat{L}}. \tag{2.22}$$

Using the data of Problem 2.11 with $\alpha = .05$, this becomes

$$-1 - 2.02(1.41) < \mu_2 + \mu_3 - \mu_4 - \mu_5 < -1 + 2.02(1.41),$$
$$-3.85 < \mu_2 + \mu_3 - \mu_4 - \mu_5 < 1.85,$$

a much shorter interval than given by either the T-method or the S-method. Naturally, we would expect to get a shorter interval from a procedure designed to capture one prechosen contrast than from procedures that try to catch all imaginable contrasts. However, it is quite unlikely that we would specify a contrast in advance. Usually we first test the hypothesis of equal means. If this is rejected, we attempt to discover contrasts that are responsible. It is very difficult to find significance levels associated with several intervals of the type (2.22). Thus we should use intervals given by the T-method or S-method which may be computed for contrasts that are selected after the experiment is conducted and for which we can make an exact probability statement.

EXERCISES

2.12 (a) For the data of Exercise 2.11 use both the T-method and the S-method to obtain confidence limits for $L = 4\mu_1 - \mu_2 - \mu_3 - \mu_4 - \mu_5$. What do these limits imply about L?

(b) Using the methods suggested in (a), one may select a contrast after the experiment has been performed. Suppose, however, that we had decided in advance that this is the only contrast of interest. Now what confidence interval do we get?

2.13 Suppose that the textbook-notes-lab manual experiment of Section 2-12 yields $SS_T = 24,400$, $T_{.1} = 1,400$, $T_{.2} = 2,000$, $T_{.3} = 1,500$, $T_{.4} = 2,100$. First perform the F-test for the hypothesis of equal means. If this is rejected, use the T-method to determine which treatments are significantly better than which others.

2.14 Suppose that in Exercise 2.5 the same book is used for all four classes. The classes are composed of:

> Class A : mathematics majors
> Class B : engineers
> Class C : social science majors
> Class D : business majors.

The real purpose of the experiment is to compare mathematics majors with the others. What is the conclusion to be drawn? After seeing the data, the professor believes that there is some interest in comparing the larger classes (B, C) and smaller (A, D). What conclusions come from this comparison?

2-15 THE RANDOM EFFECTS MODEL

Occasionally a situation will arise where we are interested in a large set of populations, not just the r populations that we sample. The r populations are then considered to be a random sample of populations drawn from the large set.

As an example, suppose that we wish to study the competence in algebra of students who have just completed the ninth grade. Five high schools are selected at random and then within each school a random sample of ninth-grade graduates are given examinations. With these scores the hypothesis that the average level of competence is the same could be tested. If we happened to be interested only in the five high schools, then the fixed-effects model is the appropriate one, and the analysis would proceed along the lines discussed previously. If we want to generalize our conclusions to the population of high schools that we sampled, then we must use the random effects approach. It is quite likely that we would not be interested in the hypothesis of equal means. We may know from past experience that they are not the same and conduct the experiment only to study the variability from school to school.

The assumptions for the random-effects model are

$$x_{ij} = \mu + \beta_j + e_{ij}, \ i = 1, \ 2, \ \cdots, \ n_j, \ j = 1, \ 2, \ \cdots, \ r$$
$$e_{ij} \text{ are independently } N(0, \ \sigma^2) \hspace{2cm} (2.23)$$
$$\beta_j \text{ are independently } N(0, \ \sigma_\beta^2).$$

Thus the x_{ij}'s are a linear function of two variables instead of one as in the fixed-effects model. The β_j's are variable quantities that have a normal distribution of their own whereas before they were a set of r fixed but unknown constants.

To test the hypothesis of equal-treatment effects, we choose between

$$H_0: \ \sigma_\beta^2 = 0$$

and $\hspace{8cm}$ (2.24)

$$H_1: \ \sigma_\beta^2 \neq 0.$$

Even though the assumptions and the hypothesis take a slightly different form than in the fixed-effects model, it turns out that the F ratio used is exactly the same. The only change necessary in Table 2.3 is accomplished by replacing the EMS for among groups by $\sigma^2 + n_0 \sigma_\beta^2$ where

$$n_0 = \frac{\displaystyle\sum_{j=1}^{r} n_j - \frac{\displaystyle\sum_{j=1}^{r} n_j^2}{\displaystyle\sum_{j=1}^{r} n_j}}{r-1} \hspace{1cm} (n_0 = n \text{ if each } n_j = n).$$

If H_0 is rejected, then an unbiased estimate of σ_β^2, say $\hat{\sigma}_\beta^2$, is readily found. Since $MS_W = \hat{\sigma}^2$ is an unbiased estimate of σ^2 and MS_A is an unbiased estimate of $\sigma^2 + n_0 \sigma_\beta^2$, we have

$$\hat{\sigma}_\beta^2 = (MS_A - MS_W)/n_0.$$

It is quite likely that (2.24) will present us with a rather unrealistic choice between hypotheses. In the ninth-grade algebra example, since differences among schools are almost certain to exist, it makes little sense to test the hypothesis of no differences. However, we may feel that it is not worth the effort to attempt to make algebra instruction more uniform if $\sigma_\beta^2 \leq \sigma^2/2$, that is if variability among schools is half or less the variability among students (where variability is measured by variance). In other words, we would like to choose between

$$H_0': \quad \sigma_\beta^2 \leqq \sigma^2/2$$
$$H_1': \quad \sigma_\beta^2 > \sigma^2/2 \qquad (2.25)$$

being satisfied with the present conditions if H_0 is accepted.

The available test for (2.25) requires equal sample sizes. To choose between

$$H_0': \quad \sigma_\beta^2 \leqq R_0\sigma^2$$
$$H_1': \quad \sigma_\beta^2 > R_0\sigma^2 \qquad (2.26)$$

where R_0 is a specific value of $R = \sigma_\beta^2/\sigma^2$, the proper F ratio to use is

$$F_{r-1,\ N-r} = \frac{MS_A}{MS_W} \frac{1}{1+nR_0} \qquad (2.27)$$

with large values of the statistic providing grounds for rejection. From (2.27) it can be shown that the probability is $1-\alpha$ that the interval

$$\frac{1}{n}\left(\frac{MS_A}{MS_W} \frac{1}{F_{1-\alpha/2;\ r-1,\ N-r}} - 1\right) < R < \frac{1}{n}\left(\frac{MS_A}{MS_W} \frac{1}{F_{\alpha/2;\ r-1,\ N-r}} - 1\right) \qquad (2.28)$$

captures R.

Confidence intervals are available for σ_β^2. Scheffé [5] presents approximate intervals on pages 234-235. The approximation appears to be very good. A discussion of intervals based upon what is called fiducial probability may be found on page 258 of [2].

The power of the tests for situation (2.24) with equal sample sizes and for situation (2.26) is given by

$$\Pr\left[F_{r-1,\ N-r} > F_{1-\alpha;\ r-1,\ N-r} \frac{1+nR_0}{1+nR}\right]$$

which is relatively easy to evaluate with extensive F tables (i.e., [3], page 425). Curves giving $1-\text{Power}$ for the first of these two cases (for which $R_0 = 0$) may be found in [1] on pages 309-313. These are much like the Pearson-Hartley charts for the fixed-effects model.

We conclude the section by doing some further calculations for the ninth-grade algebra example. There are $r = 5$ groups being sampled. Suppose that $n = 10$, $\alpha = .05$ and $MS_A/MS_W = 12$ so that $r-1 = 4$ and $N-r = 45$. The tables yield $F_{.95;\ 4,\ 45} = 2.59$. Since 12 exceeds 2.59, we conclude $\sigma_\beta^2 \neq 0$. To choose between H_0' and H_1' of (2.25) with $R_0 = 1/2$, we compute $12/(1+10/2) = 2$. This is smaller than 2.59 so that $H_0': \sigma_\beta^2 \leqq \sigma^2/2$ is accepted. Finally, since

$$F_{.975;\ 4,\ 45} = 3.10$$

and

$$F_{.025;\ 4,\ 45} = 1/8.40,$$

the probability is .95 that the interval

$$\frac{1}{10}\left[\frac{12}{3.10} - 1\right] < R < \frac{1}{10}[12(8.40) - 1]$$

or

$$.29 < R < 10.0$$

captures the ratio σ_β^2/σ^2. The interval given by (2.28) could be such that one or both endpoints turn out to be negative numbers. The ratio R is, of course, necessarily positive. In such a case, the usual procedure is to replace a negative endpoint by a zero.

EXERCISES

2.15 A manufacturer builds a piece of equipment to turn out machined parts. In order to study the performance of his machines, he selects 8 at random and then selects 10 parts at random from the production of each machine. He measures the lengths of the 80 pieces and finds $SS_A = .0168$, $SS_T = .0456$.

(a) Fill out the analysis of variance table.

(b) Write out the model that seems to be appropriate.

(c) Test the hypothesis of equal-treatment effects.

(d) Find unbiased estimates for σ^2 and σ_β^2.

(e) Test the hypothesis that the ratio σ_β^2/σ^2 is $1/2$ or less.

(f) Find an interval such that the probability is .95 that this interval captures $R = \sigma_\beta^2/\sigma^2$.

2.16 Suppose that the inequality signs in (2.26) are reversed. Thus we would be choosing between

$$H_0'' : \quad \sigma_\beta^2 \geq R_0 \sigma^2$$
$$H_1'' : \quad \sigma_\beta^2 < R_0 \sigma^2$$

rejecting H_0'' if the statistic (2.27) is small. If H_0'' is rejected, we would be "reasonably sure" that H_1'' is true. The manufacturer of the previous problem would like to "prove" that $R < 1/2$. How small would MS_A/MS_W have to be to reach this decision if $\alpha = .05$?

2·16 CONCLUDING REMARKS

If it is quite obvious that the variances of the r populations in a fixed-effects model differ from one another, a test due to Welch similar to the approximate t of Equation (1.12) may be used. Examples illustrating this test may be found on page 265 of [2] and page 288 of [6]. However, studies have indicated that inequality of variances does not seriously affect the F-test for equal means if the sample sizes are equal. Thus the Welch procedure should be used only if variances are unequal and the sample sizes differ greatly.

A further assumption we made in discussing the analysis of variance techniques was normality of the observations. Although the test is derived under this assumption, investigation has shown that failure to satisfy this condition has little effect upon the F-test for equal means and the S-method.

We should make every possible effort to obtain independent random samples. Nonrandomness can very seriously affect the conclusions we draw from an experiment.

REFERENCES

[1] Bowker, A.H., and G.J. Lieberman, *Engineering Statistics* (Englewood Cliffs, N.J.: Prentice-Hall, Inc., 1959).

[2] Brownlee, K. A., *Statistical Theory and Methodology in Science and Engineering*, (New York: John Wiley & Sons, Inc., 1960).

[3] Graybill, Franklin A., *An Introduction to Linear Statistical Models* (New York: McGraw-Hill Book Co., Inc., 1961), Volume 1.

[4] Pearson, E.S., and H.O. Hartley, "Charts of the Power Function for Analysis of Variance Tests Derived from the Non-Central F-Distribution," *Biometrika*, Vol. 38 (1951), pp. 112–30.

[5] Scheffé, Henry, *The Analysis of Variance* (New York: John Wiley & Sons, Inc., 1959).

[6] Snedecor, George W., *Statistical Methods* (Ames, Iowa: Iowa State University Press, 1956).

3

Randomized Blocks

3-1 INTRODUCTION

In Section 1-15, we discussed an example involving the comparison of two teaching methods. Two procedures for conducting the experiment were mentioned. In the first, the students were assigned randomly to one of the two classes so that half of the group was taught by Method I and half by Method II. The generalization of this procedure produced the one-way classification. It was observed that perhaps a better way to conduct the experiment was to pair the students according to ability and then conduct a test based upon these pairs. The objective of the pairing is realized if scores are obtained (in this case, differences) which reflect differences attributable only to methods and not ability. After eliminating one source of variation, we may expect the scores to be less variable. Intuitively, at least, it seems that more accurate conclusions should result by way of reducing the probability of a Type II error. This is indeed the case despite the fact that degrees of freedom are lost.

In extending the method of paired comparisons to more than two treatments, we are led to the discussion of what we will call randomized blocks. Suppose 5 teaching methods instead of 2 are under consideration. If we select the top five students for one group, the next five in order of ability as another group, etc., then these groups form blocks. Within each block the assignment to treatments (teaching methods) is made at random. The experiment is then conducted and scores are recorded. Our objectives are the same as for the one-way classification. First we seek a test for the hypothesis of equal-treatment effects. Should the hypothesis be rejected, we would still like to specify which treatments are significantly better than which others.

The main difference between the two designs is found in the method by which experimental units are assigned to treatments. In the completely randomized design, units are assigned at random with no restrictions except possibly that each treatment receive the same number of experimental units. With randomized blocks, units are also assigned randomly to treatments, but not until they have first been placed into fairly homogeneous groups. The main purpose of the blocking is to eliminate a variable in which there is no interest so that more accurate conclusions may be drawn. In other words, having eliminated one source of variation, it is more likely that significant differences among treatments will be detected.

If the experimental units are relatively homogeneous with respect to the variable used to form the blocks, then a randomized block design sacrifices degrees of freedom with no compensating return. On the other hand, if the units vary greatly with respect to this variable, but can be grouped into fairly homogeneous blocks, then the use of blocks is rewarding.

Each block receives each treatment once and may be considered as a complete experiment. A block is sometimes referred to as a replicate of the experiment.

3-2 NOTATION

Very little new notation is necessary for the observational data. We will use

$$\text{Total of the } i^{\text{th}} \text{ block} = T_{i.} = \sum_{j=1}^{r} x_{ij}$$

$$\text{Mean of the } i^{\text{th}} \text{ block} = \bar{x}_{i.} = \frac{\sum_{j=1}^{r} x_{ij}}{r}.$$

Once the experiment is performed, the data may be arranged as in Table 3.1.

Table 3.1 SUMMARY OF RESULTS FOR A RANDOMIZED BLOCK EXPERIMENT

		\multicolumn{4}{c}{Treatments}				TOTALS	Means
		1	2	3	$\cdots$	r		
Blocks	1	x_{11}	x_{12}	x_{13}		x_{1r}	$T_{1.}$	$\bar{x}_{1.}$
	2	x_{21}	x_{22}	x_{23}		x_{2r}	$T_{2.}$	$\bar{x}_{2.}$
	3	x_{31}	x_{32}	x_{33}		x_{3r}	$T_{3.}$	$\bar{x}_{3.}$
	.	.	.	.		.	.	.
	.	.	.	.		.	.	.
	.	.	.	.		.	.	.
	n	x_{n1}	x_{n2}	x_{n3}		x_{nr}	$T_{n.}$	$\bar{x}_{n.}$
TOTALS		$T_{.1}$	$T_{.2}$	$T_{.3}$		$T_{.r}$	$T_{..}$	
Means		$\bar{x}_{.1}$	$\bar{x}_{.2}$	$\bar{x}_{.3}$		$\bar{x}_{.r}$		$\bar{x}_{..}$

We note that

$$T_{..} = \sum_{j=1}^{r} T_{.j} = \sum_{i=1}^{n} T_{i.} \, ,$$

that is, the grand total may be obtained by adding either the row totals or the column totals.

3-3 THE FIXED-EFFECTS MODEL FOR RANDOMIZED BLOCKS

We will assume that the x_{ij} are independently $N(\mu_{ij}, \sigma^2)$, $i = 1,$ $2, \cdots, n$, $j = 1, 2, \ldots, r$. This means (a) a random sample of size 1 is drawn from each of the rn populations, (b) all rn populations are normal, and (c) the variance of each of the rn populations is the same. These are the same assumptions that we made for the one-way classification except for the fact that rn populations instead of r populations are under consideration. One further assumption is also necessary. This is (d) the block and treatment effects are additive. Since this is a new concept, some explanation is necessary.

Let us examine the meaning of this new assumption. If

$$\mu_{ij} - \mu_{ij'} = \mu_{i'j} - \mu_{i'j'} \tag{3.1}$$

for every i, i', j, j', then treatment effects and block effects are said to be additive. This implies that the difference between average values for treatments j and j' is the same in every block. Since (3.1) can be written

$$\mu_{ij} - \mu_{i'j} = \mu_{ij'} - \mu_{i'j'} \tag{3.2}$$

it implies also that the difference between the average values for blocks i and i' is the same for each treatment. A numerical example will help clarify this idea. Suppose that $r = 3$, $n = 4$, and the 12 population means are those given in Table 3.2.

Table 3.2 MEANS FOR 12 POPULATIONS

		Treatment		
		1	2	3
	1	12	18	6
Block	2	20	26	14
	3	17	23	11
	4	23	29	17

Examination of the table reveals that the means for treatment 2 are 6 more than the means for treatment 1 in every block. The means for treatments 3 are 6 less than those for treatment 1 and 12 less than those for treatment 2 in every block. Likewise, block differences remain constant from treatment to treatment. For this set of means, block effects and treatment effects are additive.

We will use the following notation,

$$\mu_{i.} = \frac{\sum\limits_{j=1}^{r} \mu_{ij}}{r}, \quad \mu_{.j} = \frac{\sum\limits_{i=1}^{n} \mu_{ij}}{n},$$

$$\mu_{..} = \mu = \frac{\sum\limits_{j=1}^{r}\sum\limits_{i=1}^{n} \mu_{ij}}{rn}.$$

Now consider the identity

$$\mu_{ij} = \mu + (\mu_{i.} - \mu) + (\mu_{.j} - \mu) + (\mu_{ij} - \mu_{i.} - \mu_{.j} + \mu). \qquad (3.3)$$

If additivity holds so that Equation (3.1) is satisfied, we get, upon summing both sides of this equation over i' and j',

$$\sum_{j'=1}^{r}\sum_{i'=1}^{n}\mu_{ij} - \sum_{j'=1}^{r}\sum_{i'=1}^{n}\mu_{ij'} = \sum_{j'=1}^{r}\sum_{i'=1}^{n}\mu_{i'j} - \sum_{j'=1}^{r}\sum_{i'=1}^{n}\mu_{i'j'}$$

which is

$$rn\mu_{ij} - rn\mu_{i.} = rn\mu_{.j} - rn\mu.$$

Dividing each side of this equation by rn yields

$$\mu_{ij} - \mu_{i.} = \mu_{.j} - \mu$$

so that

$$\mu_{ij} - \mu_{i.} - \mu_{.j} + \mu = 0.$$

Hence if additivity holds, (3.3) can be written

$$\mu_{ij} = \mu + (\mu_{i.} - \mu) + (\mu_{.j} - \mu). \qquad (3.4)$$

Now if we let

$$\alpha_i = \mu_{i.} - \mu, \quad \beta_j = \mu_{.j} - \mu,$$

then Equation (3.3) can be written

$$\mu_{ij} = \mu + \alpha_i + \beta_j.\tag{3.5}$$

Observe that

$$\sum_{i=1}^{n} \alpha_i = \sum_{i=1}^{n} (\mu_{i.} - \mu) = \sum_{i=1}^{n} \mu_{i.} - n\mu$$

$$= \frac{\sum_{i=1}^{n}\left(\sum_{j=1}^{r} \mu_{ij}\right)}{r} - n\mu$$

$$= n\frac{\sum_{j=1}^{r}\sum_{i=1}^{n} \mu_{ij}}{rn} - n\mu$$

$$= n\mu - n\mu$$

$$= 0.$$

Similarly,

$$\sum_{j=1}^{r} \beta_j = 0.$$

In words, Equation (3.5) states that every population mean μ_{ij} can be written as (the overall mean of means) + (a constant arising from the fact that the experimental unit is in block i) + (a constant arising due to the fact that the unit is receiving treatment j).

Note that the additivity assumption does not always hold. In the teaching methods example, it may happen that some methods produce good results with good students, yet produce the opposite effect with poor students. When this unfortunate state of affairs exists, blocks and treatment are said to interact. Obviously, we cannot draw the same conclusions regarding treatments for all blocks.

We can now restate the assumptions for the fixed-effects model in more compact form. First, observe that

$$x_{ij} = \mu_{ij} + (x_{ij} - \mu_{ij})\tag{3.6}$$

is an identity. Let $e_{ij} = x_{ij} - \mu_{ij}$, which will be independently $N(0, \sigma^2)$. If additivity holds, then (3.6) can be written

$$x_{ij} = \mu + \alpha_i + \beta_j + e_{ij}.\tag{3.7}$$

Consequently, the assumptions in symbolic form are

$$x_{ij} = \mu + \alpha_i + \beta_j + e_{ij}, \ i = 1, 2, \cdots, n, \ j = 1, 2, \cdots r$$
$$e_{ij} \text{ are independently } N(0, \sigma^2)\tag{3.8}$$

$$\sum_{i=1}^{n} \alpha_i = \sum_{j=1}^{r} \beta_j = 0.$$

This mathematical formulation implies all four assumptions listed at the beginning of the section. Here the α_i and β_j are a set of fixed constants.

If all treatment means are the same, then $\mu_{.1}=\mu_{.2}=\cdots=\mu_{.r}=\mu$ which implies $\beta_1=\beta_2=\cdots=\beta_r=0$. Consequently, in testing the hypothesis of equal-treatment effects we are choosing between

$$H_0: \quad \beta_j=0, \quad j=1, 2,\cdots, r \qquad (3.9)$$
$$H_1: \quad \text{not all } \beta_j\text{'s are zero.}$$

EXERCISE

3.1 Since additivity holds for the means given in Table 3.2, each of them can be written in the form of Equation (3.5). Find the α_i and the β_j and write all 12 means as the sum of 3 components.

3-4 PARTITIONING THE SUM OF SQUARES

As in Section 2.5, the total sum of squares is divided into several sums of squares. It may be written

$$\sum_{j=1}^{r}\sum_{i=1}^{n}(x_{ij}-\bar{x}_{..})^2=\sum_{j=1}^{r}\sum_{i=1}^{n}[\,(\bar{x}_{i.}-\bar{x}_{..})+(\bar{x}_{.j}-\bar{x}_{..})+(x_{ij}-\bar{x}_{i.}-\bar{x}_{.j}+\bar{x}_{..})\,]^2$$
$$=\sum_{j=1}^{r}\sum_{i=1}^{n}(\bar{x}_{i.}-\bar{x}_{..})^2+\sum_{j=1}^{r}\sum_{i=1}^{n}(\bar{x}_{.j}-\bar{x}_{..})^2$$
$$+\sum_{j=1}^{r}\sum_{i=1}^{n}(x_{ij}-\bar{x}_{i.}-\bar{x}_{.j}+\bar{x}_{..})^2+3 \text{ cross-product terms.}$$

Let us examine the cross-product terms. One of them is

$$2\sum_{j=1}^{r}\sum_{i=1}^{n}(\bar{x}_{.j}-\bar{x}_{..})(x_{ij}-\bar{x}_{i.}-\bar{x}_{.j}+\bar{x}_{..})=2\sum_{j=1}^{r}(\bar{x}_{.j}-\bar{x}_{..})\sum_{i=1}^{n}(x_{ij}-\bar{x}_{i.}-\bar{x}_{.j}+\bar{x}_{..}).$$

Now

$$\bar{x}_{.j}=\sum_{i=1}^{n}\frac{x_{ij}}{n}, \qquad \text{so} \qquad \sum_{i=1}^{n}x_{ij}=n\bar{x}_{.j}$$

and

$$\sum_{i=1}^{n}\bar{x}_{i.}=\sum_{i=1}^{n}\sum_{j=1}^{r}\frac{x_{ij}}{r}=n\frac{\sum_{j=1}^{r}\sum_{i=1}^{n}x_{ij}}{nr}=n\bar{x} \quad .$$

Hence

$$\sum_{i=1}^{n}(x_{ij}-\bar{x}_{i.}-\bar{x}_{.j}+\bar{x}_{..})=n\bar{x}_{.j}-n\bar{x}_{..}-n\bar{x}_{.j}+n\bar{x}_{..}=0.$$

Thus the cross-product is

$$2\sum_{j=1}^{r}(\bar{x}_{.j}-\bar{x}_{..})\,(0)=0.$$

Similarly we can show that the other two cross-product terms are equal to zero.

Thus we have the identity

$$\sum_{j=1}^{r}\sum_{i=1}^{n}(x_{ij}-\bar{x}_{..})^2=\sum_{j=1}^{r}\sum_{i=1}^{n}(\bar{x}_{i.}-\bar{x}_{..})^2+\sum_{j=1}^{r}\sum_{i=1}^{n}(\bar{x}_{.j}-\bar{x}_{..})^2$$
$$+\sum_{j=1}^{r}\sum_{i=1}^{n}(x_{ij}-\bar{x}_{i.}-\bar{x}_{.j}+\bar{x}_{..})^2\,. \tag{3.10}$$

In shorthand notation we can write Equation (3.10)

$$SS_T=SS_B+SS_{Tr}+SS_E \tag{3.11}$$

where SS_T, SS_B, SS_{Tr}, and SS_E stand for sum of squares for total, sum of squares for blocks, sum of squares for treatments, and sum of squares for error respectively. Observe that SS_{Tr} is exactly the same quantity that was designated by SS_A in Chapter 2. What was called SS_W is now divided into two parts, $SS_W=SS_B+SS_E$. In other words, the error sum of squares is nothing more than the old sum of squares within groups reduced by the sum of squares for blocks. That is, $SS_E=SS_W-SS_B$.

The computing formulas for SS_T and SS_{Tr} are the same as those given for the one-way classification. These are

$$SS_T=\sum_{j=1}^{r}\sum_{i=1}^{n}x_{ij}^2-\frac{T_{..}^2}{rn}, \tag{3.12}$$

$$SS_{Tr}=\sum_{j=1}^{r}\frac{T_{.j}^2}{n}-\frac{T_{..}^2}{rn}. \tag{3.13}$$

It is easily shown that

$$SS_B=\sum_{i=1}^{n}\frac{T_{i.}^2}{r}-\frac{T_{..}^2}{rn}. \tag{3.14}$$

The error sum of squares is obtained by subtraction and is

$$SS_E=SS_T-SS_B-SS_{Tr}. \tag{3.15}$$

EXERCISES

3.2   The other cross-product terms referred to are

$$2\sum_{j=1}^{r}\sum_{i=1}^{n}(\bar{x}_{i.}-\bar{x}_{..})\,(x_{ij}-\bar{x}_{i.}-\bar{x}_{.j}+\bar{x}_{..})$$

and

$$2\sum_{j=1}^{r}\sum_{i=1}^{n}(\bar{x}_{i.}-\bar{x}_{..})\,(\bar{x}_{.j}-\bar{x}_{..}).$$

Show that each one of these is zero.

3.3 Show that

$$SS_B = \sum_{j=1}^{r} \sum_{i=1}^{n} (\bar{x}_{i.} - \bar{x}_{..})^2 = \sum_{i=1}^{n} \frac{T_{i.}^2}{r} - \frac{T_{..}^2}{rn}.$$

3-5 TESTING THE HYPOTHESIS OF EQUAL-TREATMENT EFFECTS

With the four assumptions implied by (3.8), it may be shown that the average values of SS_E and SS_{Tr} are $(n-1)(r-1)\sigma^2$ and $(r-1)\sigma^2 + n\sum_{j=1}^{r} \beta_j^2$.   Thus

$$MS_E = \frac{SS_E}{(n-1)(r-1)} \quad \text{and} \quad MS_{Tr} = \frac{SS_{Tr}}{r-1}$$

have average values σ^2 and

$$\sigma^2 + \frac{n}{r-1} \sum_{j=1}^{r} \beta_j^2.$$

If $\beta_1 = \beta_2 = \cdots = \beta_r = 0$, then MS_E and MS_{Tr} should consequently have compatible values so that it seems reasonable to compare them in an F-ratio.   It may be shown that

$$F_{r-1,\,(n-1)(r-1)} = \frac{MS_{Tr}}{MS_E}$$

is the ratio to use to test the hypothesis of equal-treatment effects.   Since MS_{Tr} is large if the sample treatment means differ greatly, but small if they are nearly the same, only large values of F lie in the critical region. The results of the analysis may be presented in the form of Table 3.3.

Table 3.3   ANALYSIS OF VARIANCE FOR RANDOMIZED BLOCKS

Source	SS	d.f.	MS	EMS	F
Blocks	SS_B	$n-1$	MS_B	$\sigma^2 + \dfrac{r}{n-1} \sum_{i=1}^{n} \alpha_i^2$	
Treatments	SS_{Tr}	$r-1$	MS_{Tr}	$\sigma^2 + \dfrac{n}{r-1} \sum_{j=1}^{r} \beta_j^2$	$\dfrac{MS_{Tr}}{MS_E}$
Error	SS_E	$(n-1)(r-1)$	MS_E	σ^2	
TOTAL	SS_T	$nr-1$			

The mean square for blocks is

$$MS_B = \frac{SS_B}{n-1}.$$

EXERCISES

3.4 Four varieties of oats are being compared for yield. A four-acre plot is selected in 10 localities that differ considerably with respect to soil fertility. One variety is assigned at random to a one-acre plot. After the harvest the yield in bushels is recorded in each locality. A composite map from the ten localities with variety listed first, yield second is as follows:

Locality 1		Locality 2		Locality 3	
1–33	4–48	3–28	1–46	2–32	4–46
3–36	2–13	4–22	2–15	3–40	1–39

Locality 4		Locality 5		Locality 6	
1–44	3–41	4–81	1–51	2–46	3–79
4–53	2–26	3–61	2–53	4–78	1–74

Locality 7		Locality 8		Locality 9	
2–59	1–61	1–88	4–96	2–93	1–93
3–74	4–92	3–92	2–66	4–100	3–82

Locality 10	
1–69	3–83
4–108	2–85

Using randomized blocks analysis, what conclusion can be reached concerning the four varieties? Suppose that the completely randomized analysis had been used incorrectly. Would this change the conclusion?

3.5 Suppose a study is being conducted to compare tire mileage for four brands of tires. It is recognized that mileage will vary according to road conditions and climate. These are listed and it is decided that 10 categories sufficiently cover these variations. Each of the brands is assigned randomly to a wheel of a car and this is repeated until assignment has been made to 10 cars. Then one car is assigned at random to a road and climate category. The mileage required to wear out each tire is recorded in thousands of miles. The results are recorded below.

		Brand			
		A	F	G	R
Road and climate category	1	38	29	41.5	39
	2	24.5	36	35.5	25
	3	37.5	38.5	31.5	29.5
	4	20.5	33.5	29.5	21.5
	5	29.5	35	34	11
	6	22	33	35	17
	7	29	37.5	38	18.5
	8	25	21.5	28	18
	9	26	35.5	28	17
	10	17	23.5	34	16.5

Do all four brands give the same average mileage?

3-6 COMPARISON OF THE F AND t TESTS WHEN $r=2$

In Section 1-15, we observed that $t_{n-1} = \bar{d}\sqrt{n} / s_d$ could be used to choose between

$$H_0: \quad \mu_d = \mu_1 - \mu_2 = 0$$
$$H_1: \quad \mu_d \neq 0,$$

rejecting H_0 when t is large or small. Rewriting t in terms of our present notation, we get

$$t_{n-1} = \frac{(\bar{x}_{.1} - \bar{x}_{.2})\sqrt{n}}{\sqrt{\sum\limits_{i=1}^{n} \frac{[(x_{i1} - x_{i2}) - (\bar{x}_{.1} - \bar{x}_{.2})]^2}{n-1}}} .$$

When we use the F test for randomized blocks with only two treatments, we compute

$$F_{1,\,n-1} = \frac{SS_{Tr}}{\dfrac{SS_E}{n-1}} .$$

Now

$$SS_{Tr} = \sum_{i=1}^{n} \sum_{j=1}^{2} (\bar{x}_{.j} - \bar{x}_{..})^2 = n \left[(\bar{x}_{.1} - \bar{x}_{..})^2 + (\bar{x}_{.2} - \bar{x}_{..})^2 \right].$$

Since

$$\bar{x}_{..} = \frac{\bar{x}_{.1} + \bar{x}_{.2}}{2} ,$$

we see that

$$(\bar{x}_{.1} - \bar{x}_{..})^2 = \frac{(\bar{x}_{.1} - \bar{x}_{.2})^2}{4} ,$$

$$(\bar{x}_{.2} - \bar{x}_{..})^2 = \frac{(\bar{x}_{.1} - \bar{x}_{.2})^2}{4} ,$$

so that

$$SS_{Tr} = \frac{n}{2} (\bar{x}_{.1} - \bar{x}_{.2})^2.$$

Next

$$SS_E = \sum_{i=1}^{n} \sum_{j=1}^{2} (x_{ij} - \bar{x}_{i.} - \bar{x}_{.j} + \bar{x}_{..})^2$$

$$= \sum_{i=1}^{n} [(x_{i1} - \bar{x}_{i.} - \bar{x}_{.1} + \bar{x}_{..})^2 + (x_{i2} - \bar{x}_{i.} - \bar{x}_{.2} + \bar{x}_{..})^2].$$

Because there are only two treatments

$$\bar{x}_{i.} = \frac{x_{i1} + x_{i2}}{2}$$

and therefore we may write

$$(x_{i1} - \bar{x}_{i.} - \bar{x}_{.1} + \bar{x}_{..})^2 = \left[x_{i1} - \frac{x_{i1} + x_{i2}}{2} - \bar{x}_{.1} + \frac{\bar{x}_{.1} + \bar{x}_{.2}}{2} \right]^2$$

$$= \frac{[(x_{i1} - x_{i2}) - (\bar{x}_{.1} - \bar{x}_{.2})]^2}{4}.$$

Similarly,

$$(x_{i2} - \bar{x}_{i.} - \bar{x}_{.2} + \bar{x}_{..})^2 = \frac{[(x_{i1} - x_{i2}) - (\bar{x}_{.1} - \bar{x}_{.2})]^2}{4}.$$

Thus

$$SS_E = \frac{1}{2} \sum_{i=1}^{n} [(x_{i1} - x_{i2}) - (\bar{x}_{.1} - \bar{x}_{.2})]^2$$

and

$$F_{1, n-1} = \frac{n(\bar{x}_{.1} - \bar{x}_{.2})^2}{\sum_{i=1}^{n} \frac{[(x_{i1} - x_{i2}) - (\bar{x}_{.1} - \bar{x}_{.2})]^2}{n-1}} = t_{n-1}^2$$

since the $1/2$'s divide out. Exactly the same quantity is computed in each case except that one is the square of the other. We have previously noted in Section 2-10 that the critical regions for the two statistics correspond to one another. Thus the same decision is reached with both tests.

It might be pointed out that the t-test is slightly more general than the F-test of randomized blocks. The t-test (but not the F-test) can be used in situations where the observations are paired data (i. e., before-and-after-type experiments).

EXERCISE

3.6 Use both F and t to test the hypothesis of equal means for the following data:

| | Treatment | |
	1	2
1	7	10
2	2	6
Blocks 3	11	5
4	4	13
5	1	6

Verify that $t^2 = F$ for this example.

3-7 THE TUKEY TEST FOR NONADDITIVITY

In case there is reason to doubt additivity, it may be wise to investigate the reasonableness of this assumption. A test for this purpose has been proposed by Tukey. The hypothesis and the alternate are

$$H_0: \quad (\alpha\beta)_{ij} = 0, \ \imath = 1, \ 2, \cdots, \ n, \ j = 1, \ 2, \cdots, \ r$$

$$H_1: \quad \text{not all } (\alpha\beta)_{ij} \text{ are zero}$$

where $(\alpha\beta)_{ij} = \mu_{ij} - \mu_{i.} - \mu_{.j} + \mu$. The procedure requires that we compute

$$SS_N = \frac{\left[\sum\limits_{j=1}^{r} \sum\limits_{i=1}^{n} x_{ij} \ (\bar{x}_{i.} - \bar{x}_{..}) \ (\bar{x}_{.j} - \bar{x}_{..}) \right]^2}{\sum\limits_{i=1}^{n} (\bar{x}_{i.} - \bar{x}_{..})^2 \sum\limits_{j=1}^{r} (\bar{x}_{.j} - \bar{x}_{..})^2}, \tag{3.16}$$

which is called the sum of squares for nonadditivity. It may be shown that if the hypothesis is true, then

$$F_{1, (n-1)(r-1)-1} = \frac{SS_N}{\dfrac{SS_E - SS_N}{(n-1)(r-1)-1}}. \tag{3.17}$$

If this is large, the assumption of additivity is rejected. The results can be summarized in the form of Table 3.4.

Table 3.4 TEST FOR NONADDITIVITY

Source	SS	d.f.	MS	F
Nonadditivity	SS_N	1	MS_N	$\dfrac{MS_N}{MS_R}$
Remainder	$SS_E - SS_N$	$(n-1)(r-1)-1$	MS_R	
Error	SS_E	$(n-1)(r-1)$		

As usual, the MS's are obtained by dividing SS's by degrees of freedom.

For computational purposes, Equation (3.16) may be rewritten. Expanding the numerator into four terms, one gets after a little manipulation

$$SS_N = \frac{\left[\sum_{j=1}^{r}\sum_{i=1}^{n} x_{ij}\, T_{i.}\, T_{.j} - T_{..}\left(\sum_{j=1}^{r}\frac{T_{.j}^2}{n} + \sum_{i=1}^{n}\frac{T_{i.}^2}{r} - \frac{T_{..}^2}{rn}\right)\right]^2}{rn\,(SS_B)\,(SS_{Tr})}. \qquad (3.18)$$

The only term here that gives any difficulty is $\sum_{j=1}^{r}\sum_{i=1}^{n} x_{ij}\, T_{i.}\, T_{.j}$. This can be more easily calculated by writing it as

$$\sum_{j=1}^{r} T_{.j}\left[\sum_{i=1}^{n} x_{ij}\, T_{i.}\right]. \qquad (3.19)$$

That is, find the sum of the bracket for each column as a preliminary calculation. In the numerator of (3.18)

$$\sum_{j=1}^{r}\frac{T_{.j}^2}{n} + \sum_{i=1}^{n}\frac{T_{i.}^2}{r} - \frac{T_{..}^2}{rn}$$

can be replaced by $SS_B + SS_{Tr} + T_{..}^2/rn$ if one so prefers.

The power of this test and the average value of SS_N are unknown. If H_0 is rejected, interpretation becomes difficult. It is then likely that the choice of treatment depends upon the block. For example, one teaching method may be best with good students, another with poor students.

EXERCISES

3.7 Test the additivity assumption for the data of Exercise 3.5.
3.8 Show that Equation (3.16) can be put in the form of Equation (3.18).

3-8 MISSING OBSERVATIONS

In the process of conducting an experiment one or more of the observations may be lost. For example, in a teaching methods study, a student may leave school before the experiment is completed. Since the randomized block design requires r treatments in each block, some change in the testing procedure might be expected.

Denote the missing observation by y_{ij}. Then all sums of squares are computed in the usual way except, of course, they all involve y_{ij}. It is an elementary calculus problem to select y_{ij} so that it minimizes SS_E. Exercise 3.4 illustrates the desirability of a small SS_E since then a false hypothesis is more likely to be rejected. When y_{ij} is chosen this way, the result is

$$y_{ij} = \frac{rT_{.j}' + nT_{i.}' - T_{..}'}{(r-1)(n-1)} \qquad (3.20)$$

where $T_{.j}'$, $T_{i.}'$ and $T_{..}'$ are the usual totals with the one value missing.

If y_{ij} obtained from (3.20) is substituted for the missing value, then SS_B, SS_{Tr}, SS_E and SS_T can be computed in the usual way. Let

$$SS'_{Tr} = SS_{Tr} - \frac{[T'_{i.} - (r-1)\, y_{ij}]^2}{r\,(r-1)} = SS_{Tr} - a^2. \tag{3.21}$$

Then

$$F_{r-1,\,(n-1)(r-1)-1} = \frac{\dfrac{SS'_{Tr}}{r-1}}{\dfrac{SS_E}{(n-1)(r-1)-1}} \tag{3.22}$$

can be used to test the hypothesis of equal-treatment effects. Thus not only is SS_{Tr} reduced, but SS_E loses 1 degree of freedom. Table 3.5 gives a summary of the results.

Table 3.5   ANALYSIS OF VARIANCE FOR RANDOMIZED BLOCKS
WITH ONE MISSING OBSERVATION

Source	SS	d.f.	MS	F
Blocks	SS_B	$n-1$	MS_B	
Treatments	SS'_{Tr}	$r-1$	MS'_{Tr}	$\dfrac{MS'_{Tr}}{MS'_E}$
Error	SS_E	$(n-1)(r-1)-1$	MS'_E	
TOTAL	$SS_T - a^2$	$nr-2$		

Here

$$MS'_{Tr} = \frac{SS'_{Tr}}{r-1} \quad \text{and} \quad MS'_E = \frac{SS_E}{(n-1)(r-1)-1}.$$

The procedure for handling the case with two missing plots may be found on page 304 of Reference [4]. Further discussion of missing value techniques may be found in all five references listed at the end of the chapter.

EXERCISE

3.9 Use the first three blocks of Exercise 3.4 to test the hypothesis that mean yields are equal for the four varieties. Assume that x_{23} is not available, because the plot was flooded. Therefore the missing value procedure must be used.

3-9 THE POWER OF THE F-TEST

The discussion of power for the one-way classification in Section 2-11 is applicable to randomized blocks. The only difference is in the definition of β_j which for the block design is $\beta_j = \mu_{.j} - \mu$. The parameter ϕ again has the value

$$\phi = \frac{\sqrt{\dfrac{n}{r} \sum_{j=1}^{r} \beta_j^2}}{\sigma} \tag{3.23}$$

so that once more it is convenient to choose the β_j's as multiples of σ. Here $\nu_1 = r - 1$ and $\nu_2 = (n-1)(r-1)$.

EXERCISE

3.10 Taking $\alpha = .01$, find the probability of rejecting the hypothesis of equal-treatment effects for Exercise 3.4 if three-treatment effects are equal and the fourth exceeds these three by σ. How many replications are necessary to raise this probability to .90? If the largest difference among the four-treatment effects is 2σ, find the least value for the power.

3-10 TESTS INVOLVING CONTRASTS, THE T-METHOD, THE S-METHOD

The results of Sections 2-12, 2-13 and 2-14 are still applicable with a few minor modifications. First, contrasts of interest will involve the $\mu_{.j}$ or β_j and will be of the form

$$\begin{aligned} L &= c_1\mu_{.1} + c_2\mu_{.2} + \cdots + c_r\mu_{.r} \\ &= c_1\beta_1 + c_2\beta_2 + \cdots + c_r\beta_r \end{aligned} \tag{3.24}$$

where, as before,

$\sum_{j=1}^{r} c_j = 0$ and the estimate of L is given by (2.11). Second, MS_E replaces MS_W and $(n-1)(r-1)$ replaces $N-r$ in degrees of freedom entries. Thus, for example, for the T-method

$$T = \frac{1}{\sqrt{n}} \, q_{1-\alpha; \; r, \, (n-1)(r-1)} \tag{3.25}$$

and for the S-method

$$S^2 = (r-1) F_{1-\alpha; \; r-1, \, (n-1)(r-1)} \, . \tag{3.26}$$

Other modifications are made just as easily.

All other comments relative to use, advantages, and disadvantages of these procedures hold without change.

EXERCISES

3.11 In Exercise 3.4 the hypothesis of equal-treatment effects was rejected. Use the T-method on this data to determine which treatments are significantly better than other treatments.

3.12 In Exercise 3.4 suppose that Variety 1 is the standard type of oats grown and Varieties 2, 3, and 4 are new hybrids. A reasonable hypothesis might be $\mu_{.1} = (\mu_{.2} + \mu_{.3} + \mu_{.4})/3$ or what is the same thing, $\beta_1 = (\beta_2 + \beta_3 + \beta_4)/3$. In words this says that the average yield for the hybrids is the same as for the standard type. Use the S-method, T-method and the t distribution to obtain confidence limits for

$$L = 3\mu_{.1} - \mu_{.2} - \mu_{.3} - \mu_{.4}.$$

Explain why they are different. Use $\alpha = .05$ in each case.

3.13 One hundred students are given a college entrance examination in mathematics. Their scores are used to divide them into blocks of four. Then one of each block is assigned at random to one of the following four classes in beginning college mathematics:

Class   I   Prof. North using a theoretical text
Class II   Prof. North using an applied text
Class III   Prof. South using a theoretical text
Class IV   Prof. South using an applied text.

After completing the course, each student is given the same final examination. Using these scores it is found that $T_{.1} = 1,200$, $T_{.2} = 1,800$, $T_{.3} = 1,300$, $T_{.4} = 1,700$, $SS_T = 22,500$, $SS_B = 4,900$. It is particularly desirable to know if there is a difference between theoretical and applied texts. Select a reasonable set of orthogonal contrasts and test to see if each of these contrasts is zero.

3-11 THE EFFICIENCY OF RANDOMIZED BLOCKS

In Exercise 3.4, we observed the consequences of using the completely randomized analysis on a randomized block experiment. Since rather large block effects were present, the denominator in the F ratio was so much larger that the completely randomized analysis failed to detect the existing differences. The correct analysis gave a highly significant F. In both cases, the numerator was exactly the same.

If randomized blocks analysis is used in Exercise 2.6, then the denominator of the F ratio is increased for another reason. There is no reason to regard these data as an 11-block experiment. If this is done, SS_B is found to be a relatively small quantity so that SS_E and SS_W do not differ greatly. Consequently, MS_W is smaller than MS_E because of the larger denominator. In other words, degrees of freedom are needlessly sacrificed. As a result, a false hypothesis is again more apt to be accepted.

Thus we see that it is advantageous to choose a design that makes the denominator of the F ratio small. False hypotheses are less likely to be accepted and the probability of committing a Type II error is reduced.

It seems desirable to have some quantitative measure by which complete randomization and randomized blocks can be compared. Such a quantity is

$$E_1 \ (RB/CR) = \frac{(n-1)\left[\sigma^2 + \frac{r}{n-1}\sum_{i=1}^{n}\alpha_i^2\right] + n\ (r-1)\ \sigma^2}{(nr-1)\ \sigma^2}, \qquad (3.27)$$

called the relative efficiency of randomized blocks with respect to complete randomization. Since (3.27) involves unknown parameters, it cannot be computed. However, the analysis of variance provides unbiased estimates of the parameters so that

$$\hat{E}_1 = \frac{(n-1)\ MS_B + n\ (r-1)\ MS_E}{(nr-1)\ MS_E} \qquad (3.28)$$

can be taken as an estimate of the relative efficiency. $\hat{E}_1 = 1.25$ may be interpreted to mean that the randomized blocks design is 125 percent as efficient as complete randomization. On the other hand, a fraction less than 1 indicates that introducing the block variable makes for a less efficient design, probably a result of loss of degrees of freedom. In this case if the experiment were repeated, it is likely that blocks would be eliminated.

In general, efficiency is defined as ratio of variances. For example, both $\bar{x}$, the sample mean, and $\tilde{x}$, the sample median, are unbiased estimates of the population mean μ. Suppose, for a given sample size, we are able to compute the variances of these estimates and it turns out that the ratio

$$\sigma_{\bar{x}}^2/\sigma_{\tilde{x}}^2 = .80.$$

With this result we would state that $\tilde{x}$ is only 80 percent as efficient as $\bar{x}$ in estimating μ with this sample size. Also, $\bar{x}$ is 125 percent as efficient as $\tilde{x}$. The derivation of (3.27) depends essentially upon this sort of comparison of variances.

EXERCISES

3.14 What is the relative efficiency of randomized blocks with respect to complete randomization for the data of Exercise 3.4? Exercise 3.5?

3.15 Write out the analysis of variance table for Exercise 2.6, which is to be regarded as an 11-block experiment. Note the difference between this and the previous analysis. Evaluate $\hat{E}_1$ for this data.

3-12 OTHER MODELS

Thus far in the chapter we have confined our remarks to the fixed-effects model. The experimenter may want his conclusions for a given set of treatments to apply for all possible blocks, not just the set used. If the blocks are considered a random sample from a population of blocks while the treatments are fixed, then we have a mixed model. The assumptions are:

$$x_{ij} = \mu + \alpha_i + \beta_j + e_{ij}, \quad i = 1, 2, \cdots, n \quad j = 1, 2, \cdots, r$$
$$e_{ij} \text{ are independently } N(0, \sigma^2) \tag{3.29}$$
$$\alpha_i \text{ are independently } N(0, \sigma_\alpha^2)$$

$$\beta_j \text{ are fixed constants such that } \sum_{j=1}^{r} \beta_j = 0.$$

The F test for the hypothesis of equal means is still valid and conducted in exactly the same way. In the analysis of variance table the EMS for blocks should be replaced by $\sigma^2 + r\sigma_\alpha^2$. The results concerning contrasts including the T-method and S-method are still applicable to treatment effects.

In the event that the treatments are also a random sample from a population of treatments, we have a random-effects model. In this case the last line of (3.29) should be replaced by the following statement: β_j are independently $N(0, \sigma_\beta^2)$. In the analysis of variance table the EMS's are $\sigma^2 + r\sigma_\alpha^2$ and $\sigma^2 + n\sigma_\beta^2$ for blocks and treatments. The F ratio used to test the hypothesis of equal-treatment effects is still MS_{Tr}/MS_E.

In the random-effects model, the hypothesis of equal-treatment effects may be quite unrealistic as was pointed out in Section 2-15. Again a more appropriate choice of hypothesis and alternate may be

$$H_0': \quad \sigma_\beta^2 \leq R_0 \sigma^2 \tag{3.30}$$
$$H_1': \quad \sigma_\beta^2 > R_0 \sigma^2$$

where R_0 is a specific value of $R = \sigma_\beta^2 / \sigma^2$. This hypothesis is tested by

$$F_{r-1, (n-1)(r-1)} = \frac{MS_{Tr}}{MS_E} \frac{1}{(1 + nR_0)}, \tag{3.31}$$

rejecting when F is large. The probability is $1 - \alpha$ that the interval

$$\frac{1}{n}\left(\frac{MS_{Tr}}{MS_E}\frac{1}{F_{1-\alpha/2;\ r-1,\ (n-1)(r-1)}}-1\right)<R$$

$$<\frac{1}{n}\left(\frac{MS_{Tr}}{MS_E}\frac{1}{F_{\alpha/2;\ r-1,\ (n-1)(r-1)}}-1\right) \qquad (3.32)$$

captures R. The power for (3.30) is given by

$$\Pr\left[F_{r-1,\ (n-1)(r-1)}>F_{1-\alpha;\ r-1,\ (n-1)(r-1)}\frac{1+nR_0}{1+nR}\right]$$

which requires the use of extensive F tables as indicated in Section 2-15. Thus these results are very similar to those of the previous chapter.

EXERCISE

3.16 Suppose the data of Exercise 3.4 are derived from a random-effects experiment. Test the hypothesis $R \leq R_0 = 1/5$. Use (3.32) to obtain a confidence interval for R using $\alpha = .05$. Find unbiased estimates of σ^2, σ_a^2, and σ_β^2.

REFERENCES

[1] Brownlee, K.A., *Statistical Theory and Methodology in Science and Engineering*. (New York: John Wiley & Sons, Inc., 1960).

[2] Kempthorne, Oscar, *The Design and Analysis of Experiments*. (New York: John Wiley & Sons, Inc., 1952).

[3] Li, Jerome C.R., *Introduction to Statistical Inference* (Ann Arbor, Mich.: J.W. Edwards, Publisher, Inc., 1957).

[4] Ostle, Bernard, *Statistics in Research* (Ames, Iowa: Iowa State University Press, 1956).

[5] Snedecor, George W., *Statistical Methods*, (Ames, Iowa: Iowa State University Press, 1956).

4

Latin Squares

4-1 INTRODUCTION

Another design that is sometimes useful, particularly in agricultural and industrial experimentation, is called the Latin square. We have observed how randomized blocks can be used to reduce the experimental error by removing a source of variation caused by a variable in which there is little or no interest; that is, if block effects exist, the denominator of the F ratio is reduced, thus decreasing the probability of a Type II error. If there are two sources of variation to be controlled, then a Latin square may provide the best method of analysis.

Suppose that in the tire study of Exercise 3.5 we decide that there are 4 different types of road conditions and 4 different types of climate under which we would like to conduct the test. We must cope with 16 different sets of conditions. A good way to conduct the experiment is to use randomized blocks, testing each tire under each condition. Since 16 blocks have been designated, this requires the use of 64 tires. With a Latin square we can reduce this number to 16 and have each brand of tire exposed to each climatic and each road condition just once. With a relatively inexpensive item such as tires, this saving may not be substantial to a business firm, but if the test item were missiles, then the saving would be an essential one.

In field experiments it is possible to control the effects that may be attributed to varying soil fertility in two directions perpendicular to each other by the use of a Latin square (for an example, see [3]). In studying yield of milk from cows, it may be desirable to control variation arising from the cows being of different breed and of different age. In comparing textbooks in a teaching experiment, we may try to eliminate the effects due to different teachers and different times of the day. It is not difficult to imagine other situations where a Latin square can be used advantageously.

To illustrate how a Latin square experiment is conducted, let us return to the tire example. Consider Figure 4.1.

		Road condition			
		1	2	3	4
	1	R	F	A	G
Climate	2	F	A	G	R
condition	3	G	R	F	A
	4	A	G	R	F

Figure 4.1   A Latin square arrangement.

Tire A is used four times: once with road condition 3 and climatic condition 1; once with road condition 2 and climatic condition 2; once with road condition 4 and climatic condition 3; and once with road condition 1 and climatic condition 4. Tire F is used once with road condition 2 and climatic condition 1; once with road condition 1 and climatic condition 2; etc.

We note that (a) the number of categories for both variables which we desire to control must be the same as the number of treatments, and (b) each treatment occurs exactly once in each column and in each row. The restriction imposed by (a) somewhat limits the usefulness of Latin squares. In practice, squares larger than 12×12 are seldom used.

4-2 RANDOMIZED PROCEDURES FOR LATIN SQUARES

The random selection of a Latin square can become quite complicated if the size of the square is very large. Fisher and Yates [1] have prepared tables which simplify this task for squares from size 4×4 to 12×12.

If these tables are not available, then Table 4.1 may be used to select squares of size 3×3 to 6×6. For the 3×3, 5×5, and 6×6 squares, randomize the rows, columns, and treatments of the square given in the table.   In the 4×4 case, select one of the four squares at random and then randomize rows, columns, and treatments.

Table 4.1 SELECTED LATIN SQUARES

3×3			4×4		
	(a)	(b)	(c)	(d)	
ABC	ABCD	ABCD	ABCD	ABCD	
BCA	BADC	BCDA	BDAC	BADC	
CAB	CDBA	CDAB	CADB	CDAB	
	DCAB	DABC	DCBA	DCBA	

5×5	6×6
ABCDE	ABCDEF
BAECD	BFDCAE
CDAEB	CDEFBA
DEBAC	DAFECB
ECDBA	ECABFD
	FEBADC

For larger squares, construct a square of the desired size and then randomize rows, columns, and treatments.   This procedure does not give every Latin square of a given size the same opportunity of being chosen. Even so, this procedure is satisfactory in practice.

As an illustration, suppose we select square (b) at random from those of size 4×4. First, from a table of random numbers choose an order for the rows, say 1, 4, 2, 3. Rearranging (b) yields Figure 4.2.

		Column			
		1	2	3	4
	1	A	B	C	D
Row	4	D	A	B	C
	2	B	C	D	A
	3	C	D	A	B

Figure 4.2 The square after rearranging rows.

		Column			
		2	1	4	3
	1	B	A	D	C
Row	4	A	D	C	B
	2	C	B	A	D
	3	D	C	B	A

Figure 4.3 The squares after rearranging rows and columns.

Now choose another random order for the columns, say 2, 1, 4, 3. Putting the columns in this order yields Figure 4.3.

Finally, select a random order for the treatments, say 2, 4, 3, 1. This means that A corresponds to Treatment 2, B to Treatment 4, C to Treatment 3, and to D Treatment 1. Thus the layout for the experiment will be that of Figure 4.4.

		Column variable classification			
		1	2	3	4
	1	4	2	1	3
Row variable	2	2	1	3	4
classification	3	3	4	2	1
	4	1	3	4	2

Figure 4.4 The square after assignment of rows, columns, and treatments.

4-3 NOTATION

Three subscripts will now be used for each observation. Let x_{ijk} denote the result when treatment k is applied to cell ij. If, for the tire example of Figure 4.1, we let brands A, F, G and R be treatments 1, 2, 3, 4 respectively, and use the randomization of Figure 4.4, the observed mileages can be written in the general notation as in Figure 4.5.

		Road condition			
		1	2	3	4
	1	x_{114}	x_{122}	x_{131}	x_{143}
Climate	2	x_{212}	x_{221}	x_{233}	x_{244}
condition	3	x_{313}	x_{324}	x_{332}	x_{341}
	4	x_{411}	x_{423}	x_{434}	x_{442}

Figure 4.5 Latin square for the tire experiment.

Let,

$$T_{i..} = \text{total of the } i^{\text{th}} \text{ row}, \ i=1, 2, \cdots, r,$$
$$T_{.j.} = \text{total of the } j^{\text{th}} \text{ column}, \ j=1, 2, \cdots, r,$$
$$T_{..k} = \text{total of all observations receiving treatment } k,$$
$$k=1, 2, \cdots, r,$$
$$T_{...} = \text{total of all observations in the square.}$$

If we attempt to write these in a simple summation notion, we experience a difficulty that did not appear in previous chapters. For example, in Figure 4.5 we have

$$T_{1..} = x_{114} + x_{122} + x_{131} + x_{143}.$$

It would not be consistent with our use of the summation sign to write

$$T_{1..} = \sum_{j=1}^{r} x_{ijk}.$$

Actually, when we add up the observations in the first row we are summing over both j and k, but only in the combinations as they appear in the chosen square. One way out of the difficulty would be to write

$$T_{i..} = \sum_{j,k=1}^{r} x_{ijk},$$

$$T_{.j.} = \sum_{i,k=1}^{r} x_{ijk},$$

$$T_{..k} = \sum_{i,j=1}^{r} x_{ijk},$$

$$T_{...} = \sum_{i,j,k=1}^{r} x_{ijk},$$

where it is understood that i, j, and k are summed over the proper values.

We define the means in the obvious way, that is,

$$\bar{x}_{i..} = \frac{T_{i..}}{r}, \qquad i = 1, 2, \cdots, r,$$

$$\bar{x}_{.j.} = \frac{T_{.j.}}{r}, \qquad j = 1, 2, \cdots, r,$$

$$\bar{x}_{..k} = \frac{T_{..k}}{r}, \qquad k = 1, 2, \cdots, r,$$

$$\bar{x}_{...} = \frac{T_{...}}{r^2}.$$

We note that

$$\sum_{i=1}^{r} T_{i..} = \sum_{j=1}^{r} T_{.j.} = \sum_{k=1}^{r} T_{..k} = T_{...},$$

that is, the sum of the row totals, the sum of the column totals, and the sum of the treatment totals each adds up to the overall total. The total sum of squares, which will be examined shortly, can be written

$$\sum_{i,j,k=1}^{r} (x_{ijk} - \bar{x}_{...})^2.$$

Observe that a sum which has two subscripts appearing below the summation sign yields r terms, while one with three subscripts yields r^2 terms.

4-4 THE FIXED-EFFECTS MODEL FOR THE LATIN SQUARE

Let μ_{ijk} be the mean of the population sampled in cell ij. We will assume that the x_{ijk} are independently $N(\mu_{ijk}, \sigma^2)$. This implies that, (a) a random sample of size 1 is drawn from each of the r^2 populations, (b) all r^2 populations are normal, and (c) the variance of each of the r^2 populations is the same. In addition, we will have to assume (d) row, column, and treatment effects are additive.

Let

$$\mu_{i..}=\frac{\sum\limits_{j,k=1}^{r}\mu_{ijk}}{r}, \quad \mu_{.j.}=\frac{\sum\limits_{i,k=1}^{r}\mu_{ijk}}{r},$$

$$\mu_{..k}=\frac{\sum\limits_{i,j=1}^{r}\mu_{ijk}}{r}, \quad \mu_{...}=\frac{\sum\limits_{i,j,k=1}^{r}\mu_{ijk}}{r^2}=\mu.$$

Then we may write the identity,

$$\mu_{ijk}=\mu+(\mu_{i..}-\mu)+(\mu_{.j.}-\mu)+(\mu_{..k}-\mu)$$
$$+(\mu_{ijk}-\mu_{i..}-\mu_{.j.}-\mu_{..k}+2\mu). \qquad (4.1)$$

Let

$$\alpha_i=\mu_{i..}-\mu, \quad \beta_j=\mu_{.j.}-\mu, \quad \text{and} \quad \gamma_k=\mu_{..k}-\mu.$$

If

$$\mu_{ijk}-\mu_{i..}-\mu_{.j.}-\mu_{..k}+2\mu=0, \qquad (4.2)$$

then (4.1) may be written

$$\mu_{ijk}=\mu+\alpha_i+\beta_j+\gamma_k. \qquad (4.3)$$

First, we note that

$$\sum_{i=1}^{r}\alpha_i=\sum_{j=1}^{r}\beta_j=\sum_{k=1}^{r}\gamma_k=0$$

since the sum of deviations from the mean is zero.

Second, let us comment upon the implication of (4.2). Essentially this implies that no new effects are produced by row and column variables acting together, row and treatment variables acting together, column and treatment variables acting together, or row, column, and treatment variables acting together. That is, the only effects present are those due to the row, treatment, and column variables acting individually and that they contribute to the μ_{ijk} in the fashion indicated by (4.3). We have seen in Table 3.2 what must happen when two variables do not interact. When we study factorials in Chapter 5, we will point out another condition that the means must satisfy if there is to be no three-way interaction.

Now us let restate the assumptions in the symbolic form. Observe that

$$x_{ijk}=\mu_{ijk}+(x_{ijk}-\mu_{ijk}) \qquad (4.4)$$

is an identity. Let $e_{ijk}=x_{ijk}-\mu_{ijk}$, variables which will be independently $N(0, \sigma^2)$. If no interactions are present, that is, if (4.2) holds, then (4.4) can be rewritten

$$x_{ijk}=\mu+\alpha_i+\beta_j+\gamma_k+e_{ijk}. \qquad (4.5)$$

Consequently, the assumptions written in the mathematical notation are

$$x_{ijk} = \mu + \alpha_i + \beta_j + \gamma_k + e_{ijk}, \quad i,j,k = 1, \ 2, \ \cdots, \ r$$

$$e_{ijk} \text{ are independently } N(0, \ \sigma^2) \qquad\qquad (4.6)$$

$$\sum_{i=1}^{r} \alpha_i = \sum_{j=1}^{r} \beta_j = \sum_{k=1}^{r} \gamma_k = 0.$$

Formula (4.6) implies exactly the assumptions (a), (b), (c), and (d) listed at the beginning of the section.

If all treatment means are the same, then $\mu_{..1} = \mu_{..2} = \mu_{..3} = \cdots = \mu_{..r} = \mu$ which means that $\gamma_1 = \gamma_2 = \cdots = \gamma_k = 0$. Consequently, when testing the hypothesis of equal treatment effects, we choose between

$$H_0 \colon \ \gamma_k = 0, \ k = 1, \ 2, \ \cdots, \ r$$

$$H_1 \colon \text{ not all } \gamma_k \text{'s are zero.} \qquad\qquad (4.7)$$

4-5 PARTITIONING THE SUM OF SQUARES

Again we divide the total sum of squares into components. We may write

$$\sum_{i,j,k=1}^{r} (x_{ijk} - \bar{x}_{...})^2 = \sum_{i,j,k=1}^{r} [\, (\bar{x}_{i..} - \bar{x}_{...}) + (\bar{x}_{.j.} - \bar{x}_{...}) + (\bar{x}_{..k} - \bar{x}_{...})$$

$$+ (x_{ijk} - \bar{x}_{i..} - \bar{x}_{.j.} - \bar{x}_{..k} + 2\bar{x}_{...})\,]^2$$

$$= \sum_{i,j,k=1}^{r} (\bar{x}_{i..} - \bar{x}_{...})^2 + \sum_{i,j,k=1}^{r} (\bar{x}_{.j.} - \bar{x}_{...})^2 + \sum_{i,j,k=1}^{r} (\bar{x}_{..k} - \bar{x}_{...})^2$$

$$+ \sum_{i,j,k=1}^{r} (x_{ijk} - \bar{x}_{i..} - \bar{x}_{.j.} - \bar{x}_{..k} + 2\bar{x}_{...})^2 + 6 \text{ cross-product terms.}$$

As usual, all cross-product terms can be shown to be zero.

Let

$$SS_R = \sum_{i,j,k=1}^{r} (\bar{x}_{i..} - \bar{x}_{...})^2,$$

$$SS_C = \sum_{i,j,k=1}^{r} (\bar{x}_{.j.} - \bar{x}_{...})^2,$$

and

$$SS_{Tr} = \sum_{i,j,k=1}^{r} (\bar{x}_{..k} - \bar{x}_{...})^2.$$

These sums of squares measure the variability of the sample row means, the sample column means, and the sample treatment means. Hence, we shall call them sum of squares for rows, sum of squares for columns, and sum of squares for treatments. Also let

$$SS_E = \sum_{i,j,k=1}^{r} (x_{ijk} - \bar{x}_{i..} - \bar{x}_{.j.} - \bar{x}_{..k} + 2\bar{x}_{...})^2$$

which will be called the error sum of squares. Then, since the 6 cross-product terms vanish, the identity at the beginning of the section may be written

$$SS_T = SS_R + SS_C + SS_{Tr} + SS_E. \tag{4.8}$$

The computing formulas are similar to those of the previous chapters. These are

$$SS_T = \sum_{i,j,k=1}^{r} x_{ijk}^2 - \frac{T_{...}^2}{r^2}, \tag{4.9}$$

$$SS_R = \frac{\sum_{i=1}^{r} T_{i..}^2}{r} - \frac{T_{...}^2}{r^2}, \tag{4.10}$$

$$SS_C = \frac{\sum_{j=1}^{r} T_{.j.}^2}{r} - \frac{T_{...}^2}{r^2}, \tag{4.11}$$

$$SS_{Tr} = \frac{\sum_{k=1}^{r} T_{..k}^2}{r} - \frac{T_{...}^2}{r^2}, \tag{4.12}$$

and

$$SS_E = SS_T - SS_R - SS_C - SS_{Tr}. \tag{4.13}$$

The derivation of these formulas is straightforward. For example,

$$SS_T = \sum_{i,j,k=1}^{r} (x_{ijk} - \bar{x}_{...})^2$$
$$= \sum_{i,j,k=1}^{r} (x_{ijk}^2 - 2\bar{x}_{...} x_{ijk} + \bar{x}_{...}^2)$$
$$= \sum_{i,j,k=1}^{r} x_{ijk}^2 - 2\bar{x}_{...} \sum_{i,j,k=1}^{r} x_{ijk} + r^2 \bar{x}_{...}^2$$
$$= \sum_{i,j,k=1}^{r} x_{ijk}^2 - 2\frac{T_{...}}{r^2}(T_{...}) + r^2\left(\frac{T_{...}}{r^2}\right)^2$$
$$= \sum_{i,j,k=1}^{r} x_{iik}^2 - \frac{T_{...}^2}{r^2}.$$

Actually, Formulas (4.9), (4.10), and (4.11) are the same as those used in Chapter 3 with (4.9) being adapted to the new notation.

EXERCISE

4.1 (a) Demonstrate that the cross-product term

$$2\sum_{i,j,k=1}^{r} (\bar{x}_{i..} - \bar{x}_{...})(\bar{x}_{..k} - \bar{x}_{...})$$

is zero for the square of Figure 4.5 by writing out all sixteen terms and grouping them properly.   (b) Verify that Formula (4.12) is correct.

4-6 TESTING THE HYPOTHESIS OF EQUAL-TREATMENT EFFECTS

If the assumptions for the fixed-effects model as specified by (4.6) are satisfied, then it may be shown that

$$F_{r-1,\ (r-1)\ (r-2)} = \frac{\dfrac{SS_{Tr}}{r-1}}{\dfrac{SS_E}{(r-1)\ (r-2)}} = \frac{MS_{Tr}}{MS_E} \qquad (4.14)$$

is the proper ratio to use when testing the hypothesis of equal-treatment effects, the situation specified by (4.7). The results of the analysis may be presented in the form of Table 4.2. An examination of the EMS's reveals that MS_{Tr} and MS_E should have compatible values if

$$\gamma_1 = \gamma_2 = \cdots = \gamma_r = 0.$$

Table 4.2 ANALYSIS OF VARIANCE FOR A LATIN SQUARE

Source	SS	d.f.	MS	EMS	F
Rows	SS_R	$r-1$	MS_R	$\sigma^2 + \dfrac{r}{r-1} \sum_{i=1}^{r} \alpha_i^2$	
Columns	SS_C	$r-1$	MS_C	$\sigma^2 + \dfrac{r}{r-1} \sum_{j=1}^{r} \beta_j^2$	
Treatments	SS_{Tr}	$r-1$	MS_{Tr}	$\sigma^2 + \dfrac{r}{r-1} \sum_{k=1}^{r} \gamma_k^2$	$\dfrac{MS_{Tr}}{MS_E}$
Error	SS_E	$(r-1)(r-2)$	MS_E	σ^2	
TOTAL	SS_T	r^2-1			

If the γ_k's are not all zero, then we would expect MS_{Tr} to be somewhat larger than MS_E. Hence, once more only large values of F lie in the critical region.

EXERCISES

4.2 A cab company operating in 5 different large cities is going to buy a fleet of cabs. They have obtained bids from 5 different car manufacturers and find that there is little difference in price. It is decided that they will experiment with 5 cars of each brand. Each car will be driven 10,000 miles and the cost per mile recorded. Five different drivers are hired to conduct the test. Since it is known that cost varies with the driver and the city, a Latin square experiment is conducted with these variables used for rows and columns. The results are given in the table below. Entries are in cents and the letter denotes the automobile brand. Test the hypothesis that the average cost per mile is the same for each brand.

		Cities				
		1	2	3	4	5
	1	5.83D	6.22P	7.67F	9.43C	6.57R
	2	4.80P	7.56D	10.34C	5.82R	9.86F
Drivers	3	7.43F	11.29C	7.01R	10.48D	9.27P
	4	6.60R	9.54F	11.11D	10.84P	15.05C
	5	11.24C	6.34R	11.30P	12.58F	16.04D

4.3 Describe a Latin square experiment in a field of application that interests you. Specify the row, column, and treatment variable for each category. Select a square by the suggested randomization procedure. Explain how you would collect the data.

4-7 MISSING OBSERVATION

We will consider the case of one missing observation. Denote the missing value by y_{ijk}. The sums of squares all depend upon this number. As in the randomized blocks case, y_{ijk} is selected to minimize SS_E. This leads to the result

$$y_{ijk} = \frac{r(T'_{i..} + T'_{.j.} + T'_{..k}) - 2T'_{...}}{(r-1)(r-2)} \tag{4.15}$$

where the primes indicate the previously defined totals with the one value missing. Substitute the value given by (4.15) for the missing one and compute the sum of squares in the usual way. Let

$$
\begin{aligned}
SS'_{Tr} &= SS_{Tr} - \frac{[T'_{...} - T'_{i..} - T'_{.j.} - (r-1)T'_{..k}]^2}{(r-1)^2(r-2)^2} \\
&= SS_{Tr} - b^2. \tag{4.16}
\end{aligned}
$$

Then

$$F_{r-1,\,(r-1)(r-2)-1} = \frac{\dfrac{SS'_{Tr}}{r-1}}{\dfrac{SS_E}{(r-1)(r-2)-1}} = \frac{MS'_{Tr}}{MS'_E} \tag{4.17}$$

is used to test the hypothesis of equal-treatment effects. The analysis of variance appears in Table 4.3.

Table 4.3   ANALYSIS OF VARIANCE FOR A LATIN SQUARE
WITH ONE MISSING OBSERVATION

Source	SS	d.f.	MS	F
Rows	SS_R	$r-1$	MS_R	
Columns	SS_C	$r-1$	MS_C	
Treatments	SS'_{Tr}	$r-1$	MS'_{Tr}	$\dfrac{MS'_{Tr}}{MS'_E}$
Error	SS_E	$(r-1)(r-2)-1$	MS'_E	
TOTAL	SS_T-b^2	r^2-2		

Procedures for handling cases with two or more missing plots may be
found in References [2] and [3].

EXERCISE

4.4 Test for equal-treatment effects in the following Latin square:

		Columns 1	2	3
Rows	1	28C	22B	A
	2	17B	16A	24C
	3	15A	23C	15B

4-8 THE POWER OF THE F-TEST

For the Latin square

$$\phi = \frac{\sqrt{\sum_{k=1}^{r} \gamma_k^2}}{\sigma} \qquad (4.18)$$

Except for this change, power calculations are the same as outlined in
Section 2-11. Once more it is convenient to choose the constants occurring in ϕ (here the γ_k's) as multiples of σ. Here $\nu_1 = r-1$ and
$\nu_2 = (r-1)(r-2)$.

EXERCISE

4.5 Taking $\alpha = .05$, find the probability of rejecting the hypothesis of equal-treatment effects for Exercise 4.2 if four-treatments
effects are equal and the fifth exceeds these four by σ. If the
largest difference among the five-treatment effects is σ, find the
least value for the power.

4-9 MISCELLANEOUS REMARKS

Again the results of 2-12, 2-13, and 2-14 are applicable after a few minor modifications. Contrasts will now be of the form

$$L = c_1 \mu_{..1} + c_2 \mu_{..2} + \cdots + c_r \mu_{..r} \qquad (4.19)$$
$$= c_1 \gamma_1 + c_2 \gamma_2 + \cdots + c_r \gamma_r$$

where
$$\sum_{k=1}^{r} c_k = 0 \quad \text{and} \quad \hat{L} = \sum_{k=1}^{r} c_k \bar{x}_{..k}.$$

We replace MS_W by MS_E. Wherever $N-r$ degrees of freedom appears, it is replaced by $(r-1)(r-2)$, the degrees of freedom for MS_E. In addition n is replaced by r. Thus, for example, for the T-method

$$T = \frac{1}{\sqrt{r}} \, q_{1-\alpha; \, r, \, (r-1)(r-2)}$$

and for the S-method

$$S^2 = (r-1) F_{1-\alpha; \, r-1, \, (r-1)(r-2)}.$$

Other modifications are made similarly.

Tukey [4] has constructed a test for nonadditivity in Latin squares. It is similar to the one described for randomized blocks, but the computation is a little more complicated. For further information refer to Tukey's original article or to that part of Snedecor's text [3] which uses a numerical example.

Expressions comparable to the E_1 of Equation (3.28) are available to estimate the relative efficiency of a Latin square design. The quantity

$$\hat{E}_2 = \frac{MS_R + MS_C + (r-1)MS_E}{(r+1)MS_E} \qquad (4.20)$$

can be taken as estimate of the relative efficiency of a Latin square with respect to complete randomization. An estimate of the relative efficiency of a Latin square with respect to a randomized block design is given by

$$\hat{E}_3 = \frac{MS_C + (r-1)MS_E}{rMS_E} \qquad (4.21)$$

where the row variable of the square is the block variable. In other words, if the introduction of the column variable improves the design, we would expect this to be larger than 1. If this is less than 1, we might eliminate the column variable when repeating the experiment. If the column variable of the square forms the blocks, then (4.21) should be replaced by

$$\hat{E}_4 = \frac{MS_R + (r-1)MS_E}{rMS_E} \qquad (4.22)$$

Perhaps it is worth noting that a random-effects or a mixed model could be used with a Latin square. If such were used, then Equation (4.6) and Table 4.2 would have to be modified to correspond with the concepts treated in Section 3-12.

EXERCISES

4.6 Use the T-method on the data of Exercise 4.2 to determine which treatments are significantly better than which other treatments. What recommendation would you make? Suppose that treatment subscripts 1, 2, 3, 4, and 5 refer to observations obtained from cars D, P, F, C, and R respectively. Use the S-method to obtain an interval for $L = 4\mu_{..5} - \mu_{..1} - \mu_{..2} - \mu_{..3} - \mu_{..4}$. Interpret your result.

4.7 For Exercise 4.2 compute the relative efficiency of a Latin square with respect to complete randomization. If rows are used as blocks, what is the relative efficiency of the Latin square with respect to a randomized block design? If columns are used as blocks?

REFERENCES

[1] Fisher, R.A., and F. Yates, *Statistical Tables* (Edinburgh: Oliver and Boyd, 1948).

[2] Kempthorne, Oscar, *The Design and Analysis of Experiments* (New York: John Wiley & Sons, Inc., 1952).

[3] Snedecor, George, W., *Statistical Methods*, (Ames, Iowa: Iowa State University Press, 1956).

[4] Tukey, J.W., "Queries in Biometrics," *Biometrics*, Vol. 11 (1955), p. 111.

5

Factorial Experiments

5-1 INTRODUCTION

In Chapters 2, 3, and 4 we were concerned with only one variable, the treatments. This variable is also called a factor. To investigate treatment effects we have introduced three different designs: (a) completely randomized, (b) randomized blocks, and (c) Latin squares. Often it may be desirable to investigate two or more factors in the same experiment. For example, we may wish to study the manner in which three different kinds of fertilizer affect wheat yields at the same time we are comparing four different varieties. Fertilizers and varieties are both called factors. There are four different levels, or classifications, for varieties and three different levels for fertilizers. The term factorial is used to identify this type of experiment in which two or more independent variables are considered simultaneously.

There are a number of reasons why we may want to use a factorial. First, it enables us to study the interaction of the factors. Some fertilizers may increase the yield of some varieties of wheat, but decrease it with others. This type of effect can be investigated only if fertilizers and varieties are combined in the same experiment. Secondly, a saving of time and effort results. All observations may be used to investigate the effects of each of the factors. The variety-fertilizer experiment could be conducted as two simple one-factor experiments. If this were done, then some of the observations would only yield information about varieties, and others only information about fertilizers. Consequently, more experimental units would be needed to achieve the same degree of accuracy as that obtained by a two-factor experiment. Hence one two-factor experiment is more economical than two one-factor experiments. Third, the conclusions reached have broader application. This is due to the fact that the behavior of each factor is studied with varying combinations of other factors. Thus the results are more useful than those obtained by holding all other factors constant.

We may use a factorial arrangement with any of the designs discussed in the previous chapters. Consider again the variety-fertilizer example. Each of the $4 \times 3 = 12$ combinations of varieties and fertilizers is a treatment. If 60 acres are available to conduct the experiment, then under complete randomization each of the 12-treatment combinations may be assigned randomly to five one-acre plots. If we decide to run the experiment in five different communities where soil fertility and rainfall vary, then a randomized block design with 12 one-acre plots in each community is appropriate. If the experiment is conducted in a field with fertility running in two directions perpendicular to each other, then perhaps a Latin square is desirable. The field may be divided into $12 \times 12 = 144$ square plots parallel to the directions of fertility. Since there are 12 treatments, this size square is necessary.

5-2 NOTATION FOR TWO-FACTOR COMPLETELY RANDOMIZED AND RANDOMIZED BLOCK DESIGNS

Denote the factors by A and B. Let the levels of A be numbered 1, 2, $\cdots$, a and the levels of B be 1, 2, $\cdots$, b. Assume that we have n observations for each treatment combination. Then the data can be arranged as in Table 5.1.

The symbols which we will use are defined as follows:

Total of cell ij $= T_{ij.} = \sum_{k=1}^{n} x_{ijk}$,

Mean of cell ij $= \bar{x}_{ij.} = \dfrac{T_{ij.}}{n}$,

Total of the ith row $= T_{i..} = \sum_{j=1}^{b} \sum_{k=1}^{n} x_{ijk} = \sum_{j=1}^{b} T_{ij.}$,

Mean of the ith row $= \bar{x}_{i..} = \dfrac{T_{i..}}{nb}$,

Table 5.1 ARRANGEMENT OF DATA FOR A TWO-FACTOR EXPERIMENT

A \ B	1	2	$\cdots$	b	TOTALS	Means
1	x_{111} . . . x_{11n}	x_{121} . . . x_{12n}	$\cdots$	x_{1b1} . . . x_{1bn}	$T_{1..}$	$\bar{x}_{1..}$
2	x_{211} . . . x_{21n}	x_{211} . . . x_{22n}	$\cdots$	x_{2b1} . . . x_{2bn}	$T_{2..}$	$\bar{x}_{2..}$
. . .	. . .	. . .	$\cdots$	. . .		
a	x_{a11} . . . x_{a1n}	x_{a21} . . . x_{a2n}	$\cdots$	x_{ab1} . . . x_{abn}	$T_{a..}$	$\bar{x}_{a..}$
TOTALS	$T_{.1.}$	$T_{.2.}$		$T_{.b.}$	$T_{...}$	
Means	$\bar{x}_{.1.}$	$\bar{x}_{.2.}$		$\bar{x}_{.b.}$		$\bar{x}_{...}$

Total of the jth column $= T_{.j.} = \sum_{i=1}^{a} \sum_{k=1}^{n} x_{ijk} = \sum_{i=1}^{a} T_{ij.}$,

Mean of the jth column $= \bar{x}_{.j.} = \dfrac{T_{.j.}}{na}$,

Overall total $= T_{...}$

$$= \sum_{i=1}^{a} \sum_{j=1}^{b} \sum_{k=1}^{n} x_{ijk}$$

$$= \sum_{i=1}^{a} \sum_{j=1}^{b} T_{ij.}$$

$$= \sum_{i=1}^{a} T_{i..}$$

$$= \sum_{j=1}^{b} T_{.j.} ,$$

Overall mean $= \bar{x}_{...}$

$$= \dfrac{T_{...}}{nab} .$$

Previously, we have used r for the number of treatments. Here $r = ab$.

The table as it stands could be regarded as data from a completely randomized experiment. If we look upon the first observation in each cell as being in block 1, the second observation in each cell as being in block 2, $\cdots$, and the nth observation in each cell as being in block n, then the table represents data from a randomized block experiment. To help connect the notation to that used in Chapters 2 and 3, visualize a table with $r=ab$ treatments across the top with n observation or blocks forming the rows.

5-3 THE FIXED-EFFECTS MODEL FOR A TWO-FACTOR COMPLETELY RANDOMIZED DESIGN

The assumptions that we make for this model are the same as those given in Section 2-4. These are (a) the $r=ab$ cells represent r random samples of size n drawn from r populations, (b) each of the r populations is normal, and (c) each of the r populations has the same variance. In other words we assume that the x_{ijk} are independently $N(\mu_{ij},\sigma^2)$. Let

$$\mu_{i.}=\frac{\sum\limits_{j=1}^{b}\mu_{ij}}{b}, \qquad \mu_{.j}=\frac{\sum\limits_{i=1}^{a}\mu_{ij}}{a},$$

and

$$\mu_{..}=\mu=\frac{\sum\limits_{i=1}^{a}\sum\limits_{j=1}^{b}\mu_{ij}}{ab}=\frac{\sum\limits_{i=1}^{a}\mu_{i.}}{a}=\frac{\sum\limits_{j=1}^{b}\mu_{.j}}{b}.$$

We may write the following identities:

$$x_{ijk}=\mu_{ij}+(x_{ijk}-\mu_{ij})$$

and

$$\mu_{ij}=\mu+(\mu_{i.}-\mu)+(\mu_{.j}-\mu)+(\mu_{ij}-\mu_{i.}-\mu_{.j}+\mu).$$

Let

$$\alpha_i=\mu_{i.}-\mu, \quad \beta_j=\mu_{.j}-\mu,$$
$$(\alpha\beta)_{ij}=\mu_{ij}-\mu_{i.}-\mu_{.j}+\mu,$$

and

$$e_{ijk}=x_{ijk}-\mu_{ij}.$$

It may be shown that

$$\sum_{i=1}^{a}\alpha_i=\sum_{j=1}^{b}\beta_j=\sum_{i=1}^{a}(\alpha\beta)_{ij}=\sum_{j=1}^{b}(\alpha\beta)_{ij}=0.$$

Consequently the assumptions for the fixed-effects model can be written

$$x_{ijk}=\mu+\alpha_i+\beta_j+(\alpha\beta)_{ij}+e_{ijk}, \qquad \begin{matrix} i=1,\ 2,\ \cdots,\ a \\ j=1,\ 2,\ \cdots,\ b \\ k=1,\ 2,\ \cdots,\ n \end{matrix}$$

e_{ijk} are independently $N(0,\ \sigma^2)$ (5.1)

$$\sum_{i=1}^{a} \alpha_i = \sum_{j=1}^{b} \beta_j = \sum_{i=1}^{a} (\alpha\beta)_{ij} = \sum_{j=1}^{b} (\alpha\beta)_{ij} = 0.$$

The three main hypotheses of interest together with their alternates are

$$H_0' : \alpha_i = 0, \qquad i = 1, 2, \cdots, a$$
$$H_1' : \text{not all } \alpha_i \text{ are zero,} \tag{5.2}$$

$$H_0'' : \beta_j = 0, \qquad j = 1, 2, \cdots, b$$
$$H_1'' : \text{not all } \beta_j \text{ are zero,} \tag{5.3}$$

and

$$H_0''' : (\alpha\beta)_{ij} = 0, \quad i = 1, 2, \cdots, a, \quad j = 1, 2, \cdots, b$$
$$H_1''' : \text{not all } (\alpha\beta)_{ij} \text{ are zero.} \tag{5.4}$$

If H_0' is true, then there is no difference between the means of the various levels of A. Similarly, if H_0'' is true, then there is no difference in the various levels of B. The third hypothesis, H_0''', which may be rewritten

$$\mu_{ij} - \mu_{i.} - \mu_{.j} + \mu = 0, \quad i = 1, 2, \cdots, a, \quad j = 1, 2, \cdots, b$$

says that effects due to factors A and B are additive.

If H_0''' is rejected, the conclusion is that these factors are not additive or that factors A and B interact. If this happens, H_0' can still be tested, but the results of such tests are usually of no interest. When interactions are present, the best treatment combinations, rather than the best levels of A or B, are usually the prime concern. In this situation the acceptance of H_0' should be interpreted as meaning that there are no differences in the various levels of A when averaged over the levels of B. Similarly, if H_0'' is accepted, the interpretation is that there is no difference in the various levels of B when averaged over the levels of A.

The analysis is much simpler if we conclude that factors A and B do not interact. Then inferences concerning the α_i are the same for all levels of B while inferences concerning the β_j are the same for all levels of A.

EXERCISE

5.1 Show that $\sum_{i=1}^{a} (\alpha\beta)_{ij} = 0$ and $\sum_{j=1}^{b} (\alpha\beta)_{ij} = 0$.

5-4 PARTITIONING THE SUM OF SQUARES FOR A TWO-FACTOR COMPLETELY RANDOMIZED EXPERIMENT

For the one-way classification we have already shown that

$$SS_T = SS_{Tr} + SS_E. \tag{5.5}$$

In Section 2-5, however, we used the terms among samples and within samples instead of treatments and error. The Identity (5.5), or its equivalent (2.3), converted to our present notation is

$$\sum_{i=1}^{a} \sum_{j=1}^{b} \sum_{k=1}^{n} (x_{ijk} - \bar{x}_{...})^2 = \sum_{i=1}^{a} \sum_{j=1}^{b} \sum_{k=1}^{n} (\bar{x}_{ij.} - \bar{x}_{...})^2$$

$$+ \sum_{i=1}^{a} \sum_{j=1}^{b} \sum_{k=1}^{n} (x_{ijk} - \bar{x}_{ij.})^2. \qquad (5.6)$$

Next SS_{Tr}, the first term on the right-hand side of Equation (5.6), is partitioned into three parts. We write

$$\sum_{i=1}^{a} \sum_{j=1}^{b} \sum_{k=1}^{n} (\bar{x}_{ij.} - \bar{x}_{...})^2$$

$$= \sum_{i=1}^{a} \sum_{j=1}^{b} \sum_{k=1}^{n} [(\bar{x}_{i..} - \bar{x}_{...}) + (\bar{x}_{.j.} - \bar{x}_{...}) + (\bar{x}_{ij.} - \bar{x}_{i..} - \bar{x}_{.j.} + \bar{x}_{...})]^2$$

$$= \sum_{i=1}^{a} \sum_{j=1}^{b} \sum_{k=1}^{n} (\bar{x}_{i..} - \bar{x}_{...})^2 + \sum_{i=1}^{a} \sum_{j=1}^{b} \sum_{k=1}^{n} (\bar{x}_{.j.} - \bar{x}_{...})^2$$

$$+ \sum_{i=1}^{a} \sum_{j=1}^{b} \sum_{k=1}^{n} (\bar{x}_{ij.} - \bar{x}_{i..} - \bar{x}_{.j.} + \bar{x}_{...})^2 + 3 \text{ cross-product terms.} \qquad (5.7)$$

It is easily shown that all cross-product terms are zero. In shorthand notation, (5.7) can be written

$$SS_{Tr} = SS_A + SS_B + SS_{AB}. \qquad (5.8)$$

We have already discussed in Section 2-5 what is measured by the sums of squares for total, treatment, and error. Let us examine the three new sums of squares that appear on the right-hand sides of Equations (5.7) and (5.8). The first term, SS_A, is a measure of the variability of the sample means obtained for the various levels of A. If these sample means are nearly alike, then this term is small. The more these sample means vary, the larger this term becomes. Similarly, SS_B measures the variation of the sample means for the levels of B. The third term, SS_{AB}, measures a new kind of effect which is called interaction. If the cell sample means possessed the property of additivity discussed in Section 3-3, then this term would be zero. The more they depart from this situation, the larger this term becomes. The interpretation is that SS_{AB} measures effects that factors A and B produce together, which are not attributable to either A or B alone.

In Section 2-7 we developed the computing formulas for Equation (5.5). Adapted to our present notation, these are

$$SS_T = \sum_{i=1}^{a} \sum_{j=1}^{b} \sum_{k=1}^{n} x_{ijk}^2 - \frac{T_{...}^2}{abn}, \qquad (5.9)$$

$$SS_{Tr} = \frac{\sum\limits_{i=1}^{a} \sum\limits_{j=1}^{b} T_{ij.}^2}{n} - \frac{T_{...}^2}{abn}, \tag{5.10}$$

and

$$SS_E = SS_T - SS_{Tr}. \tag{5.11}$$

It is easily shown that

$$SS_A = \frac{\sum\limits_{i=1}^{a} T_{i..}^2}{bn} - \frac{T_{...}^2}{abn} \tag{5.12}$$

and

$$SS_B = \frac{\sum\limits_{j=1}^{b} T_{.j.}^2}{an} - \frac{T_{...}^2}{abn}. \tag{5.13}$$

Finally

$$SS_{AB} = SS_{Tr} - SS_A - SS_B. \tag{5.14}$$

EXERCISE

5.2 (a) Prove Formula (5.12).

(b) One of the cross-product terms of Equation (5.7) is

$$2 \sum_{i=1}^{a} \sum_{j=1}^{b} \sum_{k=1}^{n} (\bar{x}_{i..} - \bar{x}_{...})(\bar{x}_{ij.} - \bar{x}_{i..} - \bar{x}_{.j.} + \bar{x}_{...}).$$

Show that this is equal to zero.

5-5 ANALYSIS OF THE TWO-FACTOR COMPLETELY RANDOMIZED EXPERIMENT (FIXED-EFFECTS MODEL)

Assume that the conditions specified by (5.1) are satisfied. If in addition H_0' is true, then it may be shown that

$$F_{a-1,\, ab(n-1)} = \frac{\dfrac{SS_A}{a-1}}{\dfrac{SS_E}{ab(n-1)}} = \frac{MS_A}{MS_E} \tag{5.15}$$

and that H_0' should be rejected when $F_{a-1,\, ab(n-1)}$ is large. Similarly,

if $$F_{b-1,\, ab(n-1)} = \frac{\dfrac{SS_B}{b-1}}{\dfrac{SS_E}{ab(n-1)}} = \frac{MS_B}{MS_E} \tag{5.16}$$

is large, reject H_0'', and if

$$F_{(a-1)(b-1),\,ab(n-1)} = \frac{\dfrac{SS_{AB}}{(a-1)(b-1)}}{\dfrac{SS_E}{ab(n-1)}} = \frac{MS_{AB}}{MS_E} \tag{5.17}$$

is large, reject H_0'''.   The results are summarized in Table 5.2.   A glance at the *EMS* column indicates the proper F ratio to form for testing each of the three main hypotheses.

Table 5.2 ANALYSIS OF VARIANCE FOR A TWO-FACTOR COMPLETELY RANDOMIZED EXPERIMENT (FIXED-EFFECTS)

Source	SS	d.f.	MS	EMS	F
TREATMENTS A	SS_A	$a-1$	MS_A	$\sigma^2 + nb\dfrac{\sum\limits_{i=1}^{a}\alpha_i^2}{a-1}$	$\dfrac{MS_A}{MS_E}$
B	SS_B	$b-1$	MS_B	$\sigma^2 + na\dfrac{\sum\limits_{j=1}^{b}\beta_j^2}{b-1}$	$\dfrac{MS_B}{MS_E}$
AB	SS_{AB}	$(a-1)(b-1)$	MS_{AB}	$\sigma^2 + n\dfrac{\sum\limits_{i=1}^{a}\sum\limits_{j=1}^{b}(\alpha\beta)_{ij}^2}{(a-1)(b-1)}$	$\dfrac{MS_{AB}}{MS_E}$
Error	SS_E	$ab(n-1)$	MS_E	σ^2	
TOTAL	SS_T	$abn-1$			

The significance levels arising from this experiment deserve some comment. First, there is a significance level for each of the F ratios making a total of three. Designate these by α', α'', and α'''. More often than not, all three of these will have the same value, say .05 or .01. However, a situation may arise in which the experimenter chooses different values. Second, there is a significance level associated with the experiment as a whole, say α. This is the probability of rejecting one or more of the three hypotheses when all are true. Kimball [1] has shown that

$$\alpha < 1 - (1-\alpha')(1-\alpha'')(1-\alpha''') . \tag{5.18}$$

For example, if $\alpha' = \alpha'' = \alpha''' = .05$, this gives $\alpha < 1 - (.95)^3$ or $\alpha < .143$. If $\alpha' = \alpha'' = \alpha''' = .01$, then $\alpha < .0297$. One should keep in mind all four significance levels when interpreting the results of an experiment.

If either A effects or B effects are found, then either the T-method or the S-method may be used to uncover contrasts which are significantly different from zero. Contrasts among the A means will be of the form

$$L = c_1\mu_{1.} + c_2\mu_{2.} + \cdots + c_a\mu_{a.} \tag{5.19}$$

which we would estimate by

$$\hat{L}=c_1\bar{x}_{1..}+c_2\bar{x}_{2..}+\cdots+c_a\bar{x}_{a..}.$$

The modifications necessary to apply the results of Section 2-12, 2-13, and 2-14 are fairly obvious. As before, MS_E replaces MS_W and $ab(n-1)$ replaces $N-r$. The number of treatments is a instead of r. Each sample mean $\bar{x}_{i..}$ is based on bn observations; consequently bn replaces n_j. Thus for the T-method

$$T=\frac{1}{\sqrt{bn}}\; q_{1-\alpha;\,a,ab(n-1)} \qquad (5.20)$$

and for the S-method

$$S^2=(a-1)\,F_{1-\alpha;\,a-1,ab(n-1)} \qquad (5.21)$$

and

$$\hat{\sigma}_{\hat{L}}^2=\frac{MS_E}{bn}\;\sum_{i=1}^{a}c_i^2. \qquad (5.22)$$

Contrasts among the B means will be of the form

$$L=c_1\mu_{.1}+c_2\mu_{.2}+\cdots+c_b\mu_{.b}. \qquad (5.23)$$

In Formulas (5.20), (5.21), and (5.22), interchange a and b when working with B means.

If we conclude that there are interactions, then we may be interested in finding the best combination of A and B. To do this, use the T-method to investigate contrasts of the type

$$L=\mu_{ij}-\mu_{i'j'} \qquad (5.24)$$

among the cell means. Here L is estimated by

$$\hat{L}=\bar{x}_{ij.}-\bar{x}_{i'j'.}$$

and

$$T=\frac{1}{\sqrt{n}}\; q_{1-\alpha;\,ab,ab(n-1)}. \qquad (5.25)$$

Then $\hat{L}$ is significant if

$$\hat{L}>T\sqrt{MS_E}. \qquad (5.26)$$

Of course, other type contrasts among the cell means may also be investigated. The S-method can be applied as well.

Power can be calculated for each of the three F tests. When A effects are investigated, then

$$\phi = \frac{\sqrt{\dfrac{bn}{a} \sum_{i=1}^{a} \alpha_i^2}}{\sigma}, \quad \nu_1 = a-1, \text{ and } \nu_2 = ab(n-1). \qquad (5.27)$$

For B effects we have

$$\phi = \frac{\sqrt{\dfrac{an}{b} \sum_{j=1}^{b} \beta_j^2}}{\sigma}, \quad \nu_1 = b-1, \text{ and } \nu_2 = ab(n-1). \qquad (5.28)$$

Finally, when testing for interactions

$$\phi = \frac{\sqrt{\dfrac{n}{(a-1)(b-1)+1} \sum_{i=1}^{a} \sum_{j=1}^{b} (\alpha\beta)_{ij}^2}}{\sigma}, \qquad (5.29)$$

$$\nu_1 = (a-1)(b-1), \text{ and } \nu_2 = ab(n-1).$$

To illustrate the use of (5.29), let $n=4$, $a=3$, $b=3$, and $\alpha=.05$. Suppose we seek the probability of detecting interactions if one of them has a value σ and as many of the others as possible are zero. Because of the results of Exercise 5.1, three other interactions are σ, $-\sigma$, and $-\sigma$. Hence

$$\sum_{i=1}^{a} \sum_{j=1}^{b} (\alpha\beta)_{ij}^2 = 4\sigma^2$$

$$\phi = \frac{\sqrt{\dfrac{4}{5} 4\sigma^2}}{\sigma} = 1.79$$

$$\nu_1 = (a-1)(b-1) = 4, \qquad \nu_2 = ab(n-1) = 27$$

and from the Pearson-Hartley graph we find the power is about .85.

In the special case in which there is only one observation per cell, it is necessary to assume that there are no interactions. The analysis of variance table then has the same appearance as the one for randomized block which is given in Section 3-5. Blocks are replaced by levels of A, treatments by levels of B, n by a, and r by b. In the F column we write MS_A/MS_E and MS_B/MS_E.

When the cell frequencies are not equal, the analysis is more difficult. For information concerning this case, see Scheffé [3] and Snedecor [5].

EXERCISES

5.3 A completely randomized experiment is conducted with three varieties of wheat and three fertilizers with the following results:

		Wheat varieties		
		1	2	3
	1	46	41	35
		35	26	21
		19	11	31
		23	17	27
		37	49	45
Fertilizers	2	18	37	66
		18	35	61
		20	43	75
	3	32	65	34
		43	67	66
		32	58	58
		18	74	67

Test the three main hypotheses. Suppose that you choose $\alpha' = .05$, $\alpha'' = .05$, and $\alpha''' = .01$. What can be said about the significance level of the experiment as a whole?

5.4 Apply the T-method to the data of Exercise 5.3. That is, for each hypothesis that is rejected, determine which treatments are significantly better than which other treatments. Which results seem to be the most interesting for this problem?

5.5 For the experiment of Exercise 5.3, what is the probability of rejecting the null hypothesis for A-level means if two-treatment effects (that is, two of the α's) are equal and the third exceeds these two by σ? If n is increased to 10, what is the probability? Assume that the significance level is .05.

5-6 OTHER MODELS FOR THE TWO-FACTOR COMPLETELY RANDOMIZED EXPERIMENT

If both the levels of A and the levels of B are random samples from a large number of levels, then the term random-effects model is used to identify the experiment. In terms of the wheat variety-fertilizer example of Section 5-1, the random-effects model is appropriate if the four varieties are a random sample from a large population of varieties, and the three fertilizers are a random sample from a large population of fertilizers. The assumptions for this model are

$$x_{ijk} = \mu + \alpha_i + \beta_j + (\alpha\beta)_{ij} + e_{ijk}, \qquad \begin{aligned} i &= 1, 2, \cdots, a \\ j &= 1, 2, \cdots, b \\ k &= 1, 2, \cdots, n \end{aligned}$$

$$e_{ijk} \quad \text{are independently } N(0, \sigma^2)$$
$$\alpha_i \quad \text{are independently } N(0, \sigma_A^2)$$
$$\beta_j \quad \text{are independently } N(0, \sigma_B^2) \tag{5.30}$$
$$(\alpha\beta)_{ij} \text{ are independently } N(0, \sigma_{AB}^2).$$

The computations of the sums of squares and the mean squares are exactly the same as in the fixed-effects model. Now (5.2), (5.3), and (5.4) are replaced by

$$H_0' : \quad \sigma_A^2 = 0 \tag{5.31}$$
$$H_1' : \quad \sigma_A^2 \neq 0,$$

$$H_0'' : \quad \sigma_B^2 = 0 \tag{5.32}$$
$$H_1'' : \quad \sigma_B^2 \neq 0$$

and

$$H_0''' : \quad \sigma_{AB}^2 = 0 \tag{5.33}$$
$$H_1''' : \quad \sigma_{AB}^2 \neq 0.$$

The analysis of variance is the same as Table 5.2 except for the changes indicated in Table 5.3.

Table 5.3   EXPECTED MEAN SQUARES AND F RATIOS FOR THE TWO-FACTOR COMPLETELY RANDOMIZED RANDOM-EFFECTS MODEL

Source		EMS	F
Treatments	A	$\sigma^2 + n\sigma_{AB}^2 + bn\sigma_A^2$	$\dfrac{MS_A}{MS_{AB}}$
	B	$\sigma^2 + n\sigma_{AB}^2 + an\sigma_B^2$	$\dfrac{MS_B}{MS_{AB}}$
	AB	$\sigma^2 + n\sigma_{AB}^2$	$\dfrac{MS_{AB}}{MS_E}$
Error		σ^2	

Note that the denominators of the F ratios used for situations (5.31) and (5.32) have MS_{AB} as the denominator. For (5.33) the denominator is still MS_E as in the fixed-effects model.

Hypotheses other than those given above may be investigated as was done in Section 2-15. The power of the three F tests associated with (5.31), (5.32), and (5.33) can be computed. However, we will omit these topics here.

Sometimes an experimenter may be interested in a mixed model. Such a situation arises if a large number of wheat varieties and three fertilizers should be considered. The assumptions are a little more complicated (A-fixed, B-random) and are as follows:

$$x_{ijk} = \mu + \alpha_i + \beta_j + (\alpha\beta)_{ij} + e_{ijk}, \qquad \begin{array}{l} i = 1, 2, \cdots, a \\ j = 1, 2, \cdots, b \\ k = 1, 2, \cdots, n \end{array}$$

e_{ijk} are independently $N(0, \sigma^2)$

β_j and $(\alpha\beta)_{ij}$ are jointly normal with means 0

$$\sum_{i=1}^{a} \alpha_i = \sum_{i=1}^{a} (\varkappa\beta)_{ij} = 0 \tag{5.34}$$

(The term "jointly normal" implies that each set of variables by itself is normal, but that some of the variables are correlated.)

Now (5.2), (5.32), and (5.33) give the hypotheses and alternates. Again there is no change in the computational procedures for sums of squares and mean squares. The expected mean squares and F ratios are given in Table 5.4.

Table 5.4   EXPECTED MEAN SQUARES AND F RATIOS FOR THE TWO-FACTOR COMPLETELY RANDOMIZED MIXED MODEL (A-FIXED)

Source		EMS	F
Treatments	A	$\sigma^2 + n\,\sigma_{AB}^2 + nb\dfrac{\sum_{i=1}^{a}\alpha_i^2}{a-1}$	$\dfrac{MS_A}{MS_{AB}}$
	B	$\sigma^2 + na\sigma_B^2$	$\dfrac{MS_B}{MS_E}$
	AB	$\sigma^2 + n\,\sigma_{AB}^2$	$\dfrac{MS_{AB}}{MS_E}$
Error		σ^2	

Note that the F ratio for the fixed-effects variable has a different denominator than the other two. If B is fixed and A is random, then A and B would be interchanged in the discussion.

Perhaps it should be pointed out that neither the random-effects nor the mixed model seem to be appropriate in the varieties-fertilizer example. It is quite likely that the fixed-effects model will arise more often in applications.

The T- and S-methods of investigating comparisons may be used on the fixed-effects factor if the null hypothesis is rejected. If A is the fixed-effects factor, then contrasts

$$L = \sum_{i=1}^{a} c_i \mu_i.$$

are estimated by

$$\hat{L} = \sum_{i=1}^{a} c_i \bar{x}_{i..} \ .$$

Here

$$T = \frac{1}{\sqrt{bn}} \ q_{1-\alpha, a, (a-1)(b-1)} \ , \tag{5.35}$$

$$S^2 = (a-1) F_{1-\alpha; \, a-1, (a-1)(b-1)} \ , \tag{5.36}$$

MS_{AB} is used in place of MS_W with the appropriate change in degrees of freedom [$(a-1)(b-1)$ instead of $N-r$], and bn replaces n. If B is the fixed factor, then contrasts

$$L = \sum_{j=1}^{b} c_j \mu_{.j}$$

are estimated by

$$\hat{L} = \sum_{j=1}^{b} c_j \bar{x}_{.j.}$$

and a and b are interchanged in the above discussion.

EXERCISES

5.6 Write out the analysis of variance table for Exercise 5.3 if
(a) both A and B effects are random,
(b) A effects are fixed, B effects are random,
(c) A effects are random, B effects are fixed.

5.7 An experiment is being conducted to compare three different methods by which reading is taught. For this purpose five schools are selected at random from a population of schools. Within each school a class of 20 students is taught by each method. Then a reading examination is given to all students. Let methods be the row variable and schools be the column variable. The results of the examination yield

$$\bar{x}_{1..} = 60, \quad \bar{x}_{2..} = 50, \quad \bar{x}_{3..} = 64,$$
$$\bar{x}_{.1.} = 63, \quad \bar{x}_{.2.} = 67, \quad \bar{x}_{.3.} = 51, \quad \bar{x}_{.4.} = 54, \quad \bar{x}_{.5.} = 55,$$
$$SS_{AB} = 2400, \quad SS_E = 57{,}000.$$

What conclusions can be drawn? Use the T-method on the fixed-effects variable to determine which treatments are significantly better than which others.

5-7 RANDOMIZED BLOCKS WITH TWO FACTORS (FIXED-EFFECTS)

The assumptions are the same as those made previously for randomized blocks. Repeated in the present terminology, these are: (a) a random sample of size 1 is drawn from each of abn populations, (b) all abn populations are normal, (c) the variance of each of the abn populations is the same, and (d) block and treatment effects are additive.

Let μ_{ijk} be the mean of the population from which x_{ijk} is drawn.

If we let

$$\mu_{i..} = \frac{\sum_{j=1}^{b}\sum_{k=1}^{n}\mu_{ijk}}{bn} = \begin{array}{l}\text{average of the population means for the}\\ i^{\text{th}} \text{ level of factor } A,\end{array}$$

$$\mu_{.j.} = \frac{\sum_{i=1}^{a}\sum_{k=1}^{n}\mu_{ijk}}{an} = \begin{array}{l}\text{average of the population means for the}\\ j^{\text{th}} \text{ level of factor } B,\end{array}$$

$$\mu_{..k} = \frac{\sum_{i=1}^{a}\sum_{j=1}^{b}\mu_{ijk}}{ab} = \begin{array}{l}\text{average of the population means for the}\\ k^{\text{th}} \text{ block,}\end{array}$$

$$\mu_{ij.} = \frac{\sum_{k=1}^{n}\mu_{ijk}}{n} = \begin{array}{l}\text{average of the population means for cell}\\ \text{or treatment combination } ij,\end{array}$$

and $$\mu_{...} = \mu = \frac{\sum_{i=1}^{a}\sum_{j=1}^{b}\sum_{k=1}^{n}\mu_{ijk}}{abn} = \begin{array}{l}\text{average of all the } abn \text{ population}\\ \text{means,}\end{array}$$

then we may write the following identities:

$$x_{ijk} = \mu_{ijk} + (x_{ijk} - \mu_{ijk}) = \mu_{ijk} + e_{ijk} \tag{5.37}$$

and

$$\mu_{ijk} = \mu + (\mu_{i..} - \mu) + (\mu_{.j.} - \mu) + (\mu_{..k} - \mu) + (\mu_{ij.} - \mu_{i..} - \mu_{.j.} + \mu)$$
$$+ (\mu_{ijk} - \mu_{..k} - \mu_{ij.} + \mu)$$
$$= \mu + \alpha_i + \beta_j + \rho_k + (\alpha\beta)_{ij} + (\mu_{ijk} - \mu_{..k} - \mu_{ij.} + \mu). \tag{5.38}$$

If we assume that block and treatment effects are additive, then

$$\mu_{ijk} - \mu_{..k} - \mu_{ij.} + \mu = 0. \tag{5.39}$$

This is exactly the same condition that we found must hold in Section 3-3 if additivity is present. Recall that in that notation we had

$$\mu_{ij} - \mu_{i.} - \mu_{.j} + \mu = 0. \tag{5.40}$$

Combining the results of (5.37) and (5.38) we may write the assumptions for the fixed-effects model as

$$x_{ijk} = \mu + \alpha_i + \beta_j + \rho_k + (\alpha\beta)_{ij} + e_{ijk}, \qquad \begin{array}{l} i = 1, 2, \cdots, a \\ j = 1, 2, \cdots, b \\ k = 1, 2, \cdots, n \end{array}$$

e_{ijk} are independently $N(0, \sigma^2)$ \qquad (5.41)

$$\sum_{i=1}^{a}\alpha_i = \sum_{j=1}^{b}\beta_j = \sum_{k=1}^{n}\rho_k = \sum_{i=1}^{a}(\alpha\beta)_{ij} = \sum_{j=1}^{b}(\alpha\beta)_{ij} = 0.$$

It is easy to show that these last five sums are zero.

Next let us turn our attention to the partitioning of the total sum of squares. We can write

$$\sum_{i=1}^{a}\sum_{j=1}^{b}\sum_{k=1}^{n}(x_{ijk}-\bar{x}_{...})^2=\sum_{i=1}^{a}\sum_{j=1}^{b}\sum_{k=1}^{n}[(\bar{x}_{..k}-\bar{x}_{...})+(\bar{x}_{ij.}-\bar{x}_{...})$$
$$+(x_{ijk}-\bar{x}_{..k}-\bar{x}_{ij.}+\bar{x}_{...})]^2.$$

But this is exactly the same identity with which we started in Section 3-4 and which produced Equation (3.11). That is, we can again write

$$SS_T=SS_{BL}+SS_{Tr}+SS_E . \qquad (5.42)$$

In our present notation, which is given in Table 5.1, we have

$$SS_T=\sum_{i=1}^{a}\sum_{j=1}^{b}\sum_{k=1}^{n}(x_{ijk}-\bar{x}_{...})^2=\sum_{i=1}^{a}\sum_{j=1}^{b}\sum_{k=1}^{n}x_{ijk}^2-\frac{T_{...}^2}{abn} , \qquad (5.43)$$

$$SS_{BL}=\sum_{i=1}^{a}\sum_{j=1}^{b}\sum_{k=1}^{n}(\bar{x}_{..k}-\bar{x}_{...})^2=\frac{\sum_{k=1}^{n}T_{..k}^2}{ab}-\frac{T_{...}^2}{abn} , \qquad (5.44)$$

$$SS_{Tr}=\sum_{i=1}^{a}\sum_{j=1}^{b}\sum_{k=1}^{n}(\bar{x}_{ij.}-\bar{x}_{...})^2=\frac{\sum_{i=1}^{a}\sum_{j=1}^{b}T_{ij.}^2}{n}-\frac{T_{...}^2}{abn} , \qquad (5.45)$$

and

$$SS_E=SS_T-SS_{BL}-SS_{Tr} . \qquad (5.46)$$

The treatment sum of squares is divided into three parts exactly the same way as in the completely randomized arrangement. Thus Formulas (5.7), (5.8), (5.12), (5.13), and (5.14) hold without change. Hence, except for the fact that SS_{BL} is computed producing a change in SS_E, the computations for blocks and complete randomization are the same.

The assumptions given by (5.41) lead to the analysis of variance shown in Table 5.5.

The changes necessary for the T- and S-methods follow the usual pattern. Contrasts among the A means are of the form $L=\sum_{i=1}^{a}c_i\mu_{i..}$ and are estimated by $\hat{L}=\sum_{i=1}^{a}c_i\bar{x}_{i..}$. For these contrasts

$$T=\frac{1}{\sqrt{bn}}\ q_{1-\alpha;\ a,\ (n-1)(ab-1)} , \qquad (5.47)$$

$$S^2=(a-1)F_{1-\alpha;\ a-1,\ (n-1)(ab-1)} , \qquad (5.48)$$

and

$$\hat{\sigma}_{\hat{L}}^2=\frac{MS_E}{bn}\sum_{i=1}^{a}c_i^2 . \qquad (5.49)$$

Table 5.5 ANALYSIS OF VARIANCE FOR A TWO-FACTOR RANDOMIZED
BLOCK EXPERIMENT (FIXED-EFFECTS)

Source	SS	d.f.	MS	EMS	F
Blocks	SS_{BL}	$n-1$	MS_{BL}	$\sigma^2 + ab\dfrac{\sum\limits_{k=1}^{n} \rho_k^2}{n-1}$	
Treatments					
A	SS_A	$a-1$	MS_A	$\sigma^2 + bn\dfrac{\sum\limits_{i=1}^{a} \alpha_i^2}{a-1}$	$\dfrac{MS_A}{MS_E}$
B	SS_B	$b-1$	MS_B	$\sigma^2 + an\dfrac{\sum\limits_{j=1}^{b} \beta_j^2}{b-1}$	$\dfrac{MS_B}{MS_E}$
AB	SS_{AB}	$(a-1)(b-1)$	MS_{AB}	$\sigma^2 + n\dfrac{\sum\limits_{i=1}^{a}\sum\limits_{j=1}^{b} (\alpha\beta)_{ij}^2}{(a-1)(b-1)}$	$\dfrac{MS_{AB}}{MS_E}$
Error	SS_E	$(n-1)(ab-1)$	MS_E	σ^2	
TOTAL	SS_T	$abn-1$			

Contrasts among B means are of the form $L = \sum\limits_{j=1}^{b} c_j \mu_{.j.}$ and are estimated by $\hat{L} = \sum\limits_{j=1}^{b} c_j \bar{x}_{.j.}$. Formulas (5.47) and (5.48) hold if a and b are interchanged. In (5.49) the correct c's must be used in addition. Finally, contrasts among cell means are of the form $\hat{L} = \sum\limits_{i=1}^{a}\sum\limits_{j=1}^{b} c_{ij}\mu_{ij}.$ and are estimated by $\hat{L} = \sum\limits_{i=1}^{a}\sum\limits_{j=1}^{b} c_{ij}\bar{x}_{ij.}$. Now

$$T = \frac{1}{\sqrt{n}}\, q_{1-\alpha;\, ab,\, (n-1)(ab-1)}\,, \qquad (5.50)$$

$$S^2 = (ab-1)F_{1-\alpha;(ab-1),\, (n-1)(ab-1)}\,, \qquad (5.51)$$

and

$$\hat{\sigma}_{\hat{L}}^2 = \frac{MS_E}{n}\sum_{i=1}^{a}\sum_{j=1}^{b} c_{ij}^2\,. \qquad (5.52)$$

To calculate power we use the same ϕ's as with the completely randomized experiment. Hence Formulas (5.27), (5.28), and (5.29) still apply. Now $\nu_2 = (n-1)(ab-1)$ in each case.

In the event the experimenter is interested in random-effects or mixed models, the correct F ratios for the main hypotheses are those given in Tables 5.3 and 5.4. These results hold whether blocks are fixed or random. The degrees of freedom associated with MS_E is changed, being now $(n-1)(ab-1)$.

EXERCISES

5.8 Repeat Exercise 5.3 and regard the data as the result of a randomized block experiment. Then use the T-method as indicated in Exercise 5.4.

5.9 Write out the analysis of variance table for Exercise 5.8 if:
(a) both A and B effects are random.
(b) A effects are fixed, B effects are random.
(c) B effects are fixed, A effects are random.

5-8 NOTATION FOR THREE-FACTOR COMPLETELY RANDOMIZED AND RANDOMIZED BLOCKS DESIGNS

Denote the factors by A, B, and C. Let the levels be numbered 1, 2, $\cdots$, a for A; 1, 2, $\cdots$, b for B; and 1, 2, $\cdots$, c for C. Assume that we have n observations for each treatment combination. Let the observations be denoted by

$$x_{ijkm} \quad \text{where} \quad \begin{aligned} i &= 1, 2, \cdots, a \\ j &= 1, 2, \cdots, b \\ k &= 1, 2, \cdots, c \\ m &= 1, 2, \cdots, n. \end{aligned}$$

For each level of C the data could be arranged as in Table 5.1. A more convenient way of presenting the results is given in Table 5.6.

Table 5.6 ARRANGEMENT OF DATA FOR A THREE-FACTOR EXPERIMENT

		Level of A							
		1		$\cdots$		a			TOTALS
Level of B		1 $\cdots$ b				1 $\cdots$ b			
Level of C	1	$x_{1111} \cdots x_{1b11}$ $\vdots \qquad \vdots$ $x_{111n} \cdots x_{1b1n}$				$x_{a111} \cdots x_{ab11}$ $\vdots \qquad \vdots$ $x_{a11n} \cdots x_{ab1n}$			$T_{..11}$ $\Big\}\, T_{..1.}$ $T_{..1n}$
	$\vdots$	$\vdots$				$\vdots$			
	c	$x_{11c1} \cdots x_{1bc1}$ $\vdots \qquad \vdots$ $x_{11cn} \cdots x_{1bcn}$				$x_{a1c1} \cdots x_{abc1}$ $\vdots \qquad \vdots$ $x_{a1cn} \quad x_{abcn}$			$T_{..c1}$ $\Big\}\, T_{..c.}$ $T_{..cn}$
TOTALS		$T_{11..} \quad T_{1b..}$ $\underbrace{\qquad\qquad}_{T_{1...}}$				$T_{a1..} \quad T_{ab..}$ $\underbrace{\qquad\qquad}_{T_{a...}}$			$T_{....}$

Definitions of totals and means follow our standard pattern of notation. We have

Total of cell $ijk = T_{ijk.} = \sum\limits_{m=1}^{n} x_{ijkm}$,

Mean of cell $ijk = \bar{x}_{ijk.} = \dfrac{T_{ijk.}}{n}$,

Total for i^{th} level of A and j^{th} level of B $= T_{ij..} = \sum\limits_{k=1}^{c} \sum\limits_{m=1}^{n} x_{ijkm} = \sum\limits_{k=1}^{c} T_{ijk.}$,

Mean of ith level of A and j^{th} level of B $= \bar{x}_{ij..} = \dfrac{T_{ij..}}{cn}$,

Total for i^{th} level of A and k^{th} level of C $= T_{i.k.} = \sum\limits_{j=1}^{b} \sum\limits_{m=1}^{n} x_{ijkm} = \sum\limits_{j=1}^{b} T_{ijk.}$,

Mean of ith level of A and k^{th} level of C $= \bar{x}_{i.k.} = \dfrac{T_{i.k.}}{bn}$,

Total for j^{th} level of B and k^{th} level of C $= T_{.jk.} = \sum\limits_{i=1}^{a} \sum\limits_{m=1}^{n} x_{ijkm} = \sum\limits_{i=1}^{a} T_{ijk.}$,

Mean of jth level of B and k^{th} level of C $= \bar{x}_{.jk.} = \dfrac{T_{i.k.}}{an}$,

Total for i^{th} level of A $= T_{i...} = \sum\limits_{j=1}^{b} \sum\limits_{k=1}^{c} \sum\limits_{m=1}^{n} x_{ijkm} = \sum\limits_{j=1}^{b} \sum\limits_{k=1}^{c} T_{ijk.}$,

Mean of the ith level of A $= \bar{x}_{i...} = \dfrac{T_{i...}}{bcn}$,

Total for j^{th} level of $B = T_{.j..} = \sum\limits_{i=1}^{a} \sum\limits_{k=1}^{c} \sum\limits_{m=1}^{n} x_{ijkm} = \sum\limits_{i=1}^{a} \sum\limits_{k=1}^{c} T_{ijk.}$,

Mean of jth level of $B = \bar{x}_{.j..} = \dfrac{T_{.j..}}{acn}$,

Total for the kth level of C $= T_{..k.} = \sum\limits_{i=1}^{a} \sum\limits_{j=1}^{b} \sum\limits_{m=1}^{n} x_{ijkm} = \sum\limits_{i=1}^{a} \sum\limits_{j=1}^{b} T_{ijk.}$,

Mean of kth level of $C = \bar{x}_{..k.} = \dfrac{T_{..k.}}{abn}$,

Overall total $= T_{....} = \sum\limits_{i=1}^{a} \sum\limits_{j=1}^{b} \sum\limits_{k=1}^{c} \sum\limits_{m=1}^{n} x_{ijkm}$

$$= \sum\limits_{i=1}^{a} \sum\limits_{j=1}^{b} \sum\limits_{k=1}^{c} T_{ijk.}$$

$$= \sum\limits_{i=1}^{a} \sum\limits_{j=1}^{b} T_{ij..} = \sum\limits_{i=1}^{a} \sum\limits_{k=1}^{c} T_{i.k.}$$

$$= \sum\limits_{j=1}^{b} \sum\limits_{k=1}^{c} T_{.jk.}$$

$$= \sum\limits_{i=1}^{a} T_{i...} = \sum\limits_{j=1}^{b} T_{.j..} = \sum\limits_{k=1}^{c} T_{..k.}$$,

Overall mean $\quad = \bar{x}_{....} = \dfrac{T_{....}}{abcn}.$

Here the number of treatments is $r = abc$.

The table as it stands can be regarded as data from a completely randomized design with n observations for each treatment. If we regard the m subscript as a block designation, then the data may represent the results of a randomized block experiment.

5-9 THE FIXED-EFFECTS MODEL FOR A THREE-FACTOR COMPLETELY RANDOMIZED DESIGN

The assumptions are the usual ones for complete randomization. These are (a) the $r = abc$ cells represent r random samples of size n drawn from r populations, (b) each of the r populations is normal, and (c) each of the r populations has the same variance. In other words, we assume that the x_{ijkm} are independently $N(\mu_{ijk}, \sigma^2)$.

Let

$$\mu_{ij.} = \frac{\sum\limits_{k=1}^{c} \mu_{ijk}}{c}$$
the average of the population means for those populations receiving the ith level of A and the jth level of B,

$$\mu_{i.k} = \frac{\sum\limits_{j=1}^{b} \mu_{ijk}}{b}$$
the average of the population means for those populations receiving the ith level of A and the kth level of C,

$$\mu_{.jk} = \frac{\sum\limits_{i=1}^{a} \mu_{ijk}}{a}$$
the average of the population means for those populations receiving the jth level of B and the kth level of C,

$$\mu_{i..} = \frac{\sum\limits_{j=1}^{b} \sum\limits_{k=1}^{c} \mu_{ijk}}{bc}$$
the average of the population means for those populations receiving the ith level of A,

$$\mu_{.j.} = \frac{\sum\limits_{i=1}^{a} \sum\limits_{k=1}^{c} \mu_{ijk}}{ac}$$
the average of the population means for those populations receiving the jth level of B,

$$\mu_{..k} = \frac{\sum\limits_{i=1}^{a} \sum\limits_{j=1}^{b} \mu_{ijk}}{ab}$$
the average of the population means for those populations receiving the kth level of C,

$$\mu = \mu_{...} = \frac{\sum\limits_{i=1}^{a} \sum\limits_{j=1}^{b} \sum\limits_{k=1}^{c} \mu_{ijk}}{abc}$$
the average of the population means for all populations under consideration.

We may write the following identities:

$$x_{ijkm} = \mu_{ijk} + (x_{ijkm} - \mu_{ijk}) = \mu_{ijk} + e_{ijkm}$$

and
$$\mu_{ijk} = \mu + (\mu_{i..} - \mu) + (\mu_{.j.} - \mu) + (\mu_{..k} - \mu) + (\mu_{ij} - \mu_{i..} - \mu_{.j.} + \mu)$$
$$+ (\mu_{i.k} - \mu_{i..} - \mu_{.k.} + \mu) + (\mu_{.jk} - \mu_{.j.} - \mu_{..k} + \mu) + (\mu_{ijk} - \mu_{ij} - \mu_{i.k} - \mu_{.jk}$$
$$+ \mu_{i..} + \mu_{.j.} + \mu_{..k} - \mu)$$
$$= \mu + \alpha_i + \beta_j + \gamma_k + (\alpha\beta)_{ij} + (\alpha\gamma)_{ik} + (\beta\gamma)_{jk} + (\alpha\beta\gamma)_{ijk}.$$

It can easily be shown that

$$\sum_{i=1}^{a} \alpha_i = \sum_{j=1}^{b} \beta_j = \sum_{k=1}^{c} \gamma_k = \sum_{i=1}^{a} (\alpha\beta)_{ij} = \sum_{j=1}^{b} (\alpha\beta)_{ij} = \sum_{i=1}^{a} (\alpha\gamma)_{ik}$$

$$= \sum_{k=1}^{c} (\alpha\gamma)_{ik} = \sum_{j=1}^{b} (\beta\gamma)_{jk} = \sum_{k=1}^{c} (\beta\gamma)_{jk} = \sum_{i=1}^{a} (\alpha\beta\gamma)_{ijk}$$

$$= \sum_{j=1}^{b} (\alpha\beta\gamma)_{ijk} = \sum_{k=1}^{c} (\alpha\beta\gamma)_{ijk} = 0. \tag{5.53}$$

Thus the assumptions for the fixed-effects model may be written

$$x_{ijkm} = \mu + \alpha_i + \beta_j + \gamma_k + (\alpha\beta)_{ij} + (\alpha\gamma)_{ik} + (\beta\gamma)_{jk} + (\alpha\beta\gamma)_{ijk}$$
$$+ e_{ijkm} \qquad\qquad i = 1, 2, \cdots, a$$
$$j = 1, 2, \cdots, b \tag{5.54}$$
$$k = 1, 2, \cdots, c$$
$$m = 1, 2, \cdots, n$$

e_{ijkm} are independently $N(0, \sigma^2)$
The constants satisfy Eq. (5.53).

The main hypotheses of interest together with their alternates are:

$$H_0^1 : \quad \alpha_i = 0, \quad i = 1, 2, \cdots, a \tag{5.55}$$
$$H_1^1 : \quad \text{not all } \alpha_i \text{ are zero,}$$

$$H_0^2 : \quad \beta_j = 0, \quad j = 1, 2, \cdots, b \tag{5.56}$$
$$H_1^2 : \quad \text{not all } \beta_j \text{ are zero,}$$

$$H_0^3 : \quad \gamma_k = 0, \quad k = 1, 2, \cdots, c \tag{5.57}$$
$$H_1^3 : \quad \text{not all } \gamma_k \text{ are zero,}$$

$$H_0^4 : \quad (\alpha\beta)_{ij} = 0, \quad i = 1, 2, \cdots, a$$
$$j = 1, 2, \cdots, b \tag{5.58}$$
$$H_1^4 : \quad \text{not all } (\alpha\beta)_{ij} \text{ are zero,}$$

$$H_0^5 : \quad (\alpha\gamma)_{ik} = 0, \quad i = 1, 2, \cdots, a$$
$$k = 1, 2, \cdots, c \tag{5.59}$$
$$H_1^5 : \quad \text{not all } (\alpha\gamma)_{ik} \text{ are zero,}$$

$$H_0^6 : \quad (\beta\gamma)_{jk} = 0, \quad j = 1, 2, \cdots, b$$
$$k = 1, 2, \cdots, c \tag{5.60}$$
$$H_1^6 : \quad \text{not all } (\beta\gamma)_{jk} \text{ are zero}$$

$$H_0^7: \quad (\alpha\beta\gamma)_{ijk} = 0, \quad \begin{array}{l} i=1,\ 2,\ \cdots,\ a \\ j=1,\ 2,\ \cdots,\ b \\ k=1,\ 2,\ \cdots,\ c \end{array} \tag{5.61}$$

$H_1^7:$ not all $(\alpha\beta\gamma)_{ijk}$ are zero.

The interpretation of the first three hypotheses gives no trouble if there are no interactions. The first states that there is no difference between the means of the various levels of A. The second and third make similar assertions about the levels of B and C. When interactions are present, it becomes more difficult to interpret the results of the experiment and, as in the two-factor case, the prime concern may be the best treatment combination. The last four hypotheses merit further consideration.

For a two-way table of means μ_{ij}, we have remarked in Section 3-3 that no interaction implies that

$$\mu_{ij} - \mu_{ij'} - \mu_{i'j} + \mu_{i'j'} = 0 \tag{5.62}$$

for all i, i', j and j'. Equation (5.62) is true if and only if

$$\mu_{ij} - \mu_{.j} - \mu_{i.} + \mu = 0 \tag{5.63}$$

holds for all i and j. That is, if (5.62) holds, so does (5.63) and vice versa. Table 3.2 exhibits a set of means displaying this property. Now let us consider a three-way table of means μ_{ijk}, $i=1,\ 2,\ \cdots,\ a$, $j=1,\ 2,\ \cdots,\ b$, $k=1,\ 2,\ \cdots,\ c$. For each level of C we can compute terms

$$\mu_{ijk} - \mu_{ij'k} - \mu_{i'jk} + \mu_{i'j'k} . \tag{5.64}$$

For any choice of i, i', j and j', (5.65) averaged over all levels of C becomes

$$\mu_{ij.} - \mu_{ij'.} - \mu_{i'j.} + \mu_{i'j'.} . \tag{5.65}$$

If (5.65) is not zero for all i, i', j and j', then factors A and B are said to interact.

Let us turn to a numerical example illustrating no interaction between A and B. Consider an experiment that has three levels of A, three levels of B, and three levels of C. Suppose that the 27 population means are those given in Table 5.7.

Table 5.7   MEANS FOR 27 POPULATIONS ILLUSTRATING NO AB INTERACTION

First level of C				Second level of C			
	Level of B				Level of B		
	1	2	3		1	2	3
Level 1	2	7	5	Level 1	3	6	-3
of 2	4	5	1	of 2	8	2	2
A 3	5	-1	-8	A 3	0	-2	1

Third level of C			
	Level of B		
	1	2	3
Level	1	10	-4	1
of	2	6	5	3
A	3	1	3	1

It is easy to verify that A and B interact at each level of C. Now from Table 5.7 we can compute all the $\mu_{ij.}$. These are given in Table 5.8.

Table 5.8 $\mu_{ij.}$ FOR TABLE 5.7

		1	2	3
i	1	5	3	1
	2	6	4	2
	3	2	0	-2

We see that (5.65) has the value zero for all i, i', j and j'. Hence no interaction is present between A and B. Thus in a three-factor analysis, two-way interaction is a property of averages of means, not the original means themselves. Even though A and B interact at every level, these effects average out to be zero.

If Expression (5.65) is equal to zero for all i, i', j and j', then so is

$$(\alpha\beta)_{ij} = \mu_{ij.} - \mu_{i..} - \mu_{.j.} + \mu = 0 \tag{5.66}$$

and vice versa. Thus H_0^4 hypothesizes the condition exhibited by Table 5.8. Similarly if A and C do not interact, then both

$$\mu_{i.k} - \mu_{i.k'} - \mu_{i'.k} + \mu_{i'.k'} = 0$$

and

$$(\alpha\gamma)_{ik} = \mu_{i.k} - \mu_{i..} - \mu_{..k} + \mu = 0$$

hold for all values of the subscripts. Finally if B and C do not interact, then

$$\mu_{.jk} - \mu_{.jk'} - \mu_{.j'k} + \mu_{.j'k'} = 0$$

and

$$(\beta\gamma)_{jk} = \mu_{.jk} - \mu_{.j.} - \mu_{..k} + \mu = 0$$

hold for all values of the subscripts.

Next let us consider the implication of H_0^7. In general, (5.64) will have a value other than zero. If, for any choice of i, i', j and j', this quantity remains the same for all levels of C, then we say that there is no ABC interaction. In terms of an equation

$$(\mu_{ijk} - \mu_{ij'k} - \mu_{i'jk} + \mu_{i'j'k}) - (\mu_{ijk'} - \mu_{ij'k'} - \mu_{i'jk'} + \mu_{i'j'k'}) = 0 \qquad (5.67)$$

holds for all choices of the subscripts. If (5.67) is true, then so is

$$(\alpha\beta\gamma)_{ijk} = \mu_{ijk} - \mu_{ij.} - \mu_{i.k} - \mu_{.jk} + \mu_{i..} + \mu_{.j.} + \mu_{..k} - \mu = 0 \qquad (5.68)$$

and vice versa. The 27 population means in Table 5.9 illustrate a situation in which no ABC interaction is present.

Table 5.9 Means of 27 Populations Illustrating no ABC Interactions

First level of C			
	Level of B		
	1	2	3
Level of A 1	5	3	8
2	7	6	4
3	2	5	2

Second level of C			
	Level of B		
	1	2	3
Level of A 1	10	7	12
2	6	4	2
3	0	2	-1

Third level of C			
	Level of B		
	1	2	3
Level of A 1	8	7	9
2	6	6	1
3	1	5	-1

For example, if $i=1$, $i'=2$, $j=1$, $j'=2$, then $5-3-7+6=10-7-6+4=8-7-6+6=1$ so that (5.67) is $1-1=0$ for all choices of k and k'. In this discussion we have compared terms of the type (5.64) for various levels of C. Within each level of C the same levels of A and B furnish the terms for this comparison. The conclusions concerning the presence or absence of ABC interaction remains the same if the roles of A, B, and C are interchanged in the discussion.

If any two factors such as A and B interact, this means that A and B together produce an effect which is attributable to neither A nor B alone. Likewise, if A, B, and C interact, this means an effect is produced which is not attributable to differences in A, B, or C, or to A and B, A and C, or B and C in combination. If no interactions are present, then the observations may be written

$$x_{ijkm} = \mu + \alpha_i + \beta_j + \gamma_k + e_{ijkm}$$

and the three factors are said to be additive.

5-10 PARTITIONING THE SUM OF SQUARES FOR A THREE-FACTOR COMPLETELY RANDOMIZED EXPERIMENT

As in the two-factor case we begin by using the identity derived in Section 2-5. This is

$$SS_T = SS_{Tr} + SS_E$$

which in the three-factor notation may be written

$$\sum_{i=1}^{a} \sum_{j=1}^{b} \sum_{k=1}^{c} \sum_{m=1}^{n} (x_{ijkm} - \bar{x}_{....})^2$$
$$= \sum_{i=1}^{a} \sum_{j=1}^{b} \sum_{k=1}^{c} \sum_{m=1}^{n} (\bar{x}_{ijk.} - \bar{x}_{....})^2 + \sum_{i=1}^{a} \sum_{j=1}^{b} \sum_{k=1}^{c} \sum_{m=1}^{n} (x_{ijkm} - \bar{x}_{ijk.})^2.$$

Next SS_{Tr} is subdivided so that it contains sums of squares that measure the variation in A, B, and C means, and the AB, AC, BC and ABC interactions. We may write the identity

$$\bar{x}_{ijk.} - \bar{x}_{....} = (\bar{x}_{i...} - \bar{x}_{....}) + (\bar{x}_{.j..} - \bar{x}_{....}) + (\bar{x}_{..k.} - \bar{x}_{....})$$
$$+ (\bar{x}_{ij..} - \bar{x}_{i...} - \bar{x}_{.j..} + \bar{x}_{....}) + (\bar{x}_{i.k.} - \bar{x}_{i...} - \bar{x}_{..k.} + \bar{x}_{....})$$
$$+ (\bar{x}_{.jk.} - \bar{x}_{.j..} - \bar{x}_{..k.} + \bar{x}_{....})$$
$$+ (\bar{x}_{ijk.} - \bar{x}_{ij..} - \bar{x}_{i.k.} - \bar{x}_{.jk.} + \bar{x}_{i...} + \bar{x}_{.j..} + \bar{x}_{..k.} - \bar{x}_{....}).$$

Squaring each side of this identity and summing overall values of i, j, k and m yields

$$SS_{Tr} = \sum_{i=1}^{a} \sum_{j=1}^{b} \sum_{k=1}^{c} \sum_{m=1}^{n} (\bar{x}_{ijk.} - \bar{x}_{....})^2 \qquad (5.69)$$

on the left-hand side, and 28 terms on the right-hand side. Seven of these terms are sums of squares and 21 are sums of cross-products. As usual all cross-product terms may be shown to be zero. The seven sums of squares are

$$SS_A = \sum_{i=1}^{a} \sum_{j=1}^{b} \sum_{k=1}^{c} \sum_{m=1}^{n} (\bar{x}_{i...} - \bar{x}_{....})^2 \qquad (5.70)$$

$$SS_B = \sum_{i=1}^{a} \sum_{j=1}^{b} \sum_{k=1}^{c} \sum_{m=1}^{n} (\bar{x}_{.j..} - \bar{x}_{....})^2 \qquad (5.71)$$

$$SS_C = \sum_{i=1}^{a} \sum_{j=1}^{b} \sum_{k=1}^{c} \sum_{m=1}^{n} (\bar{x}_{..k.} - \bar{x}_{....})^2 \qquad (5.72)$$

$$SS_{AB} = \sum_{i=1}^{a} \sum_{j=1}^{b} \sum_{k=1}^{c} \sum_{m=1}^{n} (\bar{x}_{ij..} - \bar{x}_{i...} - \bar{x}_{.j..} + \bar{x}_{....})^2 \qquad (5.73)$$

$$SS_{AC} = \sum_{i=1}^{a} \sum_{j=1}^{b} \sum_{k=1}^{c} \sum_{m=1}^{n} (\bar{x}_{i.k.} - \bar{x}_{i...} - \bar{x}_{..k.} + \bar{x}_{....})^2 \qquad (5.74)$$

$$SS_{BC} = \sum_{i=1}^{a} \sum_{j=1}^{b} \sum_{k=1}^{c} \sum_{m=1}^{n} (\bar{x}_{.jk.} - \bar{x}_{.j..} - \bar{x}_{..k.} + \bar{x}_{....})^2 \qquad (5.75)$$

and
$$SS_{ABC} = \sum_{i=1}^{a} \sum_{j=1}^{b} \sum_{k=1}^{c} \sum_{m=1}^{n} (\bar{x}_{ijk.} - \bar{x}_{ij..} - \bar{x}_{i.k.} - \bar{x}_{.jk.} + \bar{x}_{i...} + \bar{x}_{..j.} + \bar{x}_{..k.} - \bar{x}_{....})^2. \qquad (5.76)$$

Hence the identity involving treatment sums of squares can be written

$$SS_{Tr} = SS_A + SS_B + SS_C + SS_{AB} + SS_{AC} + SS_{BC} + SS_{ABC}. \qquad (5.77)$$

It is not difficult to see that SS_A is a measure of the variability of the sample means obtained for the various levels of A. This term is zero if all sample means for the levels of A are the same. The more these sample means vary, the larger it becomes. Similarly, SS_B and SS_C measure the variation of the sample means for the levels of B and C. Since $\bar{x}_{ij..}$, $\bar{x}_{i...}$, $\bar{x}_{..j.}$, and $\bar{x}_{....}$ are estimates of $\mu_{ij.}$, $\mu_{i..}$, $\mu_{.j.}$ and μ, $\bar{x}_{ij..} - \bar{x}_{i...} - \bar{x}_{..j.} + \bar{x}_{....}$ is an estimate of $\mu_{ij} - \mu_{i.} - \mu_{.j} + \mu = (\alpha\beta)_{ij}$. Thus a small value of SS_{AB} would tend to support H_0^4 while a large value would contradict this hypothesis. Similar remarks can be made about SS_{AC} and SS_{BC} in connection with H_0^5 and H_0^6. Finally,

$$\bar{x}_{ijk.} - \bar{x}_{ij..} - \bar{x}_{i.k.} - \bar{x}_{.jk.} + \bar{x}_{i...} + \bar{x}_{..j.} + \bar{x}_{..k.} - \bar{x}_{....}$$

is an estimate of

$$\mu_{ijk} - \mu_{ij} - \mu_{i.k} - \mu_{.jk} + \mu_{i..} + \mu_{.j.} + \mu_{..k} - \mu = (\alpha\beta\gamma)_{ijk}.$$

Consequently, small values of SS_{ABC} support H_0^7 while large values discredit this hypothesis.

Computing formulas for SS_T (5.69), (5.70), (5.71) and (5.72) are obtained in the usual way. These are:

$$SS_{Tr} = \frac{\sum_{i=1}^{a} \sum_{j=1}^{b} \sum_{k=1}^{c} T_{ijk.}^2}{n} - \frac{T_{....}^2}{abcn}, \qquad (5.78)$$

$$SS_A = \frac{\sum_{i=1}^{a} T_{i...}^2}{bcn} - \frac{T_{....}^2}{abcn}, \qquad (5.79)$$

$$SS_B = \frac{\sum_{j=1}^{b} T_{.j..}^2}{acn} - \frac{T_{....}^2}{abcn}, \qquad (5.80)$$

and

$$SS_C = \frac{\sum_{k=1}^{c} T_{..k.}^2}{abn} - \frac{T_{....}^2}{abcn}. \qquad (5.81)$$

Next we note that if we square both sides of the identity

$$\bar{x}_{.j..} - \bar{x}_{....} = (\bar{x}_{i...} - \bar{x}_{....}) + (\bar{x}_{.j.} - \bar{x}_{....}) + (\bar{x}_{ij..} - \bar{x}_{i...} - \bar{x}_{.j..} + \bar{x}_{....})$$

and sum over the whole table, we get

$$\sum_{i=1}^{a}\sum_{j=1}^{b}\sum_{k=1}^{c}\sum_{m=1}^{n}(\bar{x}_{ij..}-\bar{x}_{....})^2=SS_A+SS_B+SS_{AB} \tag{5.82}$$

as the cross-product terms sum to zero. The left-hand side of (5.82) may be written

$$\frac{\sum_{i=1}^{a}\sum_{j=1}^{b}T_{ij..}^2}{cn}-\frac{T_{....}^2}{abcn}.$$

Hence

$$SS_{AB}=\frac{\sum_{i=1}^{a}\sum_{j=1}^{b}T_{ij..}^2}{cn}-\frac{T_{....}^2}{abcn}-SS_A-SS_B. \tag{5.83}$$

Similarly

$$SS_{AC}=\frac{\sum_{i=1}^{a}\sum_{k=1}^{c}T_{i.k.}^2}{bn}-\frac{T_{....}^2}{abcn}-SS_A-SS_C \tag{5.84}$$

and

$$SS_{BC}=\frac{\sum_{j=1}^{b}\sum_{k=1}^{c}T_{.jk.}^2}{an}-\frac{T_{....}^2}{abcn}-SS_B-SS_C. \tag{5.85}$$

Finally, we may obtain SS_{ABC} by subtraction. The result is

$$SS_{ABC}=SS_{Tr}-SS_A-SS_B-SS_C-SS_{AB}-SS_{AC}-SS_{BC}. \tag{5.86}$$

Before doing the computing it is helpful to construct the three auxiliary two-way Tables, 5.10, 5.11, and 5.12.

Table 5.10 TOTALS FOR A AND B LEVELS

		Levels of B			
		1	2	$\cdots$ b	TOTALS
Levels	1	$T_{11..}$	$T_{12..}$	$T_{1b..}$	$T_{1...}$
of	2	$T_{21..}$	$T_{22..}$	$T_{2b..}$	$T_{2...}$
.	:	.	.	.	.
.	:	.	.	.	.
A	a	$T_{a1..}$	$T_{a2..}$	$T_{ab..}$	$T_{a...}$
TOTALS		$T_{.1..}$	$T_{.2..}$	$T_{.b..}$	$T_{....}$

Table 5.11 Totals for A and C Levels

		Levels of C			
		1	2 $\cdots$ b		Totals
Levels	1	$T_{1.1.}$	$T_{1.2.}$	$T_{1.c.}$	$T_{1...}$
of	2	$T_{2.1.}$	$T_{2.2.}$	$T_{2.c.}$	$T_{2...}$
.		.	.	.	.
.		.	.	.	.
.		.	.	.	.
A	a	$T_{a.1.}$	$T_{a.2.}$	$T_{a.c.}$	$T_{a...}$
Totals		$T_{..1.}$	$T_{..2.}$	$T_{..c.}$	$T_{....}$

Table 5.12 Totals for B and C Levels

		Levels of C			
		1	2 $\cdots$ c		Totals
Levels	1	$T_{.11.}$	$T_{.12.}$	$T_{.2c.}$	$T_{.1..}$
of	2	$T_{.21.}$	$T_{.22.}$	$T_{.2c.}$	$T_{.2..}$
.		.	.	.	.
.		.	.	.	.
.		.	.	.	.
B	b	$T_{.b1.}$	$T_{.b2.}$	$T_{.bc.}$	$T_{.b..}$
Totals		$T_{..1.}$	$T_{..2.}$	$T_{..c.}$	$T_{....}$

EXERCISE

5.10 Show

(a) $\displaystyle \sum_{i=1}^{a} \sum_{j=1}^{b} \sum_{k=1}^{c} \sum_{m=1}^{n} (\bar{x}_{.j..} - \bar{x}_{....})(\bar{x}_{i.k.} - \bar{x}_{i...} - \bar{x}_{..k.} + \bar{x}_{....}) = 0$

(b) Formula (5.84) is correct by following the scheme used to establish (5.83).

5-11 ANALYSIS OF THE THREE-FACTOR COMPLETELY RANDOMIZED EXPERIMENT (FIXED-EFFECTS MODEL)

If the assumptions given by (5.54) are satisfied, then it may be shown that the analysis of variance is that given in Table 5.13. The *EMS* column indicates the proper F ratio to form for testing each of the seven main hypotheses.

As in the two-factor case, it is worthwhile to consider the significance level of the experiment as a whole. Let α^1, α^2, $\cdots$, α^7 be the significance levels associated with the seven hypotheses. If α is the probability of rejecting one or more of the hypotheses when all are true, then

$$\alpha < 1 - (1 - \alpha^1)(1 - \alpha^2) \cdots (1 - \alpha^7). \tag{5.87}$$

This is, of course, an extension of (5.18). If $\alpha^1 = \alpha^2 = \cdots = \alpha^7 = .05$, then $\alpha < 1 - (.95)^7$ or $\alpha < .302$. If $\alpha^1 = \alpha^2 = \cdots = \alpha^7 = .01$, then $\alpha < 1 - (.99)^7$ or $\alpha < .068$.

Unless the factors are additive, it may be very difficult to make recommendations. If it is decided that no interactions are present and effects due to one or more of the factors are found, then we may be interested in determining which levels are significantly better than which others. If interactions are present, we may wish to determine which of the $r = abc$ treatments are significantly better than which others.

Table 5.13   ANALYSIS OF VARIANCE FOR A THREE-FACTOR COMPLETELY RANDOMIZED DESIGN (FIXED-EFFECTS MODEL)

Source	SS	d.f.	MS	EMS	F
Treatments					
A	SS_A	$a-1$	MS_A	$\sigma^2 + bcn \sum\limits_{i=1}^{a} \dfrac{\alpha_i^2}{a-1}$	$\dfrac{MS_A}{MS_E}$
B	SS_B	$b-1$	MS_B	$\sigma^2 + acn \sum\limits_{j=1}^{b} \dfrac{\beta_j^2}{b-1}$	$\dfrac{MS_B}{MS_E}$
C	SS_C	$c-1$	MS_C	$\sigma^2 + abn \sum\limits_{k=1}^{c} \dfrac{\gamma_k^2}{c-1}$	$\dfrac{MS_C}{MS_E}$
AB	SS_{AB}	$(a-1)(b-1)$	MS_{AB}	$\sigma^2 + cn \dfrac{\sum\limits_{i=1}^{a}\sum\limits_{j=1}^{b}(\alpha\beta)_{ij}^2}{(a-1)(b-1)}$	$\dfrac{MS_{AB}}{MS_E}$
AC	SS_{AC}	$(a-1)(c-1)$	MS_{AC}	$\sigma^2 + bn \dfrac{\sum\limits_{i=1}^{a}\sum\limits_{k=1}^{c}(\alpha\gamma)_{ik}^2}{(a-1)(c-1)}$	$\dfrac{MS_{AC}}{MS_E}$
BC	SS_{BC}	$(b-1)(c-1)$	MS_{BC}	$\sigma^2 + an \dfrac{\sum\limits_{j=1}^{b}\sum\limits_{k=1}^{c}(\beta\gamma)_{jk}^2}{(b-1)(c-1)}$	$\dfrac{MS_{BC}}{MS_E}$
ABC	SS_{ABC}	$(a-1)(b-1)(c-1)$	MS_{ABC}	$\sigma^2 + n \dfrac{\sum\limits_{i=1}^{a}\sum\limits_{j=1}^{b}\sum\limits_{k=1}^{c}(\alpha\beta\gamma)_{ijk}^2}{(a-1)(b-1)(c-1)}$	$\dfrac{MS_{ABC}}{MS_E}$
Error	SS_E	$abc(n-1)$	MS_E	σ^2	
TOTAL	SS_T	$abcn-1$			

The T- and S-methods may be used in the usual way to investigate contrasts. For example, if H_0^1 is rejected indicating differences in the levels of A, we may investigate contrasts in A means. These would be of the form

$$L = c_1\mu_{1..} + c_2\mu_{2..} + \cdots + c_a\mu_{a..} \qquad (5.88)$$

which would be estimated by

$$\hat{L} = c_1\bar{x}_{1...} + c_2\bar{x}_{2...} + \cdots + c_a\bar{x}_{a...}.$$

Each sample mean is based upon bcn observations. Consequently, for the T-method

$$T = \frac{1}{\sqrt{bcn}}\, q_{1-\alpha;\, a,\, abc(n-1)} \tag{5.89}$$

and for the S-method

$$S^2 = (a-1) F_{1-\alpha;\, a-1,\, abc(n-1)} \tag{5.90}$$

and

$$\hat{\sigma}^2_{\hat{L}} = \frac{MS_E}{bcn} \sum_{i=1}^{a} c_i^2. \tag{5.91}$$

To investigate contrasts among B means, interchange the role of a and b in this discussion. If contrasts among C means are to be investigated, interchange the role of a and c. Next suppose that we are interested in contrasts among the $r = abc$ means. Then

$$L = c_1 \mu_{111} + c_2 \mu_{211} + \cdots + c_r \mu_{abc} \tag{5.92}$$

is estimated by

$$\hat{L} = c_1 \bar{x}_{111.} + c_2 \bar{x}_{211.} + \cdots + c_r \bar{x}_{abc.} \cdot$$

Here we have

$$T = \frac{1}{\sqrt{n}}\, q_{1-\alpha;\, r,\, abc(n-1)}\,, \tag{5.93}$$

$$S^2 = (r-1) F_{1-\alpha;\, r-1,\, abc(n-1)}\,, \tag{5.94}$$

and

$$\hat{\sigma}^2_{\hat{L}} = \frac{MS_E}{n} \sum_{i=1}^{r} c_i^2. \tag{5.95}$$

Power can be computed for each of the seven F tests. In each case ϕ can be obtained with the aid of Table 5.13 and the second term in the EMS column. For each of the seven hypotheses

$$\phi = \frac{\sqrt{\text{second term in } EMS \text{ column with denominator increased by 1}}}{\sigma} \tag{5.96}$$

For example, associated with H_0^3 is

$$\phi = \frac{\sqrt{\dfrac{abn}{c} \sum_{k=1}^{c} \gamma_k^2}}{\sigma} \tag{5.97}$$

and with H_0^7

$$\phi = \frac{\sqrt{\dfrac{n}{(a-1)(b-1)(c-1)+1} \sum_{i=1}^{a} \sum_{j=1}^{b} \sum_{k=1}^{c} (\alpha\beta\gamma)_{ijk}^2}}{\sigma} \tag{5.98}$$

The ν_1 in each case is the entry from the degrees of freedom column and $\nu_2 = abc(n-1)$.

An examination of Table 5.13 reveals that if $n = 1$, there are no degrees of freedom for error. In this case we would have to assume some interactions are zero. Most likely we would assume that there is no ABC interaction. In the analysis of variance table ABC would be replaced by error under source and by E under SS and MS. Because of the new assumption, the EMS for error is σ^2. The first six F ratios are used to test H_0^1 through H_0^6 as before with this new MS_E as the denominator.

EXERCISES

5.11 Two methods of plowing, three kinds of fertilizer, and four wheat varieties are being investigated in the same experiment. Each of the 24-treatment combinations is assigned at random to three acres of land in a 72-acre field. Yields are recorded in bushels per acre. The results appear in Table 5.14. Analyze the data. Use the T-method when it seems to be appropriate.

5.12 Suppose that in Exercise 5.11 we have used $\alpha = .05$ to test H_0^7. What is the probability of rejecting H_0^7 if one $(\alpha\beta\gamma)_{ijk}$ is $3\sigma/4$ and as many of the rest as possible are zero? Note the last three sums in (5.53).

Table 5.14 DATA FOR EXERCISE 5.11

| | | | Kind of fertilizer | | | | |
| | | 1 | | 2 | | 3 | |
Plowing methods		1	2	1	2	1	2
	1	52	48	38	32	44	20
		44	44	38	18	29	8
		43	51	21	13	27	1
	2	57	48	62	43	32	26
		69	51	43	25	13	20
Wheat		53	42	39	34	27	11
varieties	3	65	58	64	37	27	32
		76	36	46	51	50	16
		79	73	63	48	50	48
	4	74	68	73	51	43	39
		70	61	65	50	44	34
		104	77	50	74	50	30

5-12 OTHER MODELS FOR THE THREE-FACTOR COMPLETELY RANDOMIZED EXPERIMENT

As in the two-factor case discussed in Section 5-6, an experimenter may be interested in a random-effects model or mixed models. Sums of squares, degrees of freedom, and mean squares are exactly the same as in the fixed-effects model. However, the assumptions and F ratios are different.

Let us consider first the random-effects model. The assumptions are

$$x_{ijkm} = \mu + \alpha_i + \beta_j + \gamma_k + (\alpha\beta)_{ij} + (\alpha\gamma)_{ik} + (\beta\gamma)_{jk} + (\alpha\beta\gamma)_{ijk} + e_{ijkm}$$

α_i, β_j, γ_k, $(\alpha\beta)_{ij}$, $(\alpha\gamma)_{ik}$, $(\beta\gamma)_{jk}$, $(\alpha\beta\gamma)_{ijk}$ and e_{ijkm} (5.99)

are independently normal with means zero and variances

σ_A^2, σ_B^2, σ_C^2, σ_{AB}^2, σ_{AC}^2, σ_{BC}^2, σ_{ABC}^2 and σ^2, respectively.

This is only a slight generalization of the assumptions for the two-factor case given by (5.30). The seven null hypotheses now specify $\sigma_A^2 = 0$, $\sigma_B^2 = 0$, $\sigma_C^2 = 0$, $\sigma_{AB}^2 = 0$, $\sigma_{AC}^2 = 0$, $\sigma_{BC}^2 = 0$, and $\sigma_{ABC}^2 = 0$. Table 5.15 gives the expected mean squares and the F ratios. We note that the F column has been left blank opposite A, B, and C. In fact, no exact test exists for the null hypotheses about A, B, and C effects. An approximate procedure due to Satterthwaite [2] is used in this situation. Since $MS_{AB} + MS_{AC} - MS_{ABC}$ and MS_A both have the same expected values if $\sigma_A^2 = 0$, it seems logical to try to compare these two quantities in an F ratio.

Table 5.15 EXPECTED MEAN SQUARES AND F RATIOS FOR THE THREE-FACTOR COMPLETELY RANDOMIZED RANDOM-EFFECTS MODEL

Source	EMS	F
Treatments A	$\sigma^2 + n\sigma_{ABC}^2 + cn\sigma_{AB}^2 + bn\sigma_{AC}^2 + bcn\sigma_A^2$	
B	$\sigma^2 + n\sigma_{ABC}^2 + cn\sigma_{AB}^2 + an\sigma_{BC}^2 + acn\sigma_B^2$	
C	$\sigma^2 + n\sigma_{ABC}^2 + bn\sigma_{AC}^2 + an\sigma_{BC}^2 + abn\sigma_C^2$	
AB	$\sigma^2 + n\sigma_{ABC}^2 + cn\sigma_{AB}^2$	$\dfrac{MS_{AB}}{MS_{ABC}}$
AC	$\sigma^2 + n\sigma_{ABC}^2 + bn\sigma_{AC}^2$	$\dfrac{MS_{AC}}{MS_{ABC}}$
BC	$\sigma^2 + n\sigma_{ABC}^2 + an\sigma_{BC}^2$	$\dfrac{MS_{BC}}{MS_{ABC}}$
ABC	$\sigma^2 + n\sigma_{ABC}^2$	$\dfrac{MS_{ABC}}{MS_E}$
Error	σ^2	

To choose between

$$H_0^1: \quad \sigma_A^2 = 0$$
$$H_1^1: \quad \sigma_A^2 \neq 0$$

we use
$$F'_{a-1, \, \hat{\nu}} = \frac{MS_A}{MS_{AB} + MS_{AC} - MS_{ABC}} \qquad (5.100)$$

which has an approximate F distribution. Here

$$\hat{\nu} = \frac{(MS_{AB} + MS_{AC} - MS_{ABC})^2}{\dfrac{(MS_{AB})^2}{(a-1)(b-1)} + \dfrac{(MS_{AC})^2}{(a-1)(c-1)} + \dfrac{(MS_{ABC})^2}{(a-1)(b-1)(c-1)}} \qquad (5.101)$$

which, in general, is not an integer. Consequently, interpolation in the F table will be necessary. In practice, however, choosing the nearest integer will suffice. To choose between

$$H_0^2: \quad \sigma_B^2 = 0$$
$$H_1^2: \quad \sigma_B^2 \neq 0$$

interchange A and B (also a and b) in the above formulas. Similarly, to choose between

$$H_0^3: \quad \sigma_C^2 = 0$$
$$H_1^3: \quad \sigma_C^2 \neq 0$$

interchange A and C (also a and c). An approximate power for these tests may be computed (see Scheffé [3], p. 248).

Next suppose that A is a fixed-effect and B and C are random. Then the assumptions are

$$x_{ijkm} = \mu + \alpha_i + \beta_j + \gamma_k + (\alpha\beta)_{ij} + (\alpha\gamma)_{ik} + (\beta\gamma)_{jk} + (\alpha\beta\gamma)_{ijk} + e_{ijkm}$$
$$e_{ijkm} \quad \text{are independently } N(0, \sigma^2) \qquad (5.102)$$

$\beta_j, \; \gamma_k, \; (\alpha\beta)_{ij}, \; (\alpha\gamma)_{ik}, \; (\beta\gamma)_{jk}, \; (\alpha\beta\gamma)_{ijk}$ are jointly normal
with means zero

$$\sum_{i=1}^{a}\alpha_i = \sum_{i=1}^{a}(\alpha\beta)_{ij} = \sum_{i=1}^{a}(\alpha\gamma)_{ik} = \sum_{i=1}^{a}(\alpha\beta\gamma)_{ijk} = 0.$$

The expected mean squares and the F ratios appear in Table 5.16. The approximate F test of (5.100) is used to choose between

$$H_0^1: \quad \alpha_i = 0, \; i = 1, \, 2, \, \cdots, \, a$$
$$H_1^1: \quad \text{not all } \alpha_i \text{ are zero.}$$

Table 5.16 EXPECTED MEAN SQUARES AND F RATIOS FOR THE THREE-FACOR
COMPLETELY RANDOMIZED MIXED MODEL
(A FIXED, B AND C RANDOM)

Source	EMS	F
Treatments A	$\sigma^2+n\sigma^2_{ABC}+cn\sigma^2_{AB}+bn\sigma^2_{AC}+bcn\dfrac{\sum_{i=1}^{a}\alpha_i^2}{a-1}$	
B	$\sigma^2+an\sigma^2_{BC}+acn\sigma^2_B$	$\dfrac{MS_B}{MS_{BC}}$
C	$\sigma^2+an\sigma^2_{BC}+abn\sigma^2_C$	$\dfrac{MS_C}{MS_{BC}}$
AB	$\sigma^2+n\sigma^2_{ABC}+cn\sigma^2_{AB}$	$\dfrac{MS_{AB}}{MS_{ABC}}$
AC	$\sigma^2+n\sigma^2_{ABC}+bn\sigma^2_{AC}$	$\dfrac{MS_{AC}}{MS_{ABC}}$
BC	$\sigma^2+an\sigma^2_{BC}$	$\dfrac{MS_{BC}}{MS_E}$
ABC	$\sigma^2+n\sigma^2_{ABC}$	$\dfrac{MS_{ABC}}{MS_E}$
Error	σ^2	

The other six F ratios test the remaining six main null hypotheses:
$$\sigma_B^2=0, \quad \sigma_C^2=0, \quad \sigma_{AB}^2=0, \quad \sigma_{AC}^2=0, \quad \sigma_{BC}^2=0, \quad \text{and} \quad \sigma_{ABC}^2=0.$$
If B is the fixed factor and A and C are random, then interchange A and B (also a and b) in Table 5.16. Similarly, if C is fixed and A and B are random, then interchange A and C (also a and c).

Finally, suppose that A and B are fixed-effects and C is random. The assumptions can now be written
$$x_{ijkm}=\mu+\alpha_i+\beta_j+\gamma_k+(\alpha\beta)_{ij}+(\alpha\gamma)_{ik}+(\beta\gamma)_{jk}+(\alpha\beta\gamma)_{ijk}+e_{ijkm}$$
e_{ijkm} are independently $N(0,\ \sigma^2)$ (5.103)
γ_k, $(\alpha\gamma)_{ik}$, $(\beta\gamma)_{jk}$, and $(\alpha\beta\gamma)_{ijk}$ are jointly normal with means 0
$$\sum_{i=1}^{a}\alpha_i=\sum_{j=1}^{b}\beta_j=\sum_{i=1}^{a}(\alpha\beta)_{ij}=\sum_{j=1}^{b}(\alpha\beta)_{ij}=\sum_{i=1}^{a}(\alpha\gamma)_{ik}=\sum_{j=1}^{b}(\beta\gamma)_{jk}$$
$$=\sum_{i=1}^{a}(\alpha\beta\gamma)_{ijk}=\sum_{j=1}^{b}(\alpha\beta\gamma)_{ijk}=0.$$

Table 5.17 gives the expected mean squares and F ratios. This time no approximate tests are necessary. If the random factor is A, interchange the role of A and C (also a and c). If the random factor is B, interchange the role of B and C (also b and c).

Checking the assumptions given by (5.99), (5.102), and (5.103), we observe that (a) if an effect contains a fixed-effects subscript, then the effect summed over that subscript is zero and (b) all effects that contain a random effects subscript are jointly normally distributed. These results extend to the situations in which there are four or more factors.

The rules formulated by Schultz [4] enable us to reproduce quickly the *EMS*'s of Tables 5.15, 5.16, and 5.17. These apply not only for the three-factor case, but also for two factors and four or more factors. First, the *EMS*'s for the random-effects model are written. To do this we observe from Table 5.15:

(1)   The *EMS* for error is σ^2.

(2)   The *EMS* for each treatment effect contains two or more terms, the first of which is σ^2.

Table 5.17   EXPECTED MEAN SQUARES AND *F* RATIOS FOR THE THREE-FACTOR COMPLETELY RANDOMIZED MIXED MODEL

(*A* AND *B* FIXED, *C* RANDOM)

Source		EMS	F
Treatments *A*		$\sigma^2 + bn\sigma^2_{AC} + bcn\dfrac{\sum\limits_{i=1}^{a} \alpha_i^2}{a-1}$	$\dfrac{MS_A}{MS_{AC}}$
	B	$\sigma^2 + an\sigma^2_{BC} + acn\dfrac{\sum\limits_{j=1}^{b} \beta_j^2}{b-1}$	$\dfrac{MS_B}{MS_{BC}}$
	C	$\sigma^2 + abn\sigma^2_C$	$\dfrac{MS_C}{MS_E}$
	AB	$\sigma^2 + n\sigma^2_{ABC} + cn\dfrac{\sum\limits_{i=1}^{a}\sum\limits_{j=1}^{b} (\alpha\beta)_{ij}^2}{(a-1)(b-1)}$	$\dfrac{MS_{AB}}{MS_{ABC}}$
	AC	$\sigma^2 + bn\sigma^2_{AC}$	$\dfrac{MS_{AC}}{MS_E}$
	BC	$\sigma^2 + an\sigma^2_{BC}$	$\dfrac{MS_{BC}}{MS_E}$
	ABC	$\sigma^2 + n\sigma^2_{ABC}$	$\dfrac{MS_{ABC}}{MS_E}$
Error		σ^2	

(3)   All other terms in each *EMS* contain both coefficients and subscripts, the total number of letters being four in each case (one more than the number of factors).

(4)   The subscript on σ^2 in the last term of each *EMS* is the same as the treatment designation.

(5)   The subscripts on all σ^2's, other than the first, contain the treatment designation. A term is present for all treatment combinations containing this letter (or letters). These are written with the combination involving the most letters (in this case, ABC) coming first. This is followed by two letter subscripts and finally by one letter subscripts (if all are necessary).

(6)   When a capital letter is omitted from a subscript, the corresponding small letter appears in the coefficient.

Following these six rules, we can reproduce all expected mean squares in Table 5.15. To obtain these for Tables 5.16 and 5.17 we need the following rules for mixed models:

(7)   In each EMS of Table 5.15 ignore the letter (or letters) that designate the effect. If any of the remaining letters correspond to a fixed-effect, delete that term from the EMS.

(8)   Replace σ^2's whose subscripts are composed of fixed-effects letters by the appropriate sum. That is,

$$\sigma_A^2 \text{ becomes } \frac{\sum_{i=1}^{a} \alpha_i^2}{a-1}, \quad \sigma_{AB}^2 \text{ becomes } \frac{\sum_{i=1}^{a}\sum_{j=1}^{b}(\alpha\beta)_{ij}^2}{(a-1)(b-1)}, \text{ etc.}$$

Actually Rule (8) is not essential since it does not affect the F ratios that are formed. Let us illustrate these rules on a four-factor case where the fourth factor is D occurring at d levels. We seek the EMS for the A effects in the random-effects model. First we write

$$\sigma^2 + (\ \ )\sigma_{ABCD}^2 + (\ \ )\sigma_{ABC}^2 + (\ \ )\sigma_{ABD}^2 + (\ \ )\sigma_{ACD}^2 + (\ \ )\sigma_{AB}^2$$
$$+ (\ \ )\sigma_{AC}^2 + (\ \ )\sigma_{AD}^2 + (\ \ )\sigma_{A}^2.$$

Next the coefficients are filled in according to Rules (3) and (6). We get

$$\sigma^2 + n\sigma_{ABCD}^2 + dn\sigma_{ABC}^2 + cn\sigma_{ABD}^2 + bn\sigma_{ACD}^2 + cdn\sigma_{AB}^2 + bdn\sigma_{AC}^2$$
$$+ bcn\sigma_{AD}^2 + bcdn\sigma_{A}^2.$$

Now if A and B are fixed, then the terms involving σ_{ABCD}^2, σ_{ABD}^2, σ_{ABC}^2 and σ_{AB}^2 are deleted according to Rule (7). Thus for this case the EMS is

$$\sigma^2 + bn\sigma_{ACD}^2 + bdn\sigma_{AC}^2 + bcn\sigma_{AD}^2 + bcdn \frac{\sum_{i=1}^{a} \alpha_i^2}{a-1}.$$

EXERCISES

5.13 Let $a=4$, $b=5$, $c=6$, $n=3$, $MS_E = 30.3$, $MS_A = 384.6$, $MS_B =$

200.1, $MS_C=85.7$, $MS_{AB}=43.2$, $MS_{AC}=40.7$, $MS_{BC}=45.3$, and $MS_{ABC}=38.1$. Write out the analysis of variance table if the appropriate model is

(a) random-effects.
(b) mixed with A fixed, B and C random.
(c) mixed with A and B fixed, C random.

Indicate which F's are significant.

5.14 Find the *EMS* for *AB* in a four-factor random-effects model. What does this become if A and B are fixed, C and D random?

5-13 RANDOMIZED BLOCKS WITH THREE FACTORS (FIXED-EFFECTS)

We have previously observed that data from a three-factor randomized block experiment can be arranged in the form of Table 5.6. The first observation in each cell goes with Block 1, the second with Block 2, etc. Thus each block contains *abc* observations.

The assumptions are the usual ones made for randomized blocks. These are: (a) a random sample of size 1 is drawn from each of the *abcn* populations, (b) all *abcn* populations are normal, (c) the variance of each of the *abcn* populations is the same, and (d) block and treatment effects are additive. The equivalent symbolic formulation of these assumptions is

$$x_{ijkm}=\mu+\alpha_i+\beta_j+\gamma_k+\rho_m+(\alpha\beta)_{ij}+(\alpha\gamma)_{ik}+(\beta\gamma)_{jk}$$
$$+(\alpha\beta\gamma)_{ijk}+e_{ijkm} \qquad (5.104)$$

e_{ijkm} are independently $N(0, \sigma^2)$

All sums of (5.53) are zero and $\sum_{m=1}^{n}\rho_m=0$.

As in the previous cases with randomized blocks, we first make the subdivision

$$SS_T=SS_{BL}+SS_{Tr}+SS_E. \qquad (5.105)$$

Here

$$SS_{BL}=\sum_{i=1}^{a}\sum_{j=1}^{b}\sum_{k=1}^{c}\sum_{m=1}^{n}(\bar{x}_{...m}-\bar{x}_{....})^2=\frac{\sum_{m=1}^{n}T^2_{...m}}{abc}-\frac{T^2_{....}}{abcn} \qquad (5.106)$$

and SS_{Tr} is the same as in the completely randomized design given by (5.69) and (5.78). Then SS_E is obtained by subtraction. The subdivision of SS_{Tr} is the same as that given by Equation (5.77).

The analysis of variance is almost the same as that given by Table 5.13. As in Table 5.5 a row must be added for blocks with $n-1$

degrees of freedom and expected mean square

$$\sigma^2 + abc\frac{\sum\limits_{m=1}^{n} \rho_m^2}{n-1}.$$

The degrees of freedom for error is $(n-1)(abc-1)$.

Changes in the T- and S-methods are fairly obvious. Formulas (5.47) through (5.52) apply if $(n-1)(ab-1)$ is replaced by $(n-1)(abc-1)$. Since there are $abcn$ means under consideration, four subscripts will be needed on all μ's (denote them by μ_{ijkm}). Thus, for example, contrasts among A means are of the form $L = \sum\limits_{i=1}^{a} c_i \mu_{i...}$ which is estimated by $\hat{L} = \sum\limits_{i=1}^{a} c_i \bar{x}_{i...}$. Power calculations are the same as in the completely randomized case.

If randomized blocks are used with a random-effects or mixed model, the correct F ratios for the main hypotheses are the same as for complete randomization. This is true whether blocks are fixed or random. The degrees of freedom associated with MS_E is changed to

$$(n-1)(abc-1).$$

EXERCISE

5.15 Make the appropriate changes in Exercise 5.11 if it is regarded as a randomized-block experiment.

5-14 NESTED OR HIERARCHICAL CLASSIFICATION

We considered the data of Table 5.1 as a cross-classification. That is, every level of factor A included in the experiment occurs with every level of factor B and vice versa. Sometimes the factors may be nested inside of one another. For example, factor A at a levels may represent a different schools, factor B at b levels may be b different teachers within each school system, and the n observations within each cell may be final examination grades in classes taught by these teachers. This might be the scheme that we would use if we were interested in comparing the the competence of students attending three different universities, who completed a course in calculus. Assume that four instructors at each university were used and that by a process of random selection 30 students were assigned to each class.

As another example, suppose that we have reason to suspect that the quantity of soap put in cartons by a manufacturer varies with the different grocery chains to whom he sells. (He may cheat slightly on quantity with one or more chains so that they can buy at a lower price and sell cheaper than their competitors.) In order to investigate this situation we might select three chains, four stores from each chain, and 30 boxes from each stock and then record weights. Again this is a nested arrangement.

To derive the analysis of variance for the fixed-effects model, it is necessary to assume that the x_{ijk} are independently $N(\mu_{ij}, \sigma^2)$. This implies (a) the $r = ab$ cells represent r random samples of size n from r populations, (b) each of the r populations is normal, and (c) each of the r populations has the same variance. We may write the following two identities:

$$x_{ijk} = \mu_{ij} + (x_{ijk} - \mu_{ij}) = \mu_{ij} + e_{ijk}$$

and

$$\mu_{ij} = \mu + (\mu_{i.} - \mu) + (\mu_{ij} - \mu_{i.})$$
$$= \mu + \alpha_i + B_{ij}$$

where

$$\sum_{i=1}^{a} \alpha_i = \sum_{j=1}^{b} B_{ij} = 0.$$

Thus the assumptions for the fixed-effects model are

$$x_{ijk} = \mu + \alpha_i + B_{ij} + e_{ijk}, \qquad \begin{aligned} i &= 1, 2, \cdots, a \\ j &= 1, 2, \cdots, b \\ k &= 1, 2, \cdots, n \end{aligned}$$

e_{ijk} are independently $N(0, \sigma^2)$ (5.107)

$$\sum_{i=1}^{a} \alpha_i = \sum_{j=1}^{b} B_{.j} = 0.$$

In both of the examples cited, the mixed-model is probably more appropriate than a fixed-effects model; that is, we prefer to consider the instructors a random sample of instructors from a particular university, and the stores a random sample from a particular chain. Then these assumptions may be written

$$x_{ijk} = \mu + \alpha_i + B_{ij} + e_{ijk}, \qquad \begin{aligned} i &= 1, 2, \cdots, a \\ j &= 1, 2, \cdots, b \\ k &= 1, 2, \cdots, n \end{aligned}$$

e_{ijk} are independently $N(0, \sigma^2)$ (5.108)

B_{ij} are independently $N(0, \sigma_B^2)$

$$\sum_{i=1}^{a} \alpha_i = 0.$$

If, in addition, we assume that we have a random sample of chains or of universities, then the random-effects model is the correct one to use, and we would write the following:

$$x_{ijk} = \mu + \alpha_i + B_{ij} + e_{ijk}, \qquad \begin{aligned} i &= 1, 2, \cdots, a \\ j &= 1, 2, \cdots, b \\ k &= 1, 2, \cdots, n \end{aligned}$$

e_{ijk}, α_i, and B_{ij} are each independently normal with   (5.109)
means zero and variances σ^2, σ_α^2, and σ_B^2, respectively.

The main hypothesis of interest is usually the one concerning the A effects. We choose between

$$H_0: \quad \alpha_i = 0, \qquad i = 1, 2, \cdots, a$$
$$H_1: \quad \text{not all } \alpha_i \text{ are zero}$$

if the A effect is fixed and between

$$H_0: \quad \sigma_\alpha^2 = 0$$
$$H_1: \quad \sigma_\alpha^2 \neq 0$$

if A is random. Similarly, if the B effect is fixed, the null hypothesis is $B_{ij} = 0$, $i = 1, 2, \cdots, a$, $j = 1, 2, \cdots, b$; and if it is random, the null hypothesis is $\sigma_B^2 = 0$.

The partitioning of the total sum of squares is similar to that of the two-factor crossed-classification. We may write

$$\sum_{i=1}^{a} \sum_{j=1}^{b} \sum_{k=1}^{n} (x_{ijk} - \bar{x}_{...})^2$$

$$= \sum_{i=1}^{a} \sum_{j=1}^{b} \sum_{k=1}^{n} [(\bar{x}_{i..} - \bar{x}_{...}) + (\bar{x}_{ij.} - \bar{x}_{i..}) + (x_{ijk} - \bar{x}_{ij.})]^2$$

$$= \sum_{i=1}^{a} \sum_{j=1}^{b} \sum_{k=1}^{n} (\bar{x}_{i..} - \bar{x}_{...})^2 + \sum_{i=1}^{a} \sum_{j=1}^{b} \sum_{k=1}^{n} (\bar{x}_{ij.} - \bar{x}_{i..})^2 + \sum_{i=1}^{a} \sum_{j=1}^{b} \sum_{k=1}^{n} (x_{ijk} - \bar{x}_{ij.})^2$$

$$(5.110)$$

since all cross-products are zero. This can be written in shorthand as

$$SS_T = SS_A + SS_{B(A)} + SS_E$$

where $B(A)$ is read "B within A." We see that SS_A measures the variation among various levels of A (universities or chains), $SS_{B(A)}$ measures the variation of levels of B within A (teachers at a given university or stores within a chain), and SS_E measures the variation of observations within the same level of B within the same level of A (students of the same teacher or cartons from the same store).

The computing formulas are

$$SS_T = \sum_{i=1}^{a} \sum_{j=1}^{b} \sum_{k=1}^{n} x_{ijk}^2 - \frac{T_{...}^2}{abn}, \qquad (5.111)$$

$$SS_A = \frac{\sum\limits_{i=1}^{a} T_{i..}^2}{bn} - \frac{T_{...}^2}{abn} , \tag{5.112}$$

$$SS_{B(A)} = \frac{\sum\limits_{i=1}^{a} \sum\limits_{j=1}^{b} T_{ij.}^2}{n} - \frac{\sum\limits_{i=1}^{a} T_{i..}^2}{bn} , \tag{5.113}$$

and

$$SS_E = SS_T - SS_A - SS_{B(A)} . \tag{5.114}$$

Formulas (5.111) and (5.112) are exactly the same as (5.9) and (5.12) of Section 5-4.

The analysis of variance for the fixed-effects model is given in Table 5.18.

Table 5.18 ANALYSIS OF VARIANCE FOR A NESTED CLASSIFICATION (FIXED-EFFECTS MODEL)

Source	SS	d.f.	MS	EMS	F
Levels of A	SS_A	$a-1$	MS_A	$\sigma^2 + bn\dfrac{\sum\limits_{i=1}^{a}\alpha_i^2}{a-1}$	$\dfrac{MS_A}{MS_E}$
Levels of B within A	$SS_{B(A)}$	$a(b-1)$	$MS_{B(A)}$	$\sigma^2 + n\dfrac{\sum\limits_{i=1}^{a}\sum\limits_{j=1}^{b}B_{ij}^2}{a(b-1)}$	$\dfrac{MS_{B(A)}}{MS_E}$
Error	SS_E	$ab(n-1)$	MS_E	σ^2	
TOTAL	SS_T	$abn-1$			

The EMS's and F ratios for the random-effects and mixed models appear in Table 5.19.

Table 5.19 EXPECTED MEAN SQUARES AND F RATIOS FOR A NESTED CLASSIFICATION

Source	EMS (A, B random)	EMS (A fixed, B random)	F
Levels of A	$\sigma^2 + n\sigma_B^2 + bn\sigma_\alpha^2$	$\sigma^2 + n\sigma_B^2 + bn\dfrac{\sum\limits_{i=1}^{a}\alpha_i^2}{a-1}$	$\dfrac{MS_A}{MS_{B(A)}}$
Levels of B within A	$\sigma^2 + n\sigma_B^2$	$\sigma^2 + n\sigma_B^2$	$\dfrac{MS_{B(A)}}{MS_E}$
Error	σ^2	σ^2	

If A is fixed and the null hypothesis concerning A effects is rejected, we may want to use the T- or S-method to investigate contrasts. Contrasts $L = \sum\limits_{i=1}^{a} c_i\mu_{i.} = \sum\limits_{i=1}^{a} c_i\alpha_i$ are estimated by $\hat{L} = \sum\limits_{i=1}^{a} c_i\bar{x}_{i..}$. If B is also fixed,

$$T = \frac{1}{\sqrt{bn}} \, q_{1-\alpha;\, a,\, ab(n-1)} \,, \qquad (5.115)$$

$$S^2 = (a-1) F_{1-\alpha;\, a-1,\, ab(n-1)} \,, \qquad (5.116)$$

MS_E is used in place of MS_W with $ab(n-1)$ replacing $N-r$, and bn replacing n. If B is random, then

$$T = \frac{1}{\sqrt{bn}} \, q_{1-\alpha;\, a,\, a(b-1)} \,, \qquad (5.117)$$

$$S^2 = (a-1) F_{1-\alpha;\, a-1,\, a(b-1)} \,, \qquad (5.118)$$

$MS_{B(A)}$ is used in place of MS_W with $a(b-1)$ replacing $N-r$, and bn replacing n.

For the fixed-effects model we can calculate power in the usual way. When A effects are being investigated, then

$$\phi = \frac{\sqrt{\dfrac{bn}{a} \sum\limits_{i=1}^{a} \alpha_i^2}}{\sigma} \,, \quad \nu_1 = a-1, \ \nu_2 = ab(n-1) \,. \qquad (5.119)$$

For B effects we have

$$\phi = \frac{\sqrt{\dfrac{n}{a(b-1)+1} \sum\limits_{i=1}^{a} \sum\limits_{j=1}^{b} B_{ij}^2}}{\sigma} \,, \quad \nu_1 = a(b-1), \ \nu_2 = ab(n-1). \qquad (5.120)$$

Table 5.6 may be regarded as data from a three-factor nested design. The analysis for this design, similar to that for the two-factor case, will not be discussed here.

EXERCISES

5.16 Use the data of Exercise 5.3 relabeling fertilizers as universities and wheat varieties as teachers within universities. Consider the observations as final examination grades in calculus. Analyze the results assuming that we are interested in only the three universities and that within each we have a random sample of teachers. Note that

$$SS_{B(A)} = SS_{Tr} - SS_A = SS_B + SS_{AB} \,.$$

5.17 Suppose the fixed-effects model is used in Exercise 5.16. (Each university has only three teachers available.) Does this change any of the conclusions? If appropriate, use the T-method in the usual way on levels of A. What is the probability of rejecting H_0: $B_{ij} = 0$, $i = 1,\ 2,\ 3$, $j = 1,\ 2,\ 3$ if over a period of time all instructors get the same average result with the exception that in one university one instructor has students who average 2σ better than the other two? Use $\alpha = .05$.

REFERENCES

[1] Kimball, A, W., "On Dependent Tests of Significance in the Analysis of Variance," *Annals of Mathematical Statistics*, Vol. 22 (1951), 600–602.

[2] Satterthwaite, F. E., "An Approximate Distribution of Estimates of Variance Components, *Biometrics Bulletin*, Vol. 2 (1946) 110–14.

[3] Scheffé, Henry, *The Analysis of Variance*, (New York: John Wiley & Sons, Inc., 1959).

[4] Schultz, E. F., Jr., "Rules of Thumb for Determining Expectations of Mean Squares in Analysis of Variance," *Biometrics*, Vol. 11, (1955), 123–48.

[3] Snedecor, George W., *Statistcal Methods*, (Ames, Iowa: Iowa State University Press, 1956).

6

Analysis of Covariance

6-1 INTRODUCTION

We have observed that randomized blocks and Latin squares can be used to eliminate effects resulting from variables in which there is no interest. When we choose one of these designs in preference to complete randomization, we hope to get a smaller denominator for the F ratio and thus increase the chances of rejecting a false hypothesis. The analysis of covariance is another technique used to accomplish this same objective. It can be used in conjunction with complete randomization, randomized blocks, Latin square, or factorial experiments.

Suppose that we are interested in comparing several different kinds of feed for their ability to put weight on animals. This might be accomplished by performing an analysis of variance using the final weights at the end of the experiment. However, the final weight depends upon the initial weight at the beginning of the experiment as well as upon the difference in feeds. The use of analysis of covariance enables us to adjust or correct these initial differences.

In a teaching-methods experiment we would use some randomizing device to assign students to classes. If, in addition, we are to " correct " each final examination score by taking into account differences in IQ, we hope that the results more accurately reflect the differences that are due to methods.   Again the analysis of covariance may be profitably used.

In each of the above examples we are interested in investigating differences caused by treatments.   The observations which we intend to use to conduct the analysis (final weight or final examination scores) are dependent variables which are influenced by a second independent variable (initial weights or IQ's).   Many books refer to the latter as the concomitant variable.   The analysis of covariance enables us to take advantage of the information furnished by the concomitant variable.

Some authors point out that care should be exercised when interpreting an analysis of covariance if the concomitant variable is influenced by the treatments.   If the independent variable can be measured before the experiment is performed, this difficulty can be avoided.   With both initial weights and IQ's, this is the case.

6-2 NOTATION FOR THE COMPLETELY RANDOMIZED DESIGN

Let the concomitant variable be denoted by x and the dependent variable by y.   The data may be arranged as in Table 2.1 except, of course, that measurements occur in pairs.   Consequently, the arrangement of the observations will be that of Table 6.1.

The symbols are defined as follows:

$$\text{Total of the } j^{\text{th}} \text{ column of } x\text{'s} = T_{x.j} = \sum_{i=1}^{n_j} x_{ij},$$

$$\text{Mean of the } j^{\text{th}} \text{ column of } x\text{'s} = \bar{x}_{.j} = \frac{T_{x.j}}{n_j},$$

$$\text{Total of the } j^{\text{th}} \text{ column of } y\text{'s} = T_{y.j} = \sum_{i=1}^{n_j} y_{ij},$$

$$\text{mean of the } j^{\text{th}} \text{ column of } y\text{'s} = \bar{y}_{.j} = \frac{T_{y.j}}{n_j},$$

$$\text{total of all } x\text{'s} \qquad = T_{x..} = \sum_{j=1}^{r} \sum_{i=1}^{n_j} x_{ij},$$

$$\text{mean of all } x\text{'s} \qquad = \bar{x}_{..} = \frac{T_{x..}}{N}, \text{ where } N = \sum_{j=1}^{r} n_j,$$

$$\text{total of all } y\text{'s} \qquad = T_{y..} = \sum_{j=1}^{r} \sum_{i=1}^{n_j} y_{ij},$$

$$\text{mean of all } y\text{'s} \qquad = \bar{y}_{..} = \frac{T_{y..}}{N}.$$

Table 6.1   ARRANGEMENT OF DATA FOR ANALYSIS OF COVARIANCE IN A COMPLETELY RANDOMIZED DESIGN

	Treatments							
	1		2		$\cdots$	r		
	x	y	x	y		x	y	
Observations	x_{11}	y_{11}	x_{12}	y_{12}		x_{1r}	y_{1r}	
	x_{21}	y_{21}	x_{22}	y_{22}		x_{2r}	y_{2r}	
	.		.			.		
	.		.			.		
	.		.			.		
	$x_{n_1 1}$	$y_{n_1 1}$	$x_{n_2 2}$	$y_{n_2 2}$		$x_{n_r r}$	$y_{n_r r}$	
Means	$T_{x.1}$	$T_{y.1}$	$T_{x.2}$	$T_{y.2}$		$T_{x.r}$	$T_{y.r}$	$T_{x..}$	$T_{y..}$
TOTALS	$\bar{x}_{.1}$	$\bar{y}_{.1}$	$\bar{x}_{.2}$	$\bar{y}_{.2}$		$\bar{x}_{.r}$	$\bar{y}_{.r}$	$\bar{x}_{..}$	$\bar{y}_{..}$

6-3 THE MODEL FOR THE COMPLETELY RANDOMIZED DESIGN

For an ordinary analysis of variance on the y's, we assume

$$y_{ij} = \mu + \beta_j + e_{ij}, \quad \begin{array}{l} i = 1, 2, \cdots, n_j \\ j = 1, 2, \cdots, r \end{array}$$

e_{ij} are independently $N(0, \sigma^2)$ (6.1)

$$\sum_{j=1}^{r} n_j \beta_j = 0.$$

For the analysis of covariance this is modified to read

$$y_{ij} = \mu + \beta_j + \gamma (x_{ij} - \bar{x}_{..}) + e_{ij}, \quad \begin{array}{l} i = 1, 2, \cdots, n_j \\ j = 1, 2, \cdots, r \end{array}$$

e_{ij} are independently $N(0, \sigma^2)$ (6.2)

$$\sum_{j=1}^{r} n_j \beta_j = 0.$$

Another way to write the assumptions given by (6.2) is

$$y_{ij} \text{ are independently } N(\mu_{ij}, \sigma^2), \quad \begin{array}{l} i = 1, 2, \cdots, n_j \\ j = 1, 2, \cdots, r \end{array}$$

$$\mu_{ij} = \mu + \beta_j + \gamma (x_{ij} - \bar{x}_{..}) \qquad\qquad (6.3)$$

$$\sum_{j=1}^{r} n_j \beta_j = 0.$$

The equation $\mu_{ij} = \mu + \beta_j + \gamma (x_{ij} - \bar{x}_{..})$ implies that the y means within each column lie on a straight line and the slope of the line is the same for each of the r groups. In other words, for the given set of x's, the y means lie upon r parallel lines. The slope measures the rate of increase of the y means with respect to x. Thus an increase in x of two units within any of the r groups produces an increase in the y means that is constant from group to group.   Since

$$y_{ij} = \mu_{ij} + (y_{ij} - \mu_{ij}) = \mu_{ij} + e_{ij}$$

we see that (6.2) and (6.3) are equivalent.

The assumptions written out in words are: (a) a random sample of size 1 is drawn from each of N populations; (b) each of the N populations is normal; (c) each of the N populations has the same variance; (d) the population means within each group lie on a straight line; and (e) the slope of the line is the same for each group.   Consequently, because of (d) and (e), it is necessary to assume more when using covariance analysis than when using a straight analysis of variance on the y's.

We note that the assumptions for the completely randomized design (and for other models which appear later in this chapter) imply that the x's are constants since nothing is mentioned about their having a distribution.   The analysis of each of the models is derived with this point of view.   However, in a number of situations it may be more realistic to consider the x's, as well as the y's, as special values taken on by a variable. If in this case we are willing to assume that the assumptions hold for all possible values of the x's, then the analysis presented in Section 6-5 is still valid.

The main objective of the analysis is to choose between

$$H_0: \quad \beta_j = 0, \; j = 1, \, 2, \cdots, \, r \tag{6.4}$$
$$H_1: \quad \text{not all } \beta_j \text{ are zero.}$$

The null hypothesis states that the "corrected" treatment effects are all equal.   The equivalent formulation in terms of the $\mu_{.j}$'s is

$$H_0: \quad \mu_{.1} - \gamma \bar{x}_{.1} = \mu_{.2} - \gamma \bar{x}_{.2} = \cdots = \mu_{.r} - \gamma \bar{x}_{.r} \tag{6.5}$$
$$H_1: \quad \text{not all } \mu_{.j} - \gamma \bar{x}_{.j} \text{ are equal.}$$

Thus we see that the adjustment factor for each treatment average is proportional to the average of the concomitant variable for that treatment.

Occasionally we may first want to choose between

$$H_0^*: \quad \gamma = 0 \tag{6.6}$$
$$H_1^*: \quad \gamma \neq 0.$$

If H_0^* is accepted, the conclusion is that the concomitant variable is unnecessary.   Consequently in this situation a straight analysis of variance would be used since (6.2) reduces to (6.1).

6-4 PARTITIONING THE SUMS OF SQUARES AND SUMS OF PRODUCTS

The total sum of squares for x and y may be partitioned in exactly the same way as in Chapter 2.   We have

$$SS_{xT} = SS_{xTr} + SS_{xE} \tag{6.7}$$

and

$$SS_{yT} = SS_{yTr} + SS_{yE}. \tag{6.8}$$

With the exceptions that the x and y subscripts are used, "among groups" has been renamed "treatments," and "within groups" has been renamed "error," (6.7) and (6.8) are reproductions of (2.3). Consequently, except for notational differences, the computing formulas are the same. These are

$$SS_{xT} = \sum_{j=1}^{r} \sum_{i=1}^{n_j} x_{ij}^2 - \frac{T_{x..}^2}{N}, \tag{6.9}$$

$$SS_{xTr} = \sum_{j=1}^{r} \frac{T_{x.j}^2}{n_j} - \frac{T_{x..}^2}{N}, \tag{6.10}$$

$$SS_{xE} = SS_{xT} - SS_{xTr}, \tag{6.11}$$

$$SS_{yT} = \sum_{j=1}^{r} \sum_{i=1}^{n_j} y_{ij}^2 - \frac{T_{y..}^2}{N}, \tag{6.12}$$

$$SS_{yTr} = \sum_{j=1}^{r} \frac{T_{y.j}^2}{n_j} - \frac{T_{y..}^2}{N}, \tag{6.13}$$

$$SS_{yE} = SS_{yT} - SS_{yTr}. \tag{6.14}$$

Next consider a term which we will call the total sum of products and designate by SP_T. This term is partitioned in exactly the same way. We have

$$
\begin{aligned}
SP_T &= \sum_{j=1}^{r} \sum_{i=1}^{n_j} (x_{ij} - \bar{x}_{..}) \, (y_{ij} - \bar{y}_{..}) \\
&= \sum_{j=1}^{r} \sum_{i=1}^{n_j} [(\bar{x}_{.j} - \bar{x}_{..}) + (x_{ij} - \bar{x}_{.j})] \, [(\bar{y}_{.j} - \bar{y}_{..}) + (\bar{y}_{ij} - \bar{y}_{.j})] \\
&= \sum_{j=1}^{r} \sum_{i=1}^{n_j} (\bar{x}_{.j} - \bar{x}_{..}) \, (\bar{y}_{.j} - \bar{y}_{..}) + \sum_{j=1}^{r} \sum_{i=1}^{n_j} (x_{ij} - \bar{x}_{.j}) \, (y_{ij} - \bar{y}_{.j})
\end{aligned}
$$
$$+ 2 \text{ zero terms.} \tag{6.15}$$

The two sums obtained on the right-hand side of (6.15) will be designated by SP_{Tr}, sum of products for treatments, and SP_E, sum of products for error. Thus

$$SP_T = SP_{Tr} + SP_E. \tag{6.16}$$

The computing formulas are obtained in the usual way. For example,

$$
\begin{aligned}
SP_T &= \sum_{j=1}^{r} \sum_{i=1}^{n_j} (x_{ij} - \bar{x}_{..}) \, (y_{ij} - \bar{y}_{..}) \\
&= \sum_{j=1}^{r} \sum_{i=1}^{n_j} x_{ij} \, y_{ij} - \bar{x}_{..} \sum_{j=1}^{r} \sum_{i=1}^{n_j} y_{ij} - \bar{y}_{..} \sum_{j=1}^{r} \sum_{i=1}^{n_j} x_{ij} + N\bar{x}_{..} \, \bar{y}_{..}
\end{aligned}
$$

$$= \sum_{j=1}^{r} \sum_{i=1}^{n_j} x_{ij} y_{ij} - \frac{T_{x..}}{N} T_{y..} - \frac{T_{y..}}{N} T_{x..} + N \frac{T_{x..}}{N} \frac{T_{y..}}{N}$$

$$= \sum_{j=1}^{r} \sum_{i=1}^{n_j} x_{ij} y_{ij} - \frac{T_{x..} T_{y..}}{N}. \tag{6.17}$$

In a similar manner we get

$$SP_{Tr} = \sum_{j=1}^{r} \frac{T_{x.j} T_{y.j}}{n_j} - \frac{T_{x..} T_{y..}}{N}. \tag{6.18}$$

By subtraction we have

$$SP_E = SP_T - SP_{Tr}. \tag{6.19}$$

Unlike a sum of squares, a sum of products does not necessarily have to be positive. Also we note that if we let $y=x$, the sum of products formulas reduce to those we have for sums of squares.

EXERCISE

6.1 (a) Write down the other two terms that arise in Equation (6.15) and show that they are zero.

(b) Show that the computing formula for SP_{Tr} is given by (6.18).

6-5 THE ANALYSIS FOR THE COMPLETELY RANDOMIZED DESIGN

Let

$$SS'_{yT} = SS_{yT} - \frac{(SP_T)^2}{SS_{xT}}, \tag{6.20}$$

$$SS'_{yE} = SS_{yE} - \frac{(SP_E)^2}{SS_{xE}}, \tag{6.21}$$

and

$$SS'_{yTr} = SS'_{yT} - SS'_{yE}. \tag{6.22}$$

If the assumptions (6.2) are true, then it may be shown

$$F_{r-1,\ N-r-1} = \frac{\dfrac{SS'_{yTr}}{r-1}}{\dfrac{SS'_{yE}}{N-r-1}} = \frac{MS'_{yTr}}{MS'_{yE}} \tag{6.23}$$

is the proper F ratio to use to test H_0. As usual the hypothesis is rejected if F is large.

For convenience results may be summarized as in Table 6.2. We note that the degrees of freedom for error (and for total) is one less than in the analysis of variance. This is due to the fact that one more parameter, γ, has to be estimated from the data.

Table 6.2 ANALYSIS OF COVARIANCE FOR THE COMPLETELY
RANDOMIZED DESIGN

Source	SS_x	SP	SS_y	SS_y'	$d.f.$	MS_y'	F
Treatments	SS_{xTr}	SP_{Tr}	SS_{yTr}	SS_{yTr}'	$r-1$	MS_{yTr}'	$\dfrac{MS_{yTr}'}{MS_{yE}'}$
Error	SS_{xE}	SP_E	SS_{yE}	SS_{yE}'	$N-r-1$	MS_{yE}'	
TOTAL	SS_{xT}	SP_T	SS_{yT}	SS_{yT}'			

If H_0 is true so that all the β_j's are zero, then $\mu_{ij}=\mu+\gamma\,(x_{ij}-\bar{x}_{..})$. This means that the r lines mentioned in the assumptions are all identical.

To test H_0^*: $\gamma=0$ we may use

$$F_{1,\;N-r-1}=\frac{\dfrac{(SP_E)^2}{SS_{xE}}}{MS_{yE}'}\,. \tag{6.24}$$

Usually we would not do this, however. If testing of H_0 depends upon the outcome of the test of H_0^*, then a troublesome problem concerning the significance level arises once more.

If H_0 is rejected, we can use the S-method (the T-method is not applicable) to obtain confidence intervals for contrasts or to determine which contrasts are significantly different from zero. A contrast may be written as

$$L=c_1(\mu_{.1}-\gamma\bar{x}_{.1})+c_2(\mu_{.2}-\gamma\bar{x}_{.2})+\cdots+c_r(\mu_{.r}-\gamma\bar{x}_{.r})$$
$$=\sum_{j=1}^{r}c_j\mu_{.j}-\gamma\sum_{j=1}^{r}c_j\bar{x}_{.j} \tag{6.25}$$

or

$$L=c_1\beta_1+c_2\beta_2+\cdots+c_r\beta_r \tag{6.26}$$

and is estimated by

$$\hat{L}=\sum_{j=1}^{r}c_j\bar{y}_{.j}-\frac{SP_E}{SS_{xE}}\sum_{j=1}^{r}c_j\bar{x}_{.j}\,. \tag{6.27}$$

Recall that the set of intervals given by the S-method is

$$\hat{L}-S\hat{\sigma}_{\hat{L}}\leq L\leq\hat{L}+S\hat{\sigma}_{\hat{L}}\,. \tag{6.28}$$

Here

$$\hat{\sigma}_{\hat{L}}^2=MS_{yE}'\left[\sum_{j=1}^{r}\frac{c_j^2}{n_j}+\frac{\left(\sum\limits_{j=1}^{r}c_j\bar{x}_{.j}\right)^2}{SS_{xE}}\right] \tag{6.29}$$

and

$$S^2 = (r-1)\ F_{1-\alpha;\ r-1,\ N-r-1}.\tag{6.30}$$

For the special case for which we usually use the T-method, we have

$$L = \beta_j - \beta_{j'} = (\mu_{.j} - \gamma\bar{x}_{.j}) - (\mu_{.j'} - \gamma\bar{x}_{.j'})$$
$$= \mu_{.j} - \mu_{.j'} - \gamma\,(\bar{x}_{.j} - \bar{x}_{.j'}),\tag{6.31}$$

$$\hat{L} = \bar{y}_{.j} - \bar{y}_{.j'} - \frac{SP_E}{SS_{xE}}\,(\bar{x}_{.j} - \bar{x}_{.j'}),\tag{6.32}$$

and

$$\hat{\sigma}_{\hat{L}}^2 = MS'_{yE}\left[\frac{1}{n_j} + \frac{1}{n_{j'}} + \frac{(\bar{x}_{.j} - \bar{x}_{.j'})^2}{SS_{xE}}\right].\tag{6.33}$$

In other words, to investigate which corrected treatment effects are better than which others we use (6.30), (6.32), and (6.33). If we are not particularly interested in the interval (6.28) but wish to know if the contrast is significantly different from zero, then the calculations are shortened by comparing $\hat{L}^2/\hat{\sigma}_{\hat{L}}^2$ to S^2. This follows since (6.28) will not include zero if $|\hat{L}| > S\hat{\sigma}_{\hat{L}}$ or

$$\frac{\hat{L}^2}{\hat{\sigma}_{\hat{L}}^2} > S^2.\tag{6.34}$$

Consequently, for contrasts of the type (6.31) involving only two corrected treatment effects, the conclusion is that treatment j is better than treatment j' if (6.34) is satisfied and $\hat{L}$ is positive. (If $\hat{L}$ is negative, then treatment j' is significantly better than treatment j).

If a contrast is selected before the experiment is conducted, then we may use the counterpart of (2.22) based upon the ordinary t-distribution. This is

$$\hat{L} - t_{1-\alpha/2;\ N-r-1}\ \hat{\sigma}_{\hat{L}} < L < \hat{L} + t_{1-\alpha/2;\ N-r-1}\ \hat{\sigma}_{\hat{L}}.\tag{6.35}$$

As before the probability is $1-\alpha$ that L is covered by this interval.

As an alternate to covariance analysis, we may use the x variable to form blocks and then proceed as in Chapter 3. With the covariance assumptions the cost is 1 degree of freedom from error while $n-1$ degrees of freedom are lost in the blocks analysis. This comparison puts the analysis of covariance in a favorable light, but we should remember that the assumptions are somewhat more demanding, requiring that means lie on a straight line. If the regression assumption is unrealistic, then blocks should be used.

EXERCISES

6.2 A teacher wishes to compare four different teaching methods. He divides 40 students into four classes of 10, making the selection with a table of random numbers. Before he starts the experiment, each student is given an IQ test. At the end of the course everyone takes the same final examination. The results are tabulated below.

METHODS

1		2		3		4	
IQ	Final	IQ	Final	IQ	Final	IQ	Final
94	14	80	38	92	55	94	37
96	19	84	34	96	53	94	24
98	17	90	43	99	55	98	22
100	38	97	43	101	52	100	43
102	40	97	61	102	35	103	49
105	26	112	63	104	46	104	41
109	41	115	93	107	57	108	26
110	28	118	74	110	55	113	70
111	36	120	76	111	42	115	63
130	66	120	79	118	81	104	24

Test the hypothesis that there is no differences in methods by using the analysis of covariance.

6.3 For the data of Exercise 6.2

(a) Test H_0^*: $\gamma = 0$.

(b) Use the S-method to determine which corrected treatment effects are significantly better than which others.

(c) Use (6.35) to obtain an interval for

$$L = 3\beta_1 - \beta_2 - \beta_3 - \beta_4$$
$$= 3\mu_{.1} - \mu_{.2} - \mu_{.3} - \mu_{.4} - \gamma(3\bar{x}_{.1} - \bar{x}_{.2} - \bar{x}_{.3} - \bar{x}_{.4}).$$

Let $\alpha = .05$. How does this compare with the interval given by (6.28)?

6-6 COVARIANCE WITH RANDOMIZED BLOCKS

In Section 6-5 we mentioned the possibility of using blocks as an alternative to the analysis of covariance. Sometimes we may want to combine the two procedures. Suppose that the x variable is IQ, which first is used to form the blocks. If within each block there is still variation in the x variable, then covariance can be used to adjust for this state of affairs.

The data may be arranged as in Table 6.3. This is the same as Table 3.1 with the exception that a column has been added for the concomitant variable under each treatment. Definitions of means and totals follow the usual pattern. Column totals and means are the same as for the completely randomized design with all n_j being equal to n. For blocks we have

$$\text{Total of } x\text{'s in the } i^{th} \text{ block} = T_{xi.} ,$$

$$\text{Mean of } x\text{'s in the } i^{th} \text{ block} = \bar{x}_{i.} = \frac{T_{xi.}}{r} ,$$

$$\text{Total of } y\text{'s in the } i^{th} \text{ block} = T_{yi.} ,$$

$$\text{Mean of } y\text{'s in the } i^{th} \text{ block} = \bar{y}_{i.} = \frac{T_{yi.}}{r} .$$

Table 6.3 SUMMARY OF RESULTS FOR THE ANALYSIS OF COVARIANCE IN A RANDOMIZED BLOCKS DESIGN

		Treatments						TOTALS	Means
		1		2		$\cdots$	r		
		x	y	x	y		x	y		
Blocks	1	x_{11}	y_{11}	x_{12}	y_{12}		x_{1r}	y_{1r}	$T_{x1.}, T_{y1.}$	$\bar{x}_{1.}, \bar{y}_{1.}$
	2	x_{21}	y_{21}	x_{22}	y_{22}		x_{2r}	y_{2r}	$T_{x2.}, T_{y2.}$	$\bar{x}_{2.}, \bar{y}_{2.}$
	$\vdots$									
	n	x_{n1}	y_{n1}	x_{n2}	y_{n2}		x_{nr}	y_{nr}	$T_{xn.}, T_{yn.}$	$\bar{x}_{n.}, \bar{y}_{n.}$
TOTALS		$T_{x.1}$	$T_{y.1}$	$T_{x.2}$	$T_{y.2}$		$T_{x.r}$	$T_{y.r}$	$T_{x..}, T_{y..}$	
Means		$\bar{x}_{.1}$	$\bar{y}_{.1}$	$\bar{x}_{.2}$	$\bar{y}_{.1}$		$\bar{x}_{.r}$	$\bar{y}_{.r}$		$\bar{x}_{..}, \bar{y}_{..}$

The assumptions are

$$y_{ij} = \mu + \alpha_i + \beta_j + \gamma (x_{ij} - \bar{x}_{..}) + e_{ij} \qquad \begin{array}{l} i = 1, 2, \cdots, n \\ j = 1, 2, \cdots, r \end{array} \qquad (6.36)$$

e_{ij} are independently $N(0, \sigma^2)$

$$\sum_{i=1}^{n} \alpha_i = \sum_{j=1}^{r} \beta_j = 0.$$

An equivalent formulation is

$$y_{ij} \text{ are independently } N(\mu_{ij}, \sigma^2), \qquad \begin{array}{l} i = 1, 2, \cdots, n \\ j = 1, 2, \cdots, r \end{array} \qquad (6.37)$$

$$\mu_{ij} = \mu + \alpha_i + \beta_j + \gamma (x_{ij} - \bar{x}_{..})$$

$$\sum_{i=1}^{n} \alpha_i = \sum_{j=1}^{r} \beta_j = 0.$$

These imply (a) a random sample of size 1 is drawn from each of rn populations, (b) each of the rn populations is normal, (c) each of the rn populations has the same variance, (d) block and treatment effects do not interact, (e) the population means within each of the rn cells lie upon a straight line, and (f) the slopes of all rn lines is the same. Thus we have all the assumptions required for the randomized block design plus the assumptions stating that the means lie on straight lines with different x's giving different means.

The main hypothesis of interest states that the " corrected " treatment effects are all zero. In other words we wish to choose between

$$H_0: \quad \beta_j = 0 \tag{6.38}$$
$$H_1: \quad \text{Not all } \beta_j \text{ are zero.}$$

In terms of the $\mu_{.j}$'s, (6.38) is

$$H_0: \quad \mu_{.1} - \gamma \bar{x}_{.1} = \mu_{.2} - \gamma \bar{x}_{.2} = \cdots = \mu_{.r} - \gamma \bar{x}_{.r}$$
$$H_1: \quad \text{not all } \mu_{.j} - \gamma \bar{x}_{.j} \text{ are equal.} \tag{6.39}$$

The total sum of squares for x and y partitioned as in a randomized block analysis of variance. We have

$$SS_{xT} = SS_{xB} + SS_{xTr} + SS_{xE} \tag{6.40}$$

and

$$SS_{yT} = SS_{yB} + SS_{yTr} + SS_{yE}. \tag{6.41}$$

Except for the x and y subscripts, (6.40) and (6.41) are reproductions of (3.11). Consequently, computing Formulas (3.12), (3.13), (3.14) and (3.15) can be used to evaluate the sums of squares that appear in (6.40) and (6.41). The total sum of products is partitioned into corresponding components. We may write

$$SP_T = \sum_{j=1}^{r} \sum_{i=1}^{n} (x_{ij} - \bar{x}_{..})(y_{ij} - \bar{y}_{..})$$
$$= \sum_{j=1}^{r} \sum_{i=1}^{n} X_{ij} Y_{ij}$$

where

$$X_{ij} = (\bar{x}_{i.} - \bar{x}_{..}) + (\bar{x}_{.j} - \bar{x}_{..}) + (x_{ij} - \bar{x}_{i.} - \bar{x}_{.j} + \bar{x}_{..}),$$
$$Y_{ij} = (\bar{y}_{i.} - \bar{y}_{..}) + (\bar{y}_{.j} - \bar{y}_{..}) + (y_{ij} - \bar{y}_{i.} - \bar{y}_{.j} + \bar{y}_{..}).$$

The product $X_{ij} Y_{ij}$ yields 9 terms. Hence

$$SP_T = \sum_{j=1}^{r} \sum_{i=1}^{n} (\bar{x}_{i.} - \bar{x}_{..})(\bar{y}_{i.} - \bar{y}_{..}) + \sum_{j=1}^{r} \sum_{i=1}^{n} (\bar{x}_{.j} - \bar{x}_{..})(\bar{y}_{.j} - \bar{y}_{..})$$

$$+ \sum_{j=1}^{r} \sum_{i=1}^{n} (x_{ij} - \bar{x}_{i.} - \bar{x}_{.j} + \bar{x}_{..})(y_{ij} - \bar{y}_{i.} - \bar{y}_{.j} + \bar{y}_{..}) + 6 \text{ zero terms.} \quad (6.42)$$

In shorthand notation (6.42) can be written

$$SP_T = SP_B + SP_{Tr} + SP_E$$

where SP_B is the sum of products for blocks. Formulas (6.17) and (6.18) with $n_j = n$ and $N = nr$ are used to compute SP_T and SP_{Tr}. It is easy to show that

$$SP_B = \frac{\sum_{i=1}^{n} T_{xi.}\, T_{yi.}}{r} - \frac{T_{x..}\, T_{y..}}{rn} \quad (6.43)$$

is the computing formula for sum of products for blocks. Finally,

$$SP_E = SP_T - SP_B - SP_{Tr}. \quad (6.44)$$

Now let

$$SS'_{yE} = SS_{yE} - \frac{(SP_E)^2}{SS_{xE}}, \quad (6.45)$$

$$SS'_{y(Tr+E)} = SS_{yTr} + SS_{yE} - \frac{(SP_{Tr} + SP_E)^2}{SS_{xTr} + SS_{xE}}, \quad (6.46)$$

and

$$SS'_{yTr} = SS'_{y(Tr+E)} - SS'_{yE}. \quad (6.47)$$

With the assumptions (6.36) it may be shown that

$$F_{r-1,\,(n-1)(r-1)-1} = \frac{\dfrac{SS'_{yTr}}{r-1}}{\dfrac{SS'_{yE}}{(n-1)(r-1)-1}} \quad (6.48)$$

is the proper F ratio to use for (6.38). The results are summarized in Table 6.4.

The proper F ratio to use to test $H_0^*: \gamma = 0$ is

$$F_{1,\,(n-1)(r-1)-1} = \frac{\dfrac{(SP_E)^2}{SS_{xE}}}{MS'_{yE}} \quad (6.49)$$

The S-method is used in the same way as in Section 6-5. Of course, now all $n_j = n$, and $N - r - 1$ is replaced by $(n-1)(r-1) - 1$. These are the only changes necessary for the use of Formulas (6.25) through (6.35).

Table 6.4 ANALYSIS OF COVARIANCE FOR THE RANDOMIZED BLOCKS DESIGN

Source	SS_x	SP	SS_y	SS'_y	d.f.	MS'_y	F
Blocks	SS_{xB}	SP_B	SS_{yB}				
Treatments	SS_{xTr}	SP_{Tr}	SS_{yTr}	SS'_{yTr}	$r-1$	MS'_{yTr}	$\dfrac{MS'_{yTr}}{MS'_{yE}}$
Error	SS_{xE}	SP_E	SS_{yE}	SS'_{yE}	$(n-1)(r-1)-1$	MS'_{yE}	
TOTAL	SS_{xT}	SP_T	SS_{yT}	$SS'_{y(Tr+E)}$			

In the literature there are a number of examples illustrating the use of covariance in randomized blocks, particularly in agricultural applications (for example, see Snedecor [2]). A few typical examples are:

(1) The treatments are different kinds of fertilizer and the blocks are plots of land with differences in soil fertility, climatic conditions, or both. The study is conducted on the basis of crop (y) yields, which are dependent upon the number of plants (x) in the block.

(2) The treatments are different varieties of some crop (say wheat or corn). The blocks, the y variable, and the x variable are the same as in (1).

(3) The treatments are different varieties of some crop with blocks being formed as in (1). The x variable represents yields when the same crop is grown upon all blocks during the year preceding the experiment. The y variable is the yields from the different varieties on the same plots during the second year when the experiment is conducted. Perhaps it is felt that the use of blocks alone does not eliminate enough of the variation contributed by soil and climatic conditions.

(4) The treatments are different feeds or diets being investigated for their ability to put weight on animals. The blocks are litters from animals of the same type. The final weight is the y variable and the initial weight is the x variable.

(5) The treatments are different environmental conditions being investigated by a psychologist. The x variable represents an examination score achieved by the subject before the experiment is conducted. The corresponding y variable represents another examination score after the experiment is over. Blocks are formed on the basis of a background variable such as the type of community from which the subject comes.

EXERCISES

6.4 Write out the analysis of covariance for Exercise 6.2 regarding this as a randomized block experiment.

6.5 A university is experimenting with 3 methods of teaching grammar to incoming freshmen who are deficient in the subject. Blocks are formed using the percentile rating based upon entrance examinations in all fields. After the course is concluded, the final examination scores are used as a basis for evaluating the experiment. However, it is decided to "correct" these by using the scores from the entrance examination in grammar. Thirty students are used in each class. The following results are obtained:

$$T_{x.1} = 900, \quad T_{x.2} = 1,500, \quad T_{x.3} = 900, \quad SS_{xB} = 18,000,$$
$$SS_{xT} = 30,000; \quad T_{y.1} = 2,100, \quad T_{y.2} = 2,700, \quad T_{y.3} = 1,800,$$
$$SS_{yB} = 23,000, \quad SS_{yT} = 90,000, \quad SP_B = 8,000, \quad SP_T = 20,000.$$

Analyze the results using analysis of covariance. Would the conclusions be different if the information provided by the concomitant variable is not used?

6-7 COVARIANCE WITH A TWO-FACTOR COMPLETELY RANDOMIZED DESIGN

The arrangement of the data will be the same as Table 5.1 except that each observation x_{ijk} is replaced by a pair (x_{ijk}, y_{ijk}). Totals and sums of squares for the y variable are defined in exactly the same way as for the x variable. We will use the x and y subscripts in the same way as in the previous sections of this chapter. Thus $T_{y...}$ is the total of all the y's, $T_{yij.}$ is the total of the y's in cell ij, etc.

The assumptions are

$$y_{ijk} = \mu + \alpha_i + \beta_j + (\alpha\beta)_{ij} + \gamma(x_{ijk} - \bar{x}_{...}) + e_{ij} \quad \begin{array}{l} i = 1, 2, \cdots, a \\ j = 1, 2, \cdots, b \\ k = 1, 2, \cdots, n \end{array}$$

e_{ijk} are independently $N(0, \sigma^2)$ \hfill (6.50)

$$\sum_{i=1}^{a} \alpha_i = \sum_{j=1}^{b} \beta_j = \sum_{i=1}^{a} (\alpha\beta)_{ij} = \sum_{j=1}^{b} (\alpha\beta)_{ij} = 0.$$

These imply (a) a random sample of size 1 is drawn from each of $N = abn$ populations, (b) each of N populations is normal, (c) each of the N populations has the same variance, (d) the population means within each cell lie on a straight line, and (e) the slope of each of the $r = ab$ lines is the same. Another way to write (6.50) is

$$i=1, 2, \cdots, a$$

y_{ijk} are independently $N(\mu_{ijk}, \sigma^2)$, $j=1, 2, \cdots, b$

$$k=1, 2, \cdots, n$$

$$\mu_{ijk} = \mu + \alpha_i + \beta_j + (\alpha\beta)_{ij} + \gamma (x_{ijk} - \bar{x}_{...}) \tag{6.51}$$

$$\sum_{i=1}^{a} \alpha_i = \sum_{j=1}^{b} \beta_j = \sum_{i=1}^{a} (\alpha\beta)_{ij} = \sum_{j=1}^{b} (\alpha\beta)_{ij} = 0.$$

The three main hypotheses of interest together with their alternate are

$$H_0': \quad \alpha_i = 0, \quad i=1, 2, \cdots, a \tag{6.52}$$
$$H_1': \quad \text{not all } \alpha_i \text{ are zero,}$$

$$H_0'': \quad \beta_j = 0, \quad j=1, 2, \cdots, b \tag{6.53}$$
$$H_1'': \quad \text{not all } \beta_j \text{ are zero,}$$

and

$$H_0''': \quad (\alpha\beta)_{ij} = 0, \quad i=1, 2, \cdots, a, \quad j=1, 2, \cdots, b \tag{6.54}$$
$$H_1''': \quad \text{not all } (\alpha\beta)_{ij} \text{ are zero.}$$

Here

$$\alpha_i = (\mu_{i..} - \mu) - \gamma (\bar{x}_{i..} - \bar{x}_{...}),$$
$$\beta_j = (\mu_{.j.} - \mu) - \gamma (\bar{x}_{.j.} - \bar{x}_{...}),$$

and

$$(\alpha\beta)_{ij} = (\mu_{ij} - \mu_{i..} - \mu_{.j.} + \mu) - \gamma (\bar{x}_{ij.} - \bar{x}_{i..} - \bar{x}_{.j.} + \bar{x}_{...})$$

which are essentially the same values given in Section 5-3 with a correction factor involving the x's. Thus (6.52) and (6.53) could be replaced by

$$H_0': \quad \mu_{1..} - \gamma\bar{x}_{1..} = \mu_{2..} - \gamma\bar{x}_{2..} = \cdots = \mu_{a..} - \gamma\bar{x}_{a..} \tag{6.55}$$
$$H_1': \quad \text{not all } \mu_{i..} - \gamma\bar{x}_{i..} \text{ are equal}$$

$$H_0'': \quad \mu_{.1.} - \gamma\bar{x}_{.1.} = \mu_{.2.} - \gamma\bar{x}_{.2.} = \cdots = \mu_{.b.} - \gamma\bar{x}_{.b.} \tag{6.56}$$
$$H_1'': \quad \text{not all } \mu_{.j.} - \gamma\bar{x}_{.j.} \text{ are equal.}$$

The total sum of squares for both x and y are partitioned as in Section 5-4. That is

$$SS_{xT} = SS_{xA} + SS_{xB} + SS_{xAB} + SS_{xE} \tag{6.57}$$

and

$$SS_{yT} = SS_{yA} + SS_{yB} + SS_{yAB} + SS_{yE}. \tag{6.58}$$

Hence the computing Formulas (5.9) through (5.14) can be used to evaluate the sums of squares appearing in (6.57) and (6.58). The total sum of products is partitioned into corresponding components yielding

$$SP_T = SP_A + SP_B + SP_{AB} + SP_E \tag{6.59}$$

where

$$SP_T = \sum_{i=1}^{a} \sum_{j=1}^{b} \sum_{k=1}^{n} (x_{ijk} - \bar{x}_{...}) \, (y_{ijk} - \bar{y}_{...}), \tag{6.60}$$

$$SP_A = \sum_{i=1}^{a} \sum_{j=1}^{b} \sum_{k=1}^{n} (\bar{x}_{i..} - \bar{x}_{...}) \, (\bar{y}_{i..} - \bar{y}_{...}), \tag{6.61}$$

$$SP_B = \sum_{i=1}^{a} \sum_{j=1}^{b} \sum_{k=1}^{n} (\bar{x}_{.j.} - \bar{x}_{...}) \, (\bar{y}_{.j.} - \bar{y}_{...}), \tag{6.62}$$

$$SP_{AB} = \sum_{i=1}^{a} \sum_{j=1}^{b} \sum_{k=1}^{n} (\bar{x}_{ij.} - \bar{x}_{i..} - \bar{x}_{.j.} + \bar{x}_{...}) \, (\bar{y}_{ij.} - \bar{y}_{i..} - \bar{y}_{.j.} + \bar{y}_{...}). \tag{6.63}$$

To show that (6.59) is true we first use (6.16) which in the two-factor notation is

$$\sum_{i=1}^{a} \sum_{j=1}^{b} \sum_{k=1}^{n} (x_{ijk} - \bar{x}_{...}) \, (y_{ijk} - \bar{y}_{...}) = \sum_{i=1}^{a} \sum_{j=1}^{b} \sum_{k=1}^{n} (\bar{x}_{ij.} - \bar{x}_{...}) \, (\bar{y}_{ij.} - \bar{y}_{...})$$

$$+ \sum_{i=1}^{a} \sum_{j=1}^{b} \sum_{k=1}^{n} (x_{ijk} - \bar{x}_{ij.}) \, (y_{ijk} - \bar{y}_{ij.}). \tag{6.64}$$

Then

$$SP_{Tr} = \sum_{i=1}^{a} \sum_{j=1}^{b} \sum_{k=1}^{n} (\bar{x}_{ij.} - \bar{x}_{...}) \, (\bar{y}_{ij.} - \bar{y}_{...})$$

$$= \sum_{i=1}^{a} \sum_{j=1}^{b} \sum_{k=1}^{n} X_{ijk} \, Y_{ijk} \tag{6.65}$$

where

$$X_{ijk} = (\bar{x}_{i..} - \bar{x}_{...}) + (\bar{x}_{.j.} - \bar{x}_{...}) + (\bar{x}_{ij.} - \bar{x}_{i..} - \bar{x}_{.j.} + \bar{x}_{...})$$

and

$$Y_{ijk} = (\bar{y}_{i..} - \bar{y}_{...}) + (\bar{y}_{.j.} - \bar{y}_{...}) + (\bar{y}_{ij.} - \bar{y}_{i..} - \bar{y}_{.j.} + \bar{y}_{...}).$$

Expanding (6.65) yields (6.59) as 6 of the terms have the value zero.

In the usual way it may be shown that the computing formulas are

$$SP_T = \sum_{i=1}^{a} \sum_{j=1}^{b} \sum_{k=1}^{n} x_{ijk} \, y_{ijk} - \frac{T_{x...} \, T_{y...}}{abn}, \tag{6.66}$$

$$SP_A = \frac{\sum\limits_{i=1}^{a} T_{xi..} \, T_{yi..}}{bn} - \frac{T_{x...} \, T_{y...}}{abn}, \tag{6.67}$$

$$SP_B = \frac{\sum\limits_{j=1}^{b} T_{x.j.} \, T_{y.j.}}{an} - \frac{T_{x...} \, T_{y...}}{abn}, \tag{6.68}$$

$$SP_{Tr} = \frac{\sum\limits_{i=1}^{a} \sum\limits_{j=1}^{b} T_{xij.} \, T_{yij.}}{n} - \frac{T_{x...} \, T_{y...}}{abn}, \tag{6.69}$$

$$SP_E = SP_T - SP_{Tr}, \tag{6.70}$$

$$SP_{AB} = SP_{Tr} - SP_A - SP_B. \tag{6.71}$$

Next let

$$SS'_{yE} = SS_{yE} - \frac{(SP_E)^2}{SS_{xE}}, \tag{6.72}$$

$$SS'_{y(A+E)} = SS_{yA} + SS_{yE} - \frac{(SP_A + SP_E)^2}{SS_{xA} + SS_{xE}}, \tag{6.73}$$

$$SS'_{yA} = SS'_{y(A+E)} - SS'_{yE}. \tag{6.74}$$

Similarly

$$SS'_{yB} = SS'_{y(B+E)} - SS'_{yE} \tag{6.75}$$

$$SS'_{yAB} = SS'_{y(AB+E)} - SS'_{yE}, \tag{6.76}$$

where $SS'_{y(B+E)}$ and $SS'_{y(AB+E)}$ are obtained from (6.73) by replacing A by B and AB respectively. With the assumptions (6.50), it may be shown that the proper F ratios to use for (6.52), (6.53) and (6.54) are

$$F_{a-1,\ ab(n-1)-1} = \frac{\dfrac{SS'_{yA}}{a-1}}{\dfrac{SS'_{yE}}{ab(n-1)-1}} = \frac{MS'_{yA}}{MS'_{yE}}, \tag{6.77}$$

$$F_{b-1,\ ab(n-1)-1} = \frac{\dfrac{SS'_{yB}}{b-1}}{MS'_{yE}} = \frac{MS'_{yB}}{MS'_{yE}}, \tag{6.78}$$

and

$$F_{(a-1)(b-1),\ ab(n-1)-1} = \frac{\dfrac{SS'_{yAB}}{(a-1)(b-1)}}{MS'_{yE}} = \frac{MS'_{yAB}}{MS'_{yE}} \tag{6.79}$$

The results are summarized in Table 6.5.

Table 6.5 ANALYSIS OF COVARIANCE FOR A TWO-FACTOR COMPLETELY RANDOMIZED DESIGN

Source	SS_x	SP	SS_y	SS'_y	d.f.	MS'_y	F
Treatments A	SS_{xA}	SP_A	SS_{yA}	SS'_{yA}	$a-1$	MS'_{yA}	$\dfrac{MS'_{yA}}{MS'_{yE}}$
B	SS_{xB}	SP_B	SS_{yB}	SS'_{yB}	$b-1$	MS'_{yB}	$\dfrac{MS'_{yB}}{MS'_{yE}}$
AB	SS_{xAB}	SP_{AB}	SS_{yAB}	SS'_{yAB}	$(a-1)(b-1)$	MS'_{yAB}	$\dfrac{MS'_{yAB}}{MS'_{yE}}$
Error	SS_{xE}	SP_E	SS_{yE}	SS'_{yE}	$ab(n-1)-1$	MS'_{yE}	
TOTAL	SS_{xT}	SP_T	SS_{yT}		$abn-2$		

The proper F ratio to use to test $H_0^*: \gamma = 0$ is

$$F_{1,\ ab(n-1)-1} = \frac{\dfrac{(SP_E)^2}{SS_{xE}}}{MS'_{yE}}. \tag{6.80}$$

The modifications needed to adapt formulas (6.25) through (6.35) to this notation are easily obtained. Contrasts among corrected A effects are of the form

$$L = \sum_{i=1}^{a} c_i \alpha_i = \sum_{i=1}^{a} c_i \mu_{i..} - \gamma \sum_{i=1}^{a} c_i \bar{x}_{i..} \tag{6.81}$$

estimated by

$$\hat{L} = \sum_{i=1}^{a} c_i \bar{y}_{i..} - \frac{SP_E}{SS_{xE}} \sum_{i=1}^{a} c_i \bar{x}_{i..}\ . \tag{6.82}$$

For the S-method we have

$$S^2 = (a-1)\ F_{1-\alpha;\ a-1,\ ab(n-1)-1} \tag{6.83}$$

and

$$\hat{\sigma}_{\hat{L}}^2 = MS'_{yE} \left[\frac{\displaystyle\sum_{i=1}^{a} c_i^2}{bn} + \frac{\left(\displaystyle\sum_{i=1}^{a} c_i \bar{x}_{i..}\right)^2}{SS_{xE}} \right]. \tag{6.84}$$

When contrasts are of the type

$$L = \alpha_i - \alpha_{i'} = \mu_{i..} - \mu_{i'..} - \gamma\ (\bar{x}_{i..} - \bar{x}_{i'..}), \tag{6.85}$$

then

$$\hat{\sigma}_{\hat{L}}^2 = MS'_{yE} \left[\frac{2}{bn} + \frac{(\bar{x}_{i..} - \bar{x}_{i'..})^2}{SS_{xE}} \right]. \tag{6.86}$$

Similarly when investigating corrected B effects

$$L = \sum_{j=1}^{b} c_j \beta_j = \sum_{j=1}^{b} c_j \mu_{.j.} - \gamma \sum_{j=1}^{b} c_j \bar{x}_{.j.}\ , \tag{6.87}$$

$$\hat{L} = \sum_{j=1}^{b} c_j \bar{y}_{.j.} - \frac{SP_E}{SS_{xE}} \sum_{j=1}^{b} c_j \bar{x}_{.j.}\ , \tag{6.88}$$

$$S^2 = (b-1)\ F_{1-\alpha;\ b-1,\ ab(n-1)-1}\ , \tag{6.89}$$

$$\hat{\sigma}_{\hat{L}}^2 = MS'_{yE} \left[\frac{\displaystyle\sum_{j=1}^{b} c_j^2}{an} + \frac{\left(\displaystyle\sum_{j=1}^{b} c_j \bar{x}_{.j.}\right)^2}{SS_{xE}} \right]. \tag{6.90}$$

If we conclude that these are interactions, then we may want to investigate contrasts among corrected cell means. In particular we may want to know which corrected cell means are significantly better than which others. Then contrasts would be of the type

$$L = \mu_{ij.} - \mu_{i'j'.} - \gamma (\bar{x}_{ij.} - \bar{x}_{i'j'.}). \tag{6.91}$$

Now

$$\hat{L} = \bar{y}_{ij.} - \bar{y}_{i'j'.} - \gamma (\bar{x}_{ij.} - \bar{x}_{i'j'.}), \tag{6.92}$$

$$S^2 = (ab-1) \ F_{1-\alpha; \ ab-1, \ ab(n-1)-1}, \tag{6.93}$$

and

$$\hat{\sigma}_{\hat{L}}^2 = MS'_{yE} \left[\frac{2}{n} + \frac{(\bar{x}_{ij.} - \bar{x}_{i'j'.})^2}{SS_{xE}} \right] \tag{6.94}$$

To use (6.35) in all three situations, replace $N-r-1$ by $ab(n-1)-1$.

EXERCISES

6.6 Regard the data of Exercise 6.2 as the results of a two-factor completely randomized experiment. Methods will be factor B which occurs at 4 levels. Let factor A be textbooks. The first 5 measurements in each column are to be considered as belonging to level 1 of factor A while the second 5 belong to level 2. Test the three main hypotheses.

6.7 Use the S-method on 6.6 in the appropriate way so that statements can be made about which corrected treatments are better than which others.

6.8 Find an interval which contains $L = 3\beta_1 - \beta_2 - \beta_3 - \beta_4$ if, after looking at the results of 6.6, it is decided this contrast is of interest. Suppose it had been decided in advance that the main purpose of conducting the experiment was to investigate L. What interval could now be given? Use $\alpha = .05$ in each case.

6-8 COVARIANCE WITH THE HIERARCHICAL CLASSIFICATION

In Section 5-14 we regarded the data of Table 5.1 as the results of a nested type of experiment. Suppose now that each observation, x_{ij}, in that table is replaced by a pair of measurements, say (x_{ij}, y_{ij}). Assuming that the hierarchical classification is appropriate, we seek the analysis of covariance.

The assumptions are

$$y_{ijk} = \mu + \alpha_. + B_{ij} + \gamma (x_{ijk} - \bar{x}_{...}) + e_{ijk}, \qquad \begin{aligned} i &= 1, 2, \cdots, a \\ j &= 1, 2, \cdots, b \\ k &= 1, 2, \cdots, n \end{aligned}$$

e_{ijk} are independently $N (0, \sigma^2)$ $\qquad\qquad (6.95)$

$$\sum_{i=1}^{a} a_i = \sum_{j=1}^{b} B_{ij} = 0.$$

As in the previous situations, we have an equivalent formulation. This is

$$y_{ijk} \text{ are independently } N(\mu_{ijk}, \sigma^2) \qquad \begin{array}{l} i=1, 2, \cdots, a \\ j=1, 2, \cdots, b \\ k=1, 2, \cdots, n \end{array}$$

$$\mu_{ijk} = \mu + \alpha_i + B_{ij} + \gamma (x_{ijk} - \bar{x}_{...}) \qquad (6.96)$$

$$\sum_{i=1}^{a} \alpha_i = \sum_{j=1}^{b} B_{ij} = 0.$$

These imply (a) a random sample of size 1 is drawn from each of $N = abn$ populations, (b) each of the N populations is normal, (c) each of the N populations has the same variance, (d) the population means within each cell lie on a straight line, and (e) the slope of the $r = ab$ lines is the same.

The main hypotheses of interest together with the alternates are

$$H_0' : \quad \alpha_i = 0, \qquad i=1, 2, \cdots, a \qquad (6.97)$$
$$H_1' : \quad \text{not all } \alpha_i \text{ are zero}$$

and

$$H_0'' : \quad B_{ij} = 0, \qquad i=1, 2, \cdots, a, \qquad j=1, 2, \cdots, b \qquad (6.98)$$
$$H_1'' : \quad \text{not all } B_{ij} \text{ are zero.}$$

Here

$$\alpha_i = (\mu_{i..} - \mu) - \gamma (\bar{x}_{i..} - \bar{x}_{...})$$

and

$$B_{ij} = (\mu_{ij.} - \mu_{i..}) - \gamma (\bar{x}_{ij.} - \bar{x}_{i..}).$$

Except for the correction factor, these are essentially the same definitions given in Section 5-14. Hence (6.97) and (6.98) can be replaced by

$$H_0' : \quad \mu_{1..} - \gamma \bar{x}_{1..} = \mu_{2..} - \gamma \bar{x}_{2..} = \cdots = \mu_{a..} - \gamma \bar{x}_{a..} \qquad (6.99)$$
$$H_1' : \quad \text{not all } \mu_{i..} - \gamma \bar{x}_{i..} \text{ are equal}$$

and

$$H_0'' : \quad \mu_{i1.} - \gamma \bar{x}_{i1.} = \mu_{i2.} - \gamma \bar{x}_{i2.} = \cdots = \mu_{ib.} - \gamma \bar{x}_{ib.} , \quad i=1, 2, \cdots, a$$
$$H_1'' : \quad \text{not all } \mu_{ij.} - \gamma \bar{x}_{ij.} \text{ are equal for each } i. \qquad (6.100)$$

If H_0' is true, then the various levels of A all have the same average value when corrected for differences in the x's. If H_0'' is true, then there is no difference in the means of factor B within A (i. e., teachers within a university) when corrected.

The total sum of squares for both x and y are partitioned as in 5-14.

That is

$$SS_{xT} = SS_{xA} + SS_{xB(A)} + SS_{xE} \qquad (6.101)$$

and

$$SS_{yT} = SS_{yA} + SS_{yB(A)} + SS_{yE} \qquad (6.102)$$

Hence the computing formulas (5.111) through (5.114) can be used to evaluate the sum of squares appearing in (6.101) and (6.102). The total sum of products is partitioned into corresponding components yielding

$$SP_T = SP_A + SP_{B(A)} + SP_E \qquad (6.103)$$

where SP_T and SP_A are given by (6.60) and (6.61),

$$SP_{B(A)} = \sum_{i=1}^{a} \sum_{j=1}^{b} \sum_{k=1}^{n} (\bar{x}_{ij.} - \bar{x}_{i...})\,(\bar{y}_{ij.} - \bar{y}_{i..}), \qquad (6.104)$$

and

$$SP_E = \sum_{i=1}^{a} \sum_{j=1}^{b} \sum_{k=1}^{n} (x_{ijk} - \bar{x}_{ij.})\,(y_{ijk} - \bar{y}_{ij.}). \qquad (6.105)$$

The Identity (6.103) is easily proved in the usual manner.

To compute SP_T and SP_A we can use (6.66) and (6.67). Also (6.104) can be reduced to

$$SP_{B(A)} = \frac{\displaystyle\sum_{i=1}^{a} \sum_{j=1}^{b} T_{xij.}\,T_{yij.}}{n} - \frac{\displaystyle\sum_{i=1}^{a} T_{xi..}\,T_{yi..}}{bn}. \qquad (6.106)$$

Finally,

$$SP_E = SP_T - SP_A - SP_{B(A)}. \qquad (6.107)$$

Next let SS'_{yE}, $SS'_{y(A+E)}$, and SS'_{yA} be given by Formulas (6.72), (6.73) and (6.74). Define

$$SS'_{y[B(A)+E]} = SS_{yB(A)} + SS_{yE} - \frac{(SP_{B(A)} + SP_E)^2}{SS_{xB(A)} + SS_{xE}} \qquad (6.108)$$

and

$$SS'_{yB(A)} = SS'_{y[B(A)+E]} - SS'_{yE}. \qquad (6.109)$$

If the assumptions (6.95) are true, then it may be shown that the proper F ratios to use for (6.97) and (6.98) are (6.77) and

$$F_{a(b-1),\,ab(n-1)-1} = \frac{\dfrac{SS'_{yB(A)}}{a(b-1)}}{\dfrac{SS'_{yE}}{ab(n-1)-1}} = \frac{MS'_{yB(A)}}{MS'_{yE}} \qquad (6.110)$$

respectively. The results are summarized in Table 6.6.

Table 6.6   ANALYSIS OF COVARIANCE FOR A TWO-FACTOR NESTED CLASSIFICATION

Source	SS_x	SP	SS_y	SS'_{yA}	d.f.	MS'_y	F
Levels of A	SS_{xA}	SP_A	SS_{yA}	SS'_{yA}	$a-1$	MS'_{yA}	$\dfrac{MS'_{yA}}{MS'_{yE}}$
Levels of B within A	$SS_{xB(A)}$	$SP_{B(A)}$	$SS_{yB(A)}$	$SS'_{yB(A)}$	$a(b-1)$	$MS'_{yB(A)}$	$\dfrac{MS'_{yB(A)}}{MS'_{yE}}$
Error	SS_{xE}	SP_E	SS_{yE}	SS'_{yE}	$ab(n-1)-1$	MS'_{yE}	
TOTAL	SS_{xT}	SP_T	SS_{yT}		$abn-2$		

To test H_0^*: $\gamma = 0$, use (6.80). Formulas (6.81) through (6.86) still apply to contrasts among A means. Also (6.35) may be used for a contrast of A means if $N-r-1$ is replaced by $ab(n-1)-1$.

EXERCISES

6.9 Regard the data of Excercise 6.2 as the results of a two-factor nested classification. Consider "methods" as factor A, and let factor B be "instructors." There are 8 instructors, two for each method, so that no instructor is used twice. The first 5 measurements in each column are associated with one instructor, the second 5 with another. Perform the analysis. Note that

$$SP_{B(A)} = SP_B + SP_{AB}.$$

If appropriate, use the S-method to determine which methods are significantly better than which others.

6.10 For the data of Exercise 6.9 use (6.35) to find an interval which attempts to capture $L = 3\alpha_1 - \alpha_2 - \alpha_3 - \alpha_4$. Find the corresponding interval based upon the S-method. Use $\alpha = .05$ in both cases. Comment upon the difference in results.

6-9 MISCELLANEOUS COMMENTS ABOUT THE ANALYSIS OF COVARIANCE

The covariance analysis is easily handled in both Latin squares and three-factor arrangement. Total sums of products are partitioned in the obvious way. The primed sum of squares are computed according to the established pattern. That is

$$SS'_{yE} = SS_{yE} - \frac{(SP_E)^2}{SS_{xE}}, \qquad (6.111)$$

$$SS'_{y(Tr+E)} = SS_{yTr} + SS_{yE} - \frac{(SP_{Tr} + SP_E)^2}{SS_{xTr} + SS_{xE}}, \qquad (6.112)$$

and

$$SS'_{yTr} = SS'_{y(Tr+E)} - SS'_{yE} \qquad (6.113)$$

still hold for the investigation of the null hypothesis concerning any treatment effects. The F ratio in each case is

$$F_{\nu_1, \nu_2} = \frac{\dfrac{SS'_{yTr}}{\nu_1}}{\dfrac{SS'_{yE}}{\nu_2}} = \frac{MS'_{yTr}}{MS'_{yE}} \qquad (6.114)$$

where ν_1 is 1 less than the number of treatments and ν_2 is 1 less than the degrees of freedom associated with error in the corresponding analysis of variance.

Occasionally, an ordinary analysis of variance is used on the variable $y - x$. Actually this amounts to assuming $\gamma = 1$, an assumption which could be regarded as a hypothesis and tested by

$$F_{1, \nu} = \frac{\dfrac{(SS_{xE} - SP_E)^2}{SS_{xE}}}{MS'_{yE}} \qquad (6.115)$$

where ν is the degrees of freedom associated with MS'_{yE}. The physical and geometrical interpretation of $\gamma = 1$ is that y and x increase at the same rate.

We have observed that analysis of variance and analysis of covariance are quite similar. When attempting to describe the difference to a layman, we might point out that covariance makes use of "corrected" observations while "uncorrected" observations are used in the analysis of variance. Although this does not tell the whole story, it does emphasize the most apparent dissimilarity. In the definition associated with (1.19), the w's were specified to be either 0 or 1 (being the coefficients of μ, α_i, β_j, $(\alpha\beta)_{ij}$, etc.). Throughout this chapter the models have included γ [another unknown quantity and an a in (1.19)] with a coefficient which is a function of the concomitant variable x and which generally is not 0 or 1. Hence according to (1.19) the covariance models do not qualify as a part of analysis of variance. We can adopt either of the following points of view:

(1) Define analysis of covariance using the model equation (1.19) but requiring that some w's be 1 and some be concomitant variables.

(2) Define analysis of variance using the model equation (1.19) and

allowing the w's to be 0's, 1's or concomitant variables. If both 1's and concomitant variables occur, this special case will be referred to as analysis of covariance (which is now regarded as a part of analysis of variance).

Perhaps (2) should be preferred to (1) since it is Scheffé's [1] approach, and some conformity in the literature is needed. In addition, (2) provides justification for including this chapter in the book.

By introducing the concomitant variable many difficulties arise over which we have passed lightly. Power calculations and EMS's now become quite complicated. Greater care must be exercised in interpreting the results. The x variable should have some sensible relationship with the y variable. If, in a wheat varieties experiment, we "correct" yields using for x the mileage to the nearest town, the results may be meaningless. The assumption of equal γ's in each subclass may not be realistic.

Possibilities for extending the procedures used in this chapter include (a) the use of more than one covariate, (b) the use of higher degree terms involving the one covariate x, and (c) a combination of both (a) and (b). We shall not discuss these situations here.

REFERENCES

[1] Scheffé, Henry, *The Analysis of Variance* (New York: John Wiley & Sons, Inc., 1959).

[2] Snedecor, George W., *Statistical Methods* (Ames, Iowa: Iowa State University Press, 1956).

Appendix Tables

APPENDIX TABLE 1 THE CUMULATIVE STANDARDIZED NORMAL DISTRIBUTION FUNCTION*

* Note: $.0^21350 = .001350$

$$\text{Entry} = \Pr[Z < Z_p] = p$$

Z_p	.00	.01	.02	.03	.04	.05	.06	.07	.08	.09
-.0	.5000	.4960	.4920	.4880	.4840	.4801	.4761	.4721	.4681	.4641
-.1	.4602	.4562	.4522	.4483	.4443	.4404	.4364	.4325	.4286	.4247
-.2	.4207	.4168	.4129	.4090	.4052	.4013	.3974	.3936	.3897	.3859
-.3	.3821	.3783	.3745	.3707	.3669	.3632	.3594	.3557	.3520	.3483
-.4	.3446	.3409	.3372	.3336	.3300	.3264	.3228	.3192	.3156	.3121
-.5	.3085	.3050	.3015	.2981	.2946	.2912	.2877	.2843	.2810	.2776
-.6	.2743	.2709	.2676	.2643	.2611	.2578	.2546	.2514	.2483	.2451
-.7	.2420	.2389	.2358	.2327	.2297	.2266	.2236	.2206	.2177	.2148
-.8	.2119	.2090	.2061	.2033	.2005	.1977	.1949	.1922	.1894	.1867
-.9	.1841	.1814	.1788	.1762	.1736	.1711	.1685	.1660	.1635	.1611
-1.0	.1587	.1562	.1539	.1515	.1492	.1469	.1446	.1423	.1401	.1379
-1.1	.1357	.1335	.1314	.1292	.1271	.1251	.1230	.1210	.1190	.1170
-1.2	.1151	.1131	.1112	.1093	.1075	.1056	.1038	.1020	.1003	.09853
-1.3	.09680	.09510	.09342	.09176	.09012	.08851	.08691	.08534	.08379	.08226
-1.4	.08076	.07927	.07780	.07636	.07493	.07353	.07215	.07078	.06944	.06811
-1.5	.06681	.06552	.06426	.06301	.06178	.06057	.05938	.05821	.05705	.05592
-1.6	.05480	.05370	.05262	.05155	.05050	.04947	.04846	.04746	.04648	.04551
-1.7	.04457	.04363	.04272	.04182	.04093	.04006	.03920	.03836	.03754	.03673
-1.8	.03593	.03515	.03438	.03362	.03288	.03216	.03144	.03074	.03005	.02938
-1.9	.02872	.02807	.02743	.02680	.02619	.02559	.02500	.02442	.02385	.02330
-2.0	.02275	.02222	.02169	.02118	.02068	.02018	.01970	.01923	.01876	.01831
-2.1	.01786	.01743	.01700	.01659	.01618	.01578	.01539	.01500	.01463	.01426
-2.2	.01390	.01355	.01321	.01287	.01255	.01222	.01191	.01160	.01130	.01101
-2.3	.01072	.01044	.01017	$.0^29903$	$.0^29642$	$.0^29387$	$.0^29137$	$.0^28894$	$.0^28656$	$.0^28424$
-2.4	$.0^28198$	$.0^27976$	$.0^27760$	$.0^27549$	$.0^27344$	$.0^27143$	$.0^26947$	$.0^26756$	$.0^26569$	$.0^26387$
-2.5	$.0^26210$	$.0^26037$	$.0^25868$	$.0^25703$	$.0^25543$	$.0^25386$	$.0^25234$	$.0^25085$	$.0^24940$	$.0^24799$
-2.6	$.0^24661$	$.0^24527$	$.0^24396$	$.0^24269$	$.0^24145$	$.0^24025$	$.0^23907$	$.0^23793$	$.0^23681$	$.0^23573$
-2.7	$.0^23467$	$.0^23364$	$.0^23264$	$.0^23167$	$.0^23072$	$.0^22980$	$.0^22890$	$.0^22803$	$.0^22718$	$.0^22635$
-2.8	$.0^22555$	$.0^22477$	$.0^22401$	$.0^22327$	$.0^22256$	$.0^22186$	$.0^22118$	$.0^22052$	$.0^21988$	$.0^21926$
-2.9	$.0^21866$	$.0^21807$	$.0^21750$	$.0^21695$	$.0^21641$	$.0^21589$	$.0^21538$	$.0^21489$	$.0^21441$	$.0^21395$
-3.0	$.0^21350$	$.0^21306$	$.0^21264$	$.0^21223$	$.0^21183$	$.0^21144$	$.0^21107$	$.0^21070$	$.0^21035$	$.0^21001$

Area p → Z_p

Appendix Table 1 reprinted with permission from A. Hald, Statistical Tables and Formulas (New York: John Wiley and Sons, Inc., 1952).

THE CUMULATIVE STANDARDIZED NORMAL DISTRIBUTION FUNCTION† (Cont.)

† Note: $.9^{2}8650 = .998650$

Area p Z_p

Z_p	.00	.01	.02	.03	.04	.05	.06	.07	.08	.09
.0	.5000	.5040	.5080	.5120	.5160	.5199	.5239	.5279	.5319	.5359
.1	.5398	.5438	.5478	.5517	.5557	.5596	.5636	.5675	.5714	.5753
.2	.5793	.5832	.5871	.5910	.5948	.5987	.6026	.6064	.6103	.6141
.3	.6179	.6217	.6255	.6293	.6331	.6368	.6406	.6443	.6480	.6517
.4	.6554	.6591	.6628	.6664	.6700	.6736	.6772	.6808	.6844	.6879
.5	.6915	.6950	.6985	.7019	.7054	.7088	.7123	.7157	.7190	.7224
.6	.7257	.7291	.7324	.7357	.7389	.7422	.7454	.7486	.7517	.7549
.7	.7580	.7611	.7642	.7673	.7703	.7734	.7764	.7794	.7823	.7852
.8	.7881	.7910	.7939	.7967	.7995	.8023	.8051	.8078	.8106	.8133
.9	.8159	.8186	.8212	.8238	.8264	.8289	.8315	.8340	.8365	.8389
1.0	.8413	.8438	.8461	.8485	.8508	.8531	.8554	.8577	.8599	.8621
1.1	.8643	.8665	.8686	.8708	.8729	.8749	.8770	.8790	.8810	.8830
1.2	.8849	.8869	.8888	.8907	.8925	.8944	.8962	.8980	.8997	.90147
1.3	.90320	.90490	.90658	.90824	.90988	.91149	.91309	.91466	.91621	.91774
1.4	.91924	.92073	.92220	.92364	.92507	.92647	.92785	.92922	.93056	.93189
1.5	.93319	.93448	.93574	.93699	.93822	.93943	.94062	.94179	.94295	.94408
1.6	.94520	.94630	.94738	.94845	.94950	.95053	.95154	.95254	.95352	.95449
1.7	.95543	.95637	.95728	.95818	.95907	.95994	.96080	.96164	.96246	.96327
1.8	.96407	.96485	.96562	.96638	.96712	.96784	.96856	.96926	.96995	.97062
1.9	.97128	.97193	.97257	.97320	.97381	.97441	.97500	.97558	.97615	.97670
2.0	.97725	.97778	.97831	.97882	.97932	.97982	.98030	.98077	.98124	.98169
2.1	.98214	.98257	.98300	.98341	.98382	.98422	.98461	.98500	.98537	.98574
2.2	.98610	.98645	.98679	.98713	.98745	.98778	.98809	.98840	.98870	.98899
2.3	.98928	.98956	.98983	$.9^{2}0097$	$.9^{2}0358$	$.9^{2}0613$	$.9^{2}0863$	$.9^{2}1106$	$.9^{2}1344$	$.9^{2}1576$
2.4	$.9^{2}1802$	$.9^{2}2024$	$.9^{2}2240$	$.9^{2}2451$	$.9^{2}2656$	$.9^{2}2857$	$.9^{2}3053$	$.9^{2}3244$	$.9^{2}3431$	$.9^{2}3613$
2.5	$.9^{2}3790$	$.9^{2}3963$	$.9^{2}4132$	$.9^{2}4297$	$.9^{2}4457$	$.9^{2}4614$	$.9^{2}4766$	$.9^{2}4915$	$.9^{2}5060$	$.9^{2}5201$
2.6	$.9^{2}5339$	$.9^{2}5473$	$.9^{2}5604$	$.9^{2}5731$	$.9^{2}5855$	$.9^{2}5975$	$.9^{2}6093$	$.9^{2}6207$	$.9^{2}6319$	$.9^{2}6427$
2.7	$.9^{2}6533$	$.9^{2}6636$	$.9^{2}6736$	$.9^{2}6833$	$.9^{2}6928$	$.9^{2}7020$	$.9^{2}7110$	$.9^{2}7197$	$.9^{2}7282$	$.9^{2}7365$
2.8	$.9^{2}7445$	$.9^{2}7523$	$.9^{2}7599$	$.9^{2}7673$	$.9^{2}7744$	$.9^{2}7814$	$.9^{2}7882$	$.9^{2}7948$	$.9^{2}8012$	$.9^{2}8074$
2.9	$.9^{2}8134$	$.9^{2}8193$	$.9^{2}8250$	$.9^{2}8305$	$.9^{2}8359$	$.9^{2}8411$	$.9^{2}8462$	$.9^{2}8511$	$.9^{2}8559$	$.9^{2}8605$
3.0	$.9^{2}8650$	$.9^{2}8694$	$.9^{2}8736$	$.9^{2}8777$	$.9^{2}8817$	$.9^{2}8856$	$.9^{2}8893$	$.9^{2}8930$	$.9^{2}8965$	$.9^{2}8999$

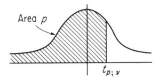

Entry $= t_{p;\,\nu}$ where $\Pr[t_\nu < t_{p;\,\nu}] = p$

$$t_{1-p;\,\nu} = -t_{p;\,\nu}$$

ν \ p	.60	.70	.80	.90	.95	.975	.990	.995	.999	.9995
1	.325	.727	1.376	3.078	6.314	12.71	31.82	63.66	318.3	636.6
2	.289	.617	1.061	1.886	2.920	4.303	6.965	9.925	22.33	31.60
3	.277	.584	.978	1.638	2.353	3.182	4.541	5.841	10.22	12.94
4	.271	.569	.941	1.533	2.132	2.776	3.747	4.604	7.173	8.610
5	.267	.559	.920	1.476	2.015	2.571	3.365	4.032	5.893	6.859
6	.265	.553	.906	1.440	1.943	2.447	3.143	3.707	5.208	5.959
7	.263	.549	.896	1.415	1.895	2.365	2.998	3.499	4.785	5.405
8	.262	.546	.889	1.397	1.860	2.306	2.896	3.355	4.501	5.041
9	.261	.543	.883	1.383	1.833	2.262	2.821	3.250	4.297	4.781
10	.260	.542	.879	1.372	1.812	2.228	2.764	3.169	4.144	4.587
11	.260	.540	.876	1.363	1.796	2.201	2.718	3.106	4.025	4.437
12	.259	.539	.873	1.356	1.782	2.179	2.681	3.055	3.930	4.318
13	.259	.538	.870	1.350	1.771	2.160	2.650	3.012	3.852	4.221
14	.258	.537	.868	1.345	1.761	2.145	2.624	2.977	3.787	4.140
15	.258	.536	.866	1.341	1.753	2.131	2.602	2.947	3.733	4.073
16	.258	.535	.865	1.337	1.746	2.120	2.583	2.921	3.686	4.015
17	.257	.534	.863	1.333	1.740	2.110	2.567	2.898	3.646	3.965
18	.257	.534	.862	1.330	1.734	2.101	2.552	2.878	3.611	3.922
19	.257	.533	.861	1.328	1.729	2.093	2.539	2.861	3.579	3.883
20	.257	.533	.860	1.325	1.725	2.086	2.528	2.845	3.552	3.850
21	.257	.532	.859	1.323	1.721	2.080	2.518	2.831	3.527	3.819
22	.256	.532	.858	1.321	1.717	2.074	2.508	2.819	3.505	3.792
23	.256	.532	.858	1.319	1.714	2.069	2.500	2.807	3.485	3.767
24	.256	.531	.857	1.318	1.711	2.064	2.492	2.797	3.467	3.745
25	.256	.531	.856	1.316	1.708	2.060	2.485	2.787	3.450	3.725
26	.256	.531	.856	1.315	1.706	2.056	2.479	2.779	3.435	3.707
27	.256	.531	.855	1.314	1.703	2.052	2.473	2.771	3.421	3.690
28	.256	.530	.855	1.313	1.701	2.048	2.467	2.763	3.408	3.674
29	.256	.530	.854	1.311	1.699	2.045	2.462	2.756	3.396	3.659
30	.256	.530	.854	1.310	1.697	2.042	2.457	2.750	3.385	3.646
40	.255	.529	.851	1.303	1.684	2.021	2.423	2.704	3.307	3.551
50	.255	.528	.849	1.298	1.676	2.009	2.403	2.678	3.262	3.495
60	.254	.527	.848	1.296	1.671	2.000	2.390	2.660	3.232	3.460
80	.254	.527	.846	1.292	1.664	1.990	2.374	2.639	3.195	3.415
100	.254	.526	.845	1.290	1.660	1.984	2.365	2.626	3.174	3.389
200	.254	.525	.843	1.286	1.653	1.972	2.345	2.601	3.131	3.339
500	.253	.525	.842	1.283	1.648	1.965	2.334	2.586	3.106	3.310
∞	.253	.524	.842	1.282	1.645	1.960	2.326	2.576	3.090	3.291

* Reprinted by permission from A. Hald, *Statistical Tables and Formulas* (New York: John Wiley and Sons, Inc., 1952). The majority of the entries are from Table III of R. A. Fisher and F. Yates, *Statistical Tables* (Edinburgh: Oliver and Boyd) and are reprinted by permission of the authors and publishers.

Entry $= \chi^2_{p;\,\nu}$ where $\Pr[\chi^2_\nu < \chi^2_{p;\,\nu}] = p$

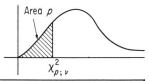

p / ν	.005	.010	.025	.050	.100	.900	.950	.975	.990	.995
1	0.0^4393	0.0^3157	0.0^3982	0.0^2393	0.0158	2.71	3.84	5.02	6.63	7.88
2	0.0100	0.0201	0.0506	0.103	0.211	4.61	5.99	7.38	9.21	10.60
3	0.072	0.115	0.216	0.352	0.584	6.25	7.81	9.35	11.34	12.84
4	0.207	0.297	0.484	0.711	1.064	7.78	9.49	11.14	13.28	14.86
5	0.412	0.554	0.831	1.145	1.61	9.24	11.07	12.83	15.09	16.75
6	0.676	0.872	1.24	1.64	2.20	10.64	12.59	14.45	16.81	18.55
7	0.989	1.24	1.69	2.17	2.83	12.02	14.07	16.01	18.48	20.28
8	1.34	1.65	2.18	2.73	3.49	13.36	15.51	17.53	20.09	21.96
9	1.73	2.09	2.70	3.33	4.17	14.68	16.92	19.02	21.67	23.59
10	2.16	2.56	3.25	3.94	4.87	15.99	18.31	20.48	23.21	25.19
11	2.60	3.05	3.82	4.57	5.58	17.28	19.68	21.92	24.72	26.76
12	3.07	3.57	4.40	5.23	6.30	18.55	21.03	23.34	26.22	28.30
13	3.57	4.11	5.01	5.89	7.04	19.81	22.36	24.74	27.69	29.82
14	4.07	4.66	5.63	6.57	7.79	21.06	23.68	26.12	29.14	31.32
15	4.60	5.23	6.26	7.26	8.55	22.31	25.00	27.49	30.58	32.80
16	5.14	5.81	6.91	7.96	9.31	23.54	26.30	28.85	32.00	34.27
17	5.70	6.41	7.56	8.67	10.09	24.77	27.59	30.19	33.41	35.72
18	6.26	7.01	8.23	9.39	10.86	25.99	28.87	31.53	34.81	37.16
19	6.84	7.63	8.91	10.12	11.65	27.20	30.14	32.85	36.19	38.58
20	7.43	8.26	9.59	10.85	12.44	28.41	31.41	34.17	37.57	40.00
21	8.03	8.90	10.28	11.59	13.24	29.62	32.67	35.48	38.93	41.40
22	8.64	9.54	10.98	12.34	14.04	30.81	33.92	36.78	40.29	42.80
23	9.26	10.20	11.69	13.09	14.85	32.01	35.17	38.08	41.64	44.18
24	9.89	10.86	12.40	13.85	15.66	33.20	36.42	39.36	42.98	45.56
25	10.52	11.52	13.12	14.61	16.47	34.38	37.65	40.65	44.31	46.93
26	11.16	12.20	13.84	15.38	17.29	35.56	38.89	41.92	45.64	48.29
27	11.81	12.88	14.57	16.15	18.11	36.74	40.11	43.19	46.96	49.64
28	12.46	13.56	15.31	16.93	18.94	37.92	41.34	44.46	48.28	50.99
29	13.21	14.26	16.05	17.71	19.77	39.09	42.56	45.72	49.59	52.34
30	13.79	14.95	16.79	18.49	20.60	40.26	43.77	46.98	50.89	53.67
40	20.71	22.16	24.43	26.51	29.05	51.80	55.76	59.34	63.69	66.77
50	27.99	29.71	32.36	34.76	37.69	63.17	67.50	71.42	76.15	79.49
60	35.53	37.48	40.48	43.19	46.46	74.40	79.08	83.30	88.38	91.95
70	43.28	45.44	48.76	51.74	55.33	85.53	90.53	95.02	100.4	104.2
80	51.17	53.54	57.15	60.39	64.28	96.58	101.9	106.6	112.3	116.3
90	59.20	61.75	65.65	69.13	73.29	107.6	113.1	118.1	124.1	128.3
100	67.33	70.06	74.22	77.93	82.36	118.5	124.3	129.6	135.8	140.2

* Reprinted with permission from E. S. Pearson and C. M. Thompson, "Tables of the Percentage Points of the Incomplete Beta Function and of the Chi-Square Distribution," *Biometrika*, Vol. 32 (1941).

$$p = .90$$

Entry $= F_{p; \, \nu_1, \, \nu_2}$ where $\Pr[F_{\nu_1, \, \nu_2} < F_{p; \, \nu_1, \, \nu_2}] = p$

Area p

$F_{p; \, \nu_1, \, \nu_2}$

ν_1 \ ν_2	1	2	3	4	5	6	7	8	9	10
1	39.86	49.50	53.59	55.83	57.24	58.20	58.91	59.44	59.86	60.19
2	8.53	9.00	9.16	9.24	9.29	9.33	9.35	9.37	9.38	9.39
3	5.54	5.46	5.39	5.34	5.31	5.28	5.27	5.25	5.24	5.23
4	4.54	4.32	4.19	4.11	4.05	4.01	3.98	3.95	3.94	3.92
5	4.06	3.78	3.62	3.52	3.45	3.40	3.37	3.34	3.32	3.30
6	3.78	3.46	3.29	3.18	3.11	3.05	3.01	2.98	2.96	2.94
7	3.59	3.26	3.07	2.96	2.88	2.83	2.78	2.75	2.72	2.70
8	3.46	3.11	2.92	2.81	2.73	2.67	2.62	2.59	2.56	2.54
9	3.36	3.01	2.81	2.69	2.61	2.55	2.51	2.47	2.44	2.42
10	3.29	2.92	2.73	2.61	2.52	2.46	2.41	2.38	2.35	2.32
11	3.23	2.86	2.66	2.54	2.45	2.39	2.34	2.30	2.27	2.25
12	3.18	2.81	2.61	2.48	2.39	2.33	2.28	2.24	2.21	2.19
13	3.14	2.76	2.56	2.43	2.35	2.28	2.23	2.20	2.16	2.14
14	3.10	2.73	2.52	2.39	2.31	2.24	2.19	2.15	2.12	2.10
15	3.07	2.70	2.49	2.36	2.27	2.21	2.16	2.12	2.09	2.06
16	3.05	2.67	2.46	2.33	2.24	2.18	2.13	2.09	2.06	2.03
17	3.03	2.64	2.44	2.31	2.22	2.15	2.10	2.06	2.03	2.00
18	3.01	2.62	2.42	2.29	2.20	2.13	2.08	2.049	2.00	1.98
19	2.99	2.61	2.40	2.27	2.18	2.11	2.06	2.02	1.98	1.96
20	2.97	2.59	2.38	2.25	2.16	2.09	2.04	2.00	1.96	1.94
21	2.96	2.57	2.36	2.23	2.14	2.08	2.02	1.98	1.95	1.92
22	2.95	2.56	2.35	2.22	2.13	2.06	2.01	1.97	1.93	1.90
23	2.94	2.55	2.34	2.21	2.11	2.05	1.99	1.95	1.92	1.89
24	2.93	2.54	2.33	2.19	2.10	2.04	1.98	1.94	1.91	1.88
25	2.92	2.53	2.32	2.18	2.09	2.02	1.97	1.93	1.89	1.87
26	2.91	2.52	2.31	2.17	2.08	2.01	1.96	1.92	1.88	1.86
27	2.90	2.51	2.30	2.17	2.07	2.00	1.95	1.91	1.87	1.85
28	2.89	2.50	2.29	2.16	2.06	2.00	1.94	1.90	1.87	1.84
29	2.89	2.50	2.28	2.15	2.06	1.99	1.93	1.89	1.86	1.83
30	2.88	2.49	2.28	2.14	2.05	1.98	1.93	1.88	1.85	1.82
40	2.84	2.44	2.23	2.09	2.00	1.93	1.87	1.83	1.79	1.76
60	2.79	2.39	2.18	2.04	1.95	1.87	1.82	1.77	1.74	1.71
120	2.75	2.35	2.13	1.99	1.90	1.82	1.77	1.72	1.68	1.65
∞	2.71	2.30	2.08	1.94	1.85	1.77	1.72	1.67	1.63	1.60

* Reprinted with permission from Table 18 of *Biometrika Tables for Statisticians*, eds. E. S. Pearson and H. O. Hartley (New York: Cambridge University Press, 1954), Vol. I.

$$p = .90$$

12	15	20	24	30	40	60	120	∞	ν_1 / ν_2
60.71	61.22	61.74	62.00	62.26	62.53	62.79	63.06	63.33	1
9.41	9.42	9.44	9.45	9.46	9.47	9.47	9.48	9.49	2
5.22	5.20	5.18	5.18	5.17	5.16	5.15	5.14	5.13	3
3.90	3.87	3.84	3.83	3.82	3.80	3.79	3.78	3.76	4
3.27	3.24	3.21	3.19	3.17	3.16	3.14	3.12	3.10	5
2.90	2.87	2.84	2.82	2.80	2.78	2.76	2.74	2.72	6
2.67	2.63	2.59	2.58	2.56	2.54	2.51	2.49	2.47	7
2.50	2.46	2.42	2.30	2.38	2.36	2.34	2.32	2.29	8
2.38	2.34	2.30	2.28	2.25	2.23	2.21	2.18	2.16	9
2.28	2.24	2.20	2.18	2.16	2.13	2.11	2.08	2.06	10
2.21	2.17	2.12	2.10	2.08	2.05	2.03	2.00	1.97	11
2.15	2.10	2.06	2.04	2.01	1.99	1.96	1.93	1.90	12
2.10	2.05	2.01	1.98	1.96	1.93	1.90	1.88	1.85	13
2.05	2.01	1.96	1.94	1.91	1.89	1.86	1.83	1.80	14
2.02	1.97	1.92	1.90	1.87	1.85	1.82	1.79	1.76	15
1.99	1.94	1.89	1.87	1.84	1.81	1.78	1.75	1.72	16
1.96	1.91	1.86	1.84	1.81	1.78	1.75	1.72	1.69	17
1.93	1.89	1.84	1.81	1.78	1.75	1.72	1.69	1.66	18
1.91	1.86	1.81	1.79	1.76	1.73	1.70	1.67	1.63	19
1.89	1.84	1.79	1.77	1.74	1.71	1.68	1.64	1.61	20
1.87	1.83	1.78	1.75	1.72	1.69	1.66	1.62	1.59	21
1.86	1.81	1.76	1.73	1.70	1.67	1.64	1.60	1.57	22
1.84	1.80	1.74	1.72	1.69	1.66	1.62	1.59	1.55	23
1.83	1.78	1.73	1.70	1.67	1.64	1.61	1.57	1.53	24
1.82	1.77	1.72	1.69	1.66	1.63	1.59	1.56	1.52	25
1.81	1.76	1.71	1.68	1.65	1.61	1.58	1.54	1.50	26
1.80	1.75	1.70	1.67	1.64	1.60	1.57	1.53	1.49	27
1.79	1.74	1.69	1.66	1.63	1.59	1.56	1.52	1.48	28
1.78	1.73	1.68	1.65	1.62	1.58	1.55	1.51	1.47	29
1.77	1.72	1.67	1.64	1.61	1.57	1.54	1.50	1.46	30
1.71	1.66	1.61	1.57	1.54	1.51	1.47	1.42	1.38	40
1.66	1.60	1.54	1.51	1.48	1.44	1.40	1.35	1.29	60
1.60	1.55	1.48	1.45	1.41	1.37	1.32	1.26	1.19	120
1.55	1.49	1.42	1.38	1.34	1.30	1.24	1.17	1.00	∞

$$p = .95$$

ν_2 \ ν_1	1	2	3	4	5	6	7	8	9	10
1	161.4	199.5	215.7	224.6	230.2	234.0	236.8	238.9	240.5	241.9
2	18.51	19.00	19.16	19.26	19.30	19.33	19.35	19.37	19.38	19.40
3	10.13	9.55	9.28	9.12	9.01	8.94	8.89	8.85	8.81	8.79
4	7.71	6.94	6.59	6.39	6.26	6.16	6.09	6.04	6.00	5.96
5	6.61	5.79	5.41	5.19	5.05	4.95	4.88	4.82	4.77	4.74
6	5.99	5.14	4.76	4.53	4.39	4.28	4.21	4.15	4.10	4.06
7	5.59	4.74	4.35	4.12	3.97	3.87	3.79	3.73	3.68	3.64
8	5.32	4.46	4.07	3.84	3.69	3.58	3.50	3.44	3.39	3.35
9	5.12	4.26	3.86	3.63	3.48	3.37	3.29	3.23	3.18	3.14
10	4.96	4.10	3.71	3.48	3.33	3.22	3.14	3.07	3.02	2.98
11	4.84	3.98	3.59	3.36	3.20	3.09	3.01	2.95	2.90	2.85
12	4.75	3.89	3.49	3.26	3.11	3.00	2.91	2.85	2.80	2.75
13	4.67	3.81	3.41	3.18	3.03	2.92	2.83	2.77	2.71	2.67
14	4.60	3.74	3.34	3.11	2.96	2.85	2.76	2.70	2.65	2.60
15	4.54	3.68	3.29	3.06	2.90	2.79	2.71	2.64	2.59	2.54
16	4.49	3.63	3.24	3.01	2.85	2.74	2.66	2.59	2.54	2.49
17	4.45	3.59	3.20	2.96	2.81	2.70	2.61	2.55	2.49	2.45
18	4.41	3.55	3.16	2.93	2.77	2.66	2.58	2.51	2.46	2.41
19	4.38	3.52	3.13	2.90	2.74	2.63	2.54	2.48	2.42	2.38
20	4.35	3.49	3.10	2.87	2.71	2.60	2.51	2.45	2.39	2.35
21	4.32	3.47	3.07	2.84	2.68	2.57	2.49	2.42	2.37	2.32
22	4.30	3.44	3.05	2.82	2.66	2.55	2.46	2.40	2.34	2.30
23	4.28	3.42	3.03	2.80	2.64	2.53	2.44	2.37	2.32	2.27
24	4.26	3.40	3.01	2.78	2.62	2.51	2.42	2.36	2.30	2.25
25	4.24	3.39	2.99	2.76	2.60	2.49	2.40	2.34	2.28	2.24
26	4.23	3.37	2.98	2.74	2.59	2.47	2.39	2.32	2.27	2.22
27	4.21	3.35	2.96	2.73	2.57	2.46	2.37	2.31	2.25	2.20
28	4.20	3.34	2.95	2.71	2.56	2.45	2.36	2.29	2.24	2.19
29	4.18	3.33	2.93	2.70	2.55	2.43	2.35	2.28	2.22	2.18
30	4.17	3.32	2.92	2.69	2.53	2.42	2.33	2.27	2.21	2.16
40	4.08	3.23	2.84	2.61	2.45	2.34	2.25	2.18	2.12	2.08
60	4.00	3.15	2.76	2.53	2.37	2.25	2.17	2.10	2.04	1.99
120	3.92	3.07	2.68	2.45	2.29	2.17	2.09	2.02	1.96	1.91
∞	3.84	3.00	2.60	2.37	2.21	2.10	2.01	1.94	1.88	1.83

$$p = .95$$

12	15	20	24	30	40	60	120	∞	ν_1 / ν_2
243.9	245.9	248.0	249.1	250.1	251.1	252.2	253.3	254.3	1
19.41	19.43	19.45	19.45	19.46	19.47	19.48	19.49	19.50	2
8.74	8.70	8.66	8.64	8.62	8.59	8.57	8.55	8.53	3
5.91	5.86	5.80	5.77	5.75	5.72	5.69	5.66	5.63	4
4.68	4.62	4.56	4.53	4.50	4.46	4.43	4.40	4.36	5
4.00	3.94	3.87	3.84	3.81	3.77	3.74	3.70	3.67	6
3.57	3.51	3.44	3.41	3.38	3.34	3.30	3.27	3.23	7
3.28	3.22	3.15	3.12	3.08	3.04	3.01	2.97	2.93	8
3.07	3.01	2.94	2.90	2.86	2.83	2.79	2.75	2.71	9
2.91	2.85	2.77	2.74	2.70	2.66	2.62	2.58	2.54	10
2.79	2.72	2.65	2.61	2.57	2.53	2.49	2.45	2.40	11
2.69	2.62	2.54	2.51	2.47	2.43	2.38	2.34	2.30	12
2.60	2.53	2.46	2.42	2.38	2.34	2.30	2.25	2.21	13
2.53	2.46	2.39	2.35	2.31	2.27	2.22	2.18	2.13	14
2.48	2.40	2.33	2.29	2.25	2.20	2.16	2.11	2.07	15
2.42	2.35	2.28	2.24	2.19	2.15	2.11	2.06	2.01	16
2.38	2.31	2.23	2.19	2.15	2.10	2.06	2.01	1.96	17
2.34	2.27	2.19	2.15	2.11	2.06	2.02	1.97	1.92	18
2.31	2.23	2.16	2.11	2.07	2.03	1.98	1.93	1.88	19
2.28	2.20	2.12	2.08	2.04	1.99	1.95	1.90	1.84	20
2.25	2.18	2.10	2.05	2.01	1.96	1.92	1.87	1.81	21
2.23	2.15	2.07	2.03	1.98	1.94	1.89	1.84	1.78	22
2.20	2.13	2.05	2.01	1.96	1.91	1.86	1.81	1.76	23
2.18	2.11	2.03	1.98	1.94	1.89	1.84	1.79	1.73	24
2.16	2.09	2.01	1.96	1.92	1.87	1.82	1.77	1.71	25
2.15	2.07	1.99	1.95	1.90	1.85	1.80	1.75	1.69	26
2.13	2.06	1.97	1.93	1.88	1.84	1.79	1.73	1.67	27
2.12	2.04	1.96	1.91	1.87	1.82	1.77	1.71	1.65	28
2.10	2.03	1.94	1.90	1.85	1.81	1.75	1.70	1.64	29
2.09	2.01	1.93	1.89	1.84	1.79	1.74	1.68	1.62	30
2.00	1.92	1.84	1.79	1.74	1.69	1.64	1.58	1.51	40
1.92	1.84	1.75	1.70	1.65	1.59	1.53	1.47	1.39	60
1.83	1.75	1.66	1.61	1.55	1.50	1.43	1.35	1.25	120
1.75	1.67	1.57	1.52	1.46	1.39	1.32	1.22	1.00	∞

APPENDIX TABLE 4   THE *F*-DISTRIBUTION   (Cont.)

p = .975

ν_1 / ν_2	1	2	3	4	5	6	7	8	9	10
1	647.8	799.5	864.2	899.6	921.8	937.1	948.2	956.7	963.3	968.6
2	38.51	39.00	39.17	39.25	39.30	39.33	39.36	39.37	39.39	39.40
3	17.44	16.04	15.44	15.10	14.88	14.73	14.62	14.54	14.47	14.42
4	12.22	10.65	9.98	9.60	9.36	9.20	9.07	8.98	8.90	8.84
5	10.01	8.43	7.76	7.39	7.15	6.98	6.85	6.76	6.68	6.62
6	8.81	7.26	6.60	6.23	5.99	5.82	5.70	5.60	5.52	5.46
7	8.07	6.54	5.89	5.52	5.29	5.12	4.99	4.90	4.82	4.76
8	7.57	6.06	5.42	5.05	4.82	4.65	4.53	4.43	4.36	4.30
9	7.21	5.71	5.08	4.72	4.48	4.32	4.20	4.10	4.03	3.96
10	6.94	5.46	4.83	4.47	4.24	4.07	3.95	3.85	3.78	3.72
11	6.72	5.26	4.63	4.28	4.04	3.88	3.76	3.66	3.59	3.53
12	6.55	5.10	4.47	4.12	3.89	3.73	3.61	3.54	3.44	3.37
13	6.41	4.97	4.35	4.00	3.77	3.60	3.48	3.39	3.31	3.25
14	6.30	4.86	4.24	3.89	3.66	3.50	3.38	3.29	3.21	3.15
15	6.20	4.77	4.15	3.80	3.58	3.41	3.29	3.20	3.12	3.06
16	6.12	4.69	4.08	3.73	3.50	3.34	3.22	3.12	3.05	2.99
17	6.04	4.62	4.01	3.66	3.44	3.28	3.16	3.06	2.98	2.92
18	5.98	4.56	3.95	3.61	3.38	3.22	3.10	3.01	2.93	2.87
19	5.92	4.51	3.90	3.56	3.33	3.17	3.05	2.96	2.88	2.82
20	5.87	4.46	3.86	3.51	3.29	3.13	3.01	2.91	2.84	2.77
21	5.83	4.42	3.82	3.48	3.25	3.09	2.97	2.87	2.80	2.73
22	5.79	4.38	3.78	3.44	3.22	3.05	2.93	2.84	2.76	2.70
23	5.75	4.35	3.75	3.41	3.18	3.02	2.90	2.81	2.73	2.67
24	5.72	4.32	3.72	3.38	3.15	2.99	2.87	2.78	2.70	2.64
25	5.69	4.29	3.69	3.35	3.13	2.97	2.85	2.75	2.68	2.61
26	5.66	4.27	3.67	3.33	3.10	2.94	2.82	2.73	2.65	2.59
27	5.63	4.24	3.65	3.31	3.08	2.92	2.80	2.71	2.63	2.57
28	5.61	4.22	3.63	3.29	3.06	2.90	2.78	2.69	2.61	2.55
29	5.59	4.20	3.61	3.27	3.04	2.88	2.76	2.67	2.59	2.53
30	5.57	4.18	3.59	3.25	3.03	2.87	2.75	2.65	2.57	2.51
40	5.42	4.05	3.46	3.13	2.90	2.74	2.62	2.53	2.45	2.39
60	5.29	3.93	3.34	3.01	2.79	2.63	2.51	2.41	2.33	2.27
120	5.15	3.80	3.23	2.89	2.67	2.52	2.39	2.30	2.22	2.16
∞	5.02	3.69	3.12	2.79	2.57	2.41	2.29	2.19	2.11	2.05

$$p = .975$$

12	15	20	24	30	40	60	120	∞	ν_1 / ν_2
976.7	984.9	993.1	997.2	1001	1006	1010	1014	1018	1
39.41	39.43	39.45	39.46	39.46	39.47	39.48	39.49	39.50	2
14.34	14.25	14.17	14.12	14.08	14.04	13.99	13.95	13.90	3
8.75	8.66	8.56	8.51	8.46	8.41	8.36	8.31	8.26	4
6.52	6.43	6.33	6.28	6.23	6.18	6.12	6.07	6.02	5
5.37	5.27	5.17	5.12	5.07	5.01	4.96	4.90	4.85	6
4.67	4.57	4.47	4.42	4.36	4.31	4.25	4.20	4.14	7
4.20	4.10	4.00	3.95	3.89	3.84	3.78	3.73	3.67	8
3.87	3.77	3.67	3.61	3.56	3.51	3.45	3.39	3.33	9
3.62	3.52	3.42	3.37	3.31	3.26	3.20	3.14	3.08	10
3.43	3.33	3.23	3.17	3.12	3.06	3.00	2.94	2.88	11
3.28	3.18	3.07	3.02	2.96	2.91	2.85	2.79	2.72	12
3.15	3.05	2.95	2.89	2.84	2.78	2.72	2.66	2.60	13
3.05	2.95	2.84	2.79	2.73	2.67	2.61	2.55	2.49	14
2.96	2.86	2.76	2.70	2.64	2.59	2.52	2.46	2.40	15
2.89	2.79	2.68	2.63	2.57	2.51	2.45	2.38	2.32	16
2.82	2.72	2.62	2.56	2.50	2.44	2.38	2.32	2.25	17
2.77	2.67	2.56	2.50	2.44	2.38	2.32	2.26	2.19	18
2.72	2.62	2.51	2.45	2.39	2.33	2.27	2.20	2.13	19
2.68	2.57	2.46	2.41	2.35	2.29	2.22	2.16	2.09	20
2.64	2.53	2.42	2.37	2.31	2.25	2.18	2.11	2.04	21
2.60	2.50	2.39	2.33	2.27	2.21	2.14	2.08	2.00	22
2.57	2.47	2.36	2.30	2.24	2.18	2.11	2.04	1.97	23
2.54	2.44	2.33	2.27	2.21	2.15	2.08	2.01	1.94	24
2.51	2.41	2.30	2.24	2.18	2.12	2.05	1.98	1.91	25
2.49	2.39	2.28	2.22	2.16	2.09	2.03	1.95	1.88	26
2.47	2.36	2.25	2.19	2.13	2.07	2.00	1.93	1.85	27
2.45	2.34	2.23	2.17	2.11	2.05	1.98	1.91	1.83	28
2.43	2.32	2.21	2.15	2.09	2.03	1.96	1.89	1.81	29
2.41	2.31	2.20	2.14	2.07	2.01	1.94	1.87	1.79	30
2.29	2.18	2.07	2.01	1.94	1.88	1.80	1.72	1.64	40
2.17	2.06	1.94	1.88	1.82	1.74	1.67	1.58	1.48	60
2.05	1.94	1.82	1.76	1.69	1.61	1.53	1.43	1.31	120
1.94	1.83	1.71	1.64	1.57	1.48	1.39	1.27	1.00	∞

$$p = .99$$

ν_1 / ν_2	1	2	3	4	5	6	7	8	9	10
1	4052	4999.5	5403	5625	5764	5859	5928	5982	6022	6056
2	98.50	99.00	99.17	99.25	99.30	99.33	99.36	99.37	99.39	99.40
3	34.12	30.82	29.46	28.71	28.24	27.91	27.67	27.49	27.35	27.23
4	21.20	18.00	16.69	15.98	15.52	15.21	14.98	14.80	14.66	14.55
5	16.26	13.27	12.06	11.39	10.97	10.67	10.46	10.29	10.16	10.05
6	13.75	10.92	9.78	9.15	8.75	8.47	8.26	8.10	7.98	7.87
7	12.25	9.55	8.45	7.85	7.46	7.19	6.99	6.84	6.72	6.62
8	11.26	8.65	7.59	7.01	6.63	6.37	6.18	6.03	5.91	5.81
9	10.56	8.02	6.99	6.42	6.06	5.80	5.61	5.47	5.35	5.26
10	10.04	7.56	6.55	5.99	5.64	5.39	5.20	5.06	4.94	4.85
11	9.65	7.21	6.22	5.67	5.32	5.07	4.89	4.74	4.63	4.54
12	9.33	6.93	5.95	5.41	5.06	4.82	4.64	4.50	4.39	4.30
13	9.07	6.70	5.74	5.21	4.86	4.62	4.44	4.30	4.19	4.10
14	8.86	6.51	5.56	5.04	4.69	4.46	4.28	4.14	4.03	3.94
15	8.68	6.36	5.42	4.89	4.56	4.32	4.14	4.00	3.89	3.80
16	8.53	6.23	5.29	4.77	4.44	4.20	4.03	3.89	3.78	3.69
17	8.40	6.11	5.18	4.67	4.34	4.10	3.93	3.79	3.68	3.59
18	8.29	6.01	5.09	4.58	4.25	4.01	3.84	3.71	3.60	3.51
19	8.18	5.93	5.01	4.50	4.17	3.94	3.77	3.63	3.52	3.43
20	8.10	5.85	4.94	4.43	4.10	3.87	3.70	3.56	3.46	3.37
21	8.02	5.78	4.87	4.37	4.04	3.81	3.64	3.51	3.40	3.31
22	7.95	5.72	4.83	4.31	3.99	3.76	3.59	3.45	3.35	3.26
23	7.88	5.66	4.76	4.26	3.94	3.71	3.54	3.41	3.30	3.21
24	7.82	5.61	4.72	4.22	3.90	3.67	3.50	3.36	3.26	3.17
25	7.77	5.57	4.68	4.18	3.85	3.63	3.46	3.32	3.22	3.13
26	7.72	5.53	4.64	4.14	3.82	3.59	3.42	3.29	3.18	3.09
27	7.68	5.49	4.60	4.11	3.78	3.56	8.39	3.26	3.15	3.06
28	7.64	5.45	4.57	4.07	3.75	3.53	3.36	3.23	3.12	3.03
29	7.60	5.42	4.54	4.04	3.73	3.50	3.33	3.20	3.09	3.00
30	7.56	5.39	4.51	4.02	3.70	3.47	3.30	3.17	3.07	2.98
40	7.31	5.18	4.31	3.83	3.51	3.29	3.12	2.99	2.89	2.80
60	7.08	4.98	4.13	3.65	3.34	3.12	2.95	2.82	2.72	2.63
120	6.85	4.79	3.95	3.48	3.17	2.96	2.79	2.66	2.56	2.47
∞	6.63	4.61	3.78	3.32	3.02	2.80	2.64	2.51	2.41	2.32

$$p = .99$$

12	15	20	24	30	40	60	120	∞	ν_1 / ν_2
6106	6157	6209	6235	6261	6287	6313	6339	6366	1
99.42	99.43	99.45	99.46	99.47	99.47	99.48	99.49	99.50	2
27.05	26.87	26.69	26.60	26.50	26.41	26.32	26.22	26.13	3
14.37	14.20	14.02	13.93	13.84	13.75	13.65	13.56	13.46	4
9.89	9.72	9.55	9.47	9.38	9.29	9.20	9.11	9.02	5
7.72	7.56	7.40	7.31	7.23	7.14	7.06	6.97	6.88	6
6.47	6.31	6.16	6.07	5.99	5.91	5.82	5.74	5.65	7
5.67	5.52	5.36	5.28	5.20	5.12	5.03	4.95	4.86	8
5.11	4.96	4.81	4.73	4.65	4.57	4.48	4.40	4.31	9
4.71	4.56	4.41	4.33	4.25	4.17	4.08	4.00	3.91	10
4.40	4.25	4.10	4.02	3.94	3.86	3.78	3.69	3.60	11
4.16	4.01	3.86	3.78	3.70	3.62	3.54	3.45	3.36	12
3.96	3.82	3.66	3.59	3.51	3.43	3.34	3.25	3.17	13
3.80	3.66	3.51	3.43	3.35	3.27	3.18	3.09	3.00	14
3.67	3.52	3.37	3.29	3.21	3.13	3.05	2.96	2.87	15
3.55	3.41	3.26	3.18	3.10	3.02	2.93	2.84	2.75	16
3.46	3.31	3.16	3.08	3.00	2.92	2.83	2.75	2.65	17
3.37	3.23	3.08	3.00	2.92	2.84	2.75	2.66	2.57	18
2.30	3.15	3.00	2.92	2.84	2.76	2.67	2.58	2.49	19
3.23	3.09	2.94	2.86	2.78	2.69	2.61	2.52	2.42	20
3.17	3.03	2.88	2.80	2.72	2.64	2.55	2.46	2.36	21
3.12	2.98	2.83	2.75	2.67	2.58	2.50	2.40	2.31	22
3.07	2.93	2.78	2.70	2.62	2.54	2.45	2.35	2.26	23
3.03	2.89	2.74	2.66	2.58	2.49	2.40	2.31	2.21	24
2.99	2.85	2.70	2.62	2.54	2.45	2.36	2.27	2.17	25
2.96	2.81	2.66	2.58	2.50	2.42	2.33	2.23	2.12	26
2.93	2.78	2.63	2.55	2.47	2.38	2.29	2.20	2.10	27
2.90	2.75	2.60	2.52	2.44	2.35	2.26	2.17	2.06	28
2.87	2.73	2.57	2.49	2.41	2.33	2.23	2.14	2.03	29
2.84	2.70	2.55	2.47	2.39	2.30	2.21	2.11	2.01	30
2.66	2.52	2.37	2.29	2.20	2.11	2.02	1.92	1.80	40
2.50	2.35	2.20	2.12	2.03	1.94	1.84	1.73	1.60	60
2.34	2.19	2.03	1.95	1.86	1.76	1.66	1.53	1.38	120
2.18	2.04	1.88	1.79	1.70	1.59	1.47	1.32	1.00	∞

$$p = .995$$

ν_2 \ ν_1	1	2	3	4	5	6	7	8	9	10
1	16211	20000	21615	22500	23056	23437	23715	23925	24091	24224
2	198.5	199.0	199.2	199.2	199.3	199.3	199.4	199.4	199.4	199.4
3	55.55	49.80	47.47	46.19	45.39	44.84	44.43	44.13	43.88	43.69
4	31.33	26.28	24.26	23.15	22.46	21.97	21.62	21.35	21.14	20.97
5	22.78	18.31	16.53	15.56	14.94	14.51	14.20	13.96	13.77	13.62
6	18.63	14.54	12.92	12.03	11.46	11.07	10.79	10.57	10.39	10.25
7	16.24	12.40	10.88	10.05	9.52	9.16	8.89	8.68	8.51	8.38
8	14.69	11.04	9.60	8.81	8.30	7.95	7.69	7.50	7.34	7.21
9	13.61	10.11	8.72	7.96	7.47	7.13	6.88	6.69	6.54	6.42
10	12.83	9.43	8.08	7.34	6.87	6.54	6.30	6.12	5.97	5.85
11	12.23	8.91	7.60	6.88	6.42	6.10	5.86	5.68	5.54	5.42
12	11.75	8.51	7.23	6.52	6.07	5.76	5.52	5.35	5.20	5.09
13	11.37	8.19	6.93	6.23	5.79	5.48	5.25	5.08	4.94	4.82
14	11.06	7.92	6.68	6.00	5.56	5.26	5.03	4.86	4.72	4.60
15	10.80	7.70	6.48	5.80	5.37	5.07	4.85	4.67	4.54	4.42
16	10.58	7.51	6.30	5.64	5.21	4.91	4.69	4.52	4.38	4.27
17	10.38	7.35	6.16	5.50	5.07	4.78	4.56	4.39	4.25	4.14
18	10.22	7.21	6.03	5.37	4.96	4.66	4.44	4.28	4.14	4.03
19	10.07	7.09	5.92	5.27	4.85	4.56	4.34	4.18	4.04	3.93
20	9.94	6.99	5.82	5.17	4.76	4.47	4.26	4.09	3.96	3.85
21	9.83	6.89	5.73	5.09	4.68	4.39	4.18	4.01	3.88	3.77
22	9.73	6.81	5.65	5.02	4.61	4.32	4.11	3.94	3.81	3.70
23	9.63	6.73	5.58	4.95	4.54	4.26	4.05	3.88	3.75	3.64
24	9.55	6.66	5.52	4.89	4.49	4.20	3.99	3.83	3.69	3.59
25	9.48	6.60	5.46	4.84	4.43	4.15	3.94	3.78	3.64	3.54
26	9.41	6.54	5.41	4.79	4.38	4.10	3.89	3.73	3.60	3.49
27	9.34	6.49	5.36	4.74	4.34	4.06	3.85	3.69	3.56	3.45
28	9.28	6.44	5.32	4.70	4.30	4.02	3.81	3.65	3.52	3.41
29	9.23	6.40	5.28	4.66	4.26	3.98	3.77	3.61	3.48	3.38
30	9.18	6.35	5.24	4.62	4.23	3.95	3.74	3.58	3.45	3.34
40	8.83	6.07	4.98	4.37	3.99	3.71	3.51	3.35	3.22	3.12
60	8.49	5.79	4.73	4.14	3.76	3.49	3.29	3.13	3.01	2.90
120	8.18	5.54	4.50	3.92	3.55	3.28	3.09	2.93	2.81	2.71
∞	7.88	5.30	4.28	3.72	3.35	3.09	2.90	2.74	2.62	2.52

p = .995

12	15	20	24	30	40	60	120	∞	ν_1 / ν_2
24426	24630	24836	24940	25044	25148	25253	25359	25465	1
199.4	199.4	199.4	199.5	199.5	199.5	199.5	199.5	199.5	2
43.39	43.08	42.78	42.62	42.47	42.31	42.15	41.99	41.83	3
20.70	20.44	20.17	20.03	19.89	19.75	19.61	19.47	19.32	4
13.38	13.15	12.90	12.78	12.66	12.53	12.40	12.27	12.14	5
10.03	9.81	9.59	9.47	9.36	9.24	9.12	9.00	8.88	6
8.18	7.97	7.75	7.65	7.53	7.42	7.31	7.19	7.08	7
7.01	6.81	6.61	6.50	6.40	6.29	6.18	6.06	5.95	8
6.23	6.03	5.83	5.73	5.62	5.52	5.41	5.30	5.19	9
5.66	5.47	5.27	5.17	5.07	4.97	4.86	4.75	4.64	10
5.24	5.05	4.86	4.76	4.65	4.55	4.44	4.34	4.23	11
4.91	4.72	4.53	4.43	4.33	4.23	4.12	4.01	3.90	12
4.64	4.46	4.27	4.17	4.07	3.97	3.87	3.76	3.65	13
4.43	4.25	4.06	3.96	3.86	3.76	3.66	3.55	3.44	14
4.25	4.07	3.88	3.79	3.69	3.58	3.48	3.37	3.26	15
4.10	3.92	3.73	3.64	3.54	3.44	3.33	3.22	3.11	16
3.97	3.79	3.61	3.51	3.41	3.31	3.21	3.10	2.98	17
3.86	3.68	3.50	3.40	3.30	3.20	3.10	2.99	2.87	18
3.76	3.59	3.40	3.31	3.21	3.11	3.00	2.89	2.78	19
3.68	3.50	3.32	3.22	3.12	3.02	2.92	2.81	2.69	20
3.60	3.43	3.24	3.15	3.05	2.95	2.84	2.73	2.61	21
3.54	3.36	3.18	3.08	2.98	2.88	2.77	2.66	2.55	22
3.47	3.30	3.12	3.02	2.92	2.82	2.71	2.60	2.48	23
3.42	3.25	3.06	2.97	2.87	2.77	2.66	2.55	2.43	24
3.37	3.20	3.01	2.92	2.82	2.72	2.61	2.50	2.38	25
3.33	3.15	2.97	2.87	2.77	2.67	2.56	2.45	2.33	26
3.28	3.11	2.95	2.83	2.73	2.63	2.52	2.41	2.29	27
3.25	3.07	2.89	2.79	2.69	2.59	2.48	2.37	2.25	28
3.21	3.04	2.86	2.76	2.66	2.56	2.45	2.33	2.21	29
3.18	3.01	2.82	2.73	2.63	2.52	2.42	2.30	2.18	30
2.95	2.78	2.60	2.50	2.40	2.30	2.18	2.06	1.93	40
2.74	2.57	2.39	2.29	2.19	2.08	1.96	1.83	1.69	60
2.54	2.37	2.19	2.09	1.98	1.87	1.75	1.61	1.43	120
2.36	2.19	2.00	1.90	1.79	1.67	1.53	1.36	1.00	∞

$p = .999$

ν_1 / ν_2	1	2	3	4	5	6	7	8	9	10
1	4053*	5000*	5404*	5625*	5764*	5859*	5929*	5981*	6023*	6056*
2	998.5	999.0	999.2	999.2	999.3	999.3	999.4	999.4	999.4	999.4
3	167.0	148.5	141.1	137.1	134.6	132.8	131.6	130.6	129.9	129.2
4	74.14	61.25	56.18	53.44	51.71	50.53	49.66	49.00	48.47	48.05
5	47.18	37.12	33.20	31.09	29.75	28.84	28.16	27.64	27.24	26.92
6	35.51	27.00	23.70	21.92	20.81	20.03	19.46	19.03	18.69	18.41
7	29.25	21.69	18.77	17.19	16.21	15.52	15.02	14.63	14.33	14.08
8	25.42	18.49	15.83	14.39	13.49	12.86	12.40	12.04	11.77	11.54
9	22.86	16.39	13.90	12.56	11.71	11.13	10.70	10.37	10.11	9.89
10	21.04	14.91	12.55	11.28	10.48	9.92	9.52	9.20	8.96	8.75
11	19.69	13.81	11.56	10.35	9.58	9.05	8.66	8.35	8.12	7.92
12	18.64	12.97	10.80	9.63	8.89	8.38	8.00	7.71	7.48	7.29
13	17.81	12.31	10.21	9.07	8.35	7.86	7.49	7.21	6.98	6.80
14	17.14	11.78	9.73	8.62	7.92	7.43	7.08	6.80	6.58	6.40
15	16.59	11.34	9.34	8.25	7.57	7.09	6.74	6.47	6.26	6.08
16	16.12	10.97	9.00	7.94	7.27	6.81	6.46	6.19	5.98	5.81
17	15.72	10.66	8.73	7.68	7.02	6.56	6.22	5.96	5.75	5.58
18	15.38	10.39	8.49	7.46	7.81	6.35	6.02	5.76	5.56	5.39
19	15.08	10.16	8.28	7.26	6.62	6.18	5.85	5.59	5.39	5.22
20	14.82	9.95	8.10	7.10	6.46	6.02	5.69	5.44	5.24	5.08
21	14.59	9.77	7.94	6.95	6.32	5.88	5.56	5.31	5.11	4.95
22	14.38	9.61	7.80	6.81	6.19	5.76	5.44	5.19	4.99	4.83
23	14.19	9.47	7.67	6.69	6.08	5.65	5.33	5.09	4.89	4.73
24	14.03	9.34	7.55	6.59	5.98	5.55	5.23	4.99	4.80	4.64
25	13.88	9.22	7.45	6.49	5.88	5.46	5.15	4.91	4.71	4.56
26	13.74	9.12	7.36	6.41	5.80	5.38	5.07	4.83	4.64	4.48
27	13.61	9.02	7.27	6.33	5.73	5.31	5.00	4.76	4.57	4.41
28	13.50	8.93	7.19	6.25	5.66	5.24	4.93	4.69	4.50	4.35
29	13.39	8.85	7.12	6.19	5.59	5.18	4.87	4.64	4.45	4.29
30	13.29	8.77	7.05	6.12	5.53	5.12	4.82	4.58	4.39	4.24
40	12.61	8.25	6.60	5.70	5.13	4.73	4.44	4.21	4.02	3.87
60	11.97	7.76	6.17	5.31	4.76	4.37	4.09	3.87	3.69	3.54
120	11.38	7.32	5.79	4.95	4.42	4.04	3.77	3.55	3.38	3.24
∞	10.83	6.91	5.42	4.62	4.10	3.74	3.47	3.27	3.10	2.96

* Multiply these entries by 100

$p = .999$

12	15	20	24	30	40	60	120	∞	ν_1 / ν_2
6107*	6158*	6209*	6235*	6261*	6287*	6313*	6340	6366	1
999.4	999.4	999.4	999.5	999.5	999.5	999.5	999.5	999.5	2
128.3	127.4	126.4	125.9	125.4	125.0	124.5	124.0	123.5	3
47.41	46.76	46.10	45.77	45.43	45.09	44.75	44.40	44.05	4
26.42	25.91	25.39	25.14	24.87	24.60	24.33	24.06	23.79	5
17.99	17.56	17.12	16.89	16.67	16.44	16.21	15.99	15.75	6
13.71	13.32	12.93	12.73	12.53	12.33	12.12	11.91	11.70	7
11.19	10.84	10.48	10.30	10.11	9.92	9.73	9.53	9.33	8
9.57	9.24	8.90	8.72	8.55	8.37	8.19	8.00	7.81	9
8.45	8.13	7.80	7.64	7.47	7.30	7.12	6.94	6.76	10
7.63	7.32	7.01	6.85	6.68	6.52	6.35	6.17	6.00	11
7.00	6.71	6.40	6.25	6.09	5.93	5.76	5.59	5.42	12
6.52	6.23	5.93	5.78	5.63	5.47	5.30	5.14	4.97	13
6.13	5.85	5.56	5.41	5.25	5.10	4.94	4.77	4.60	14
5.81	5.54	5.25	5.10	4.95	4.80	4.64	4.47	4.31	15
5.55	5.27	4.99	4.85	4.70	4.54	4.39	4.23	4.06	16
5.32	5.05	4.78	4.63	4.48	4.33	4.18	4.02	3.85	17
5.13	4.87	4.59	4.45	4.30	4.15	4.00	3.84	3.67	18
4.97	4.70	4.43	4.29	4.14	3.99	3.84	3.68	3.51	19
4.82	4.56	4.29	4.15	4.00	3.86	3.70	3.54	3.38	20
4.70	4.44	4.17	4.03	3.88	3.74	3.58	3.42	3.26	21
4.58	4.33	4.06	3.92	3.78	3.63	3.48	3.32	3.15	22
4.48	4.23	3.96	3.82	3.68	3.53	3.38	3.22	3.05	23
4.39	4.14	3.87	3.74	3.59	3.45	3.29	3.14	2.97	24
4.31	4.06	3.79	3.66	3.52	3.37	3.22	3.06	2.89	25
4.24	3.99	3.72	3.59	3.44	3.30	3.15	2.99	2.82	26
4.17	3.92	3.66	3.52	3.38	3.23	3.08	2.92	2.75	27
4.11	3.86	3.60	3.46	3.32	3.18	3.02	2.86	2.69	28
4.05	3.80	3.54	3.41	3.27	3.12	2.97	2.81	2.64	29
4.00	3.75	3.49	3.36	3.22	3.07	2.92	2.76	2.59	30
3.64	3.40	3.15	3.01	2.87	2.73	2.57	2.41	2.23	40
3.31	3.03	2.83	2.69	2.55	2.41	2.25	2.08	1.89	60
3.02	2.78	2.53	2.40	2.26	2.11	1.95	1.76	1.54	120
2.74	2.51	2.27	2.13	1.99	1.84	1.66	1.45	1.00	∞

* Multiply these entries by 100

APPENDIX TABLE 5 DISTRIBUTION OF COCHRAN'S STATISTIC*

$$p = .95$$

Entry $= R_{p;\,n,\,r}$ where $\Pr[R_{n,\,r} < R_{p;\,n,\,r}] = p$

n \ r	2	3	4	5	6	7	8	9	10	11	17	37	145	∞
2	0.9985	0.9750	0.9392	0.9057	0.8772	0.8534	0.8332	0.8159	0.8010	0.7880	0.7341	0.6602	0.5813	0.5000
3	0.9669	0.8709	0.7977	0.7457	0.7071	0.6771	0.6530	0.6333	0.6167	0.6025	0.5466	0.4748	0.4031	0.3333
4	0.9065	0.7679	0.6841	0.6287	0.5895	0.5598	0.5365	0.5175	0.5017	0.4884	0.4366	0.3720	0.3093	0.2500
5	0.8412	0.6838	0.5981	0.5441	0.5065	0.4783	0.4564	0.4387	0.4241	0.4118	0.3645	0.3066	0.2513	0.2000
6	0.7808	0.6161	0.5321	0.4803	0.4447	0.4184	0.3980	0.3817	0.3682	0.3568	0.3135	0.2612	0.2119	0.1667
7	0.7271	0.5612	0.4800	0.4307	0.3974	0.3726	0.3535	0.3384	0.3259	0.3154	0.2756	0.2278	0.1833	0.1429
8	0.6798	0.5157	0.4377	0.3910	0.3595	0.3362	0.3185	0.3043	0.2926	0.2829	0.2462	0.2022	0.1616	0.1250
9	0.6385	0.4775	0.4027	0.3584	0.3286	0.3067	0.2901	0.2768	0.2659	0.2568	0.2226	0.1820	0.1446	0.1111
10	0.6020	0.4450	0.3733	0.3311	0.3029	0.2823	0.2666	0.2541	0.2439	0.2353	0.2032	0.1655	0.1308	0.1000
12	0.5410	0.3924	0.3264	0.2880	0.2624	0.2439	0.2299	0.2187	0.2098	0.2020	0.1737	0.1403	0.1100	0.0833
15	0.4709	0.3346	0.2758	0.2419	0.2195	0.2034	0.1911	0.1815	0.1736	0.1671	0.1429	0.1144	0.0889	0.0667
20	0.3894	0.2705	0.2205	0.1921	0.1735	0.1602	0.1501	0.1422	0.1357	0.1303	0.1108	0.0879	0.0675	0.0500
24	0.3434	0.2354	0.1907	0.1656	0.1493	0.1374	0.1286	0.1216	0.1160	0.1113	0.0942	0.0743	0.0567	0.0417
30	0.2929	0.1980	0.1593	0.1377	0.1237	0.1137	0.1061	0.1002	0.0958	0.0921	0.0771	0.0604	0.0457	0.0333
40	0.2370	0.1567	0.1259	0.1082	0.0968	0.0887	0.0827	0.0780	0.0745	0.0713	0.0595	0.0462	0.0347	0.0250
60	0.1737	0.1131	0.0895	0.0765	0.0682	0.0623	0.0583	0.0552	0.0520	0.0497	0.0411	0.0316	0.0234	0.0167
120	0.0998	0.0632	0.0495	0.0419	0.0371	0.0337	0.0312	0.0292	0.0279	0.0266	0.0218	0.0165	0.0120	0.0083
∞	0	0	0	0	0	0	0	0	0	0	0	0	0	0

$$p = .99$$

r \ n	2	3	4	5	6	7	8	9	10	11	17	37	145	∞
2	0.9999	0.9950	0.9794	0.9586	0.9373	0.9172	0.8988	0.8823	0.8674	0.8539	0.7949	0.7067	0.6062	0.5000
3	0.9933	0.9423	0.8831	0.8335	0.7933	0.7606	0.7335	0.7107	0.6912	0.6743	0.6059	0.5153	0.4230	0.3333
4	0.9676	0.8643	0.7814	0.7212	0.6761	0.6410	0.6129	0.5897	0.5702	0.5536	0.4884	0.4057	0.3251	0.2500
5	0.9279	0.7885	0.6957	0.6329	0.5875	0.5531	0.5259	0.5037	0.4854	0.4697	0.4094	0.3351	0.2644	0.2000
6	0.8828	0.7218	0.6258	0.5635	0.5195	0.4866	0.4608	0.4401	0.4229	0.4084	0.3529	0.2858	0.2229	0.1667
7	0.8376	0.6644	0.5685	0.5080	0.4659	0.4347	0.4105	0.3911	0.3751	0.3616	0.3105	0.2494	0.1929	0.1429
8	0.7945	0.6152	0.5209	0.4627	0.4226	0.3932	0.3704	0.3522	0.3373	0.3248	0.2779	0.2214	0.1700	0.1250
9	0.7544	0.5727	0.4810	0.4251	0.3870	0.3592	0.3378	0.3207	0.3067	0.2950	0.2514	0.1992	0.1521	0.1111
10	0.7175	0.5358	0.4469	0.3934	0.3572	0.3308	0.3106	0.2945	0.2813	0.2704	0.2297	0.1811	0.1376	0.1000
12	0.6528	0.4751	0.3919	0.3428	0.3099	0.2861	0.2680	0.2535	0.2419	0.2320	0.1961	0.1535	0.1157	0.0833
15	0.5747	0.4069	0.3317	0.2882	0.2593	0.2386	0.2228	0.2104	0.2002	0.1918	0.1612	0.1251	0.0934	0.0667
20	0.4799	0.3297	0.2654	0.2288	0.2048	0.1877	0.1748	0.1646	0.1567	0.1501	0.1248	0.0960	0.0709	0.0500
24	0.4247	0.2871	0.2295	0.1970	0.1759	0.1608	0.1495	0.1406	0.1338	0.1283	0.1060	0.0810	0.0595	0.0417
30	0.3632	0.2412	0.1913	0.1635	0.1454	0.1327	0.1232	0.1157	0.1100	0.1054	0.0867	0.0658	0.0480	0.0333
40	0.2940	0.1915	0.1508	0.1281	0.1135	0.1033	0.0957	0.0898	0.0853	0.0816	0.0668	0.0503	0.0363	0.0250
60	0.2151	0.1371	0.1069	0.0902	0.0796	0.0722	0.0668	0.0625	0.0594	0.0567	0.0461	0.0344	0.0245	0.0167
120	0.1225	0.0759	0.0585	0.0489	0.0429	0.0387	0.0357	0.0334	0.0316	0.0302	0.0242	0.0178	0.0125	0.0083
∞	0	0	0	0	0	0	0	0	0	0	0	0	0	0

* Reprinted with permission from C. Eisenhart, M. W. Hastay, and W. A. Wallis, *Technique of Statistical Analysis* (New York: McGraw-Hill Book Co., Inc, 1947), pp. 390-91.

APPENDIX TABLE 6 THE POWER FUNCTION FOR ANALYSIS OF VARIANCE (FIXED-EFFECTS MODEL).*

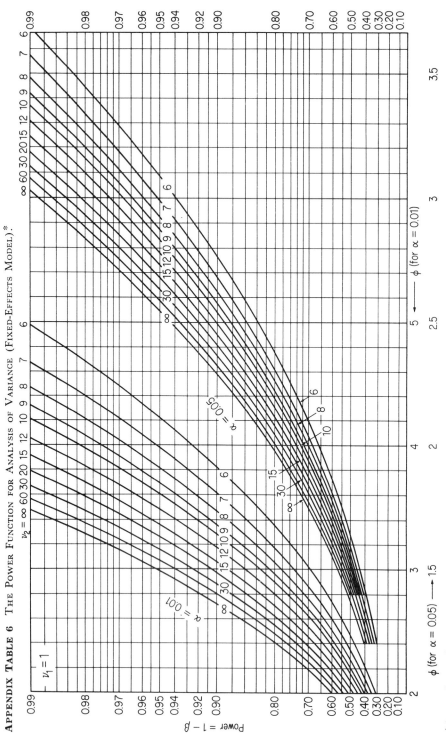

*Appendix Table 6 reprinted with permission from E. S. Pearson and H. O. Hartley,"Charts of the Power Function for Analysis of Variance Tests, Derived from the Non-Central F-Distribution," Biometrika, Vol. 38 (1951), p. 112.

APPENDIX TABLE 6 THE POWER FUNCTION FOR ANALYSIS OF VARIANCE (FIXED-EFFECTS MODEL) (Cont.)

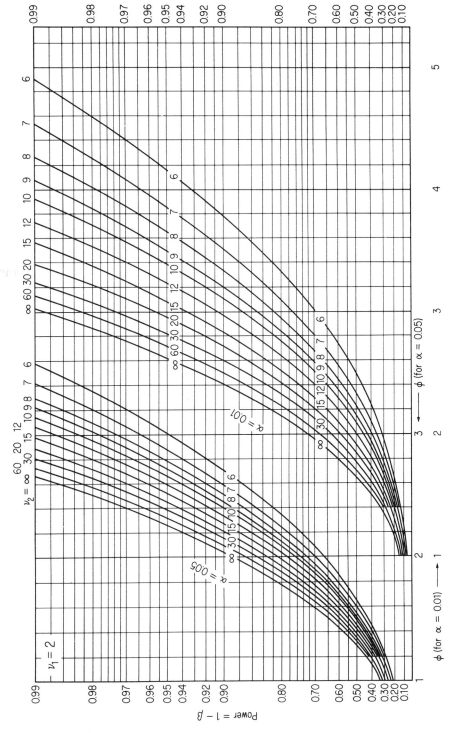

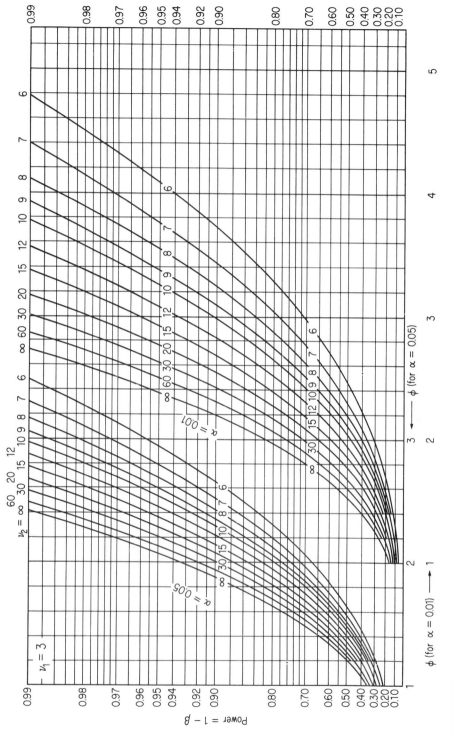

APPENDIX TABLE 6 THE POWER FUNCTION FOR ANALYSIS OF VARIANCE (FIXED-EFFECTS MODEL) (Cont.)

189

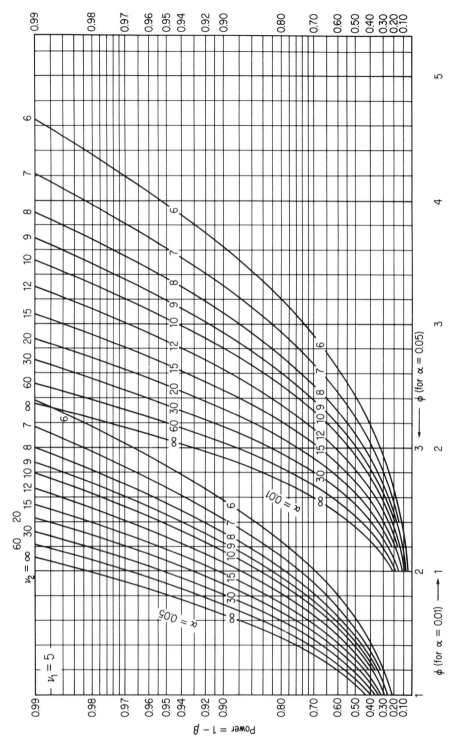

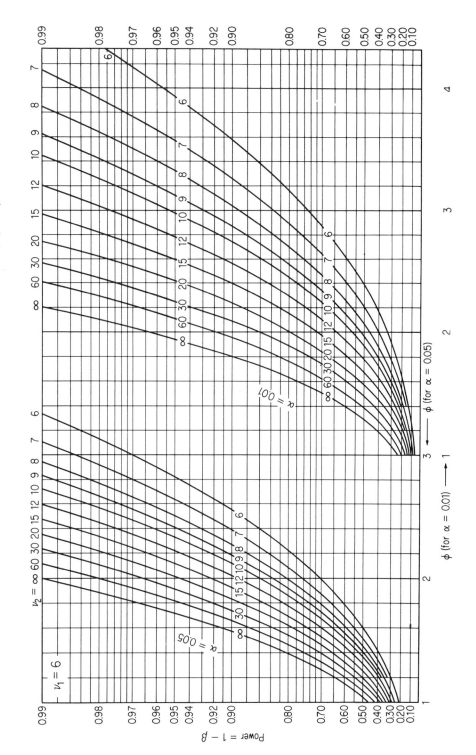

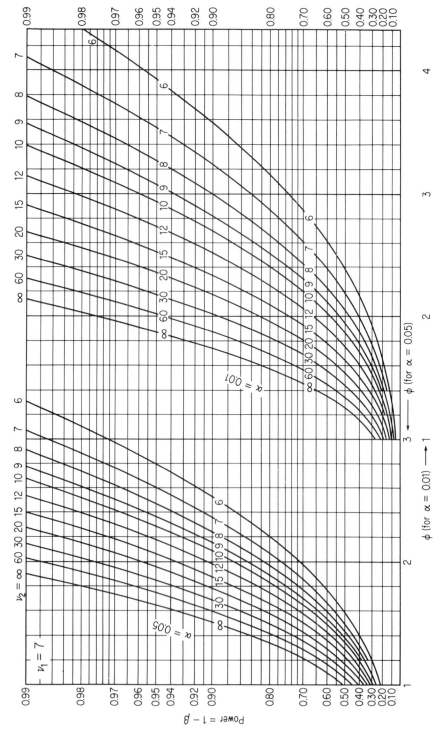

192

APPENDIX TABLE 6 THE POWER FUNCTION FOR ANALYSIS OF VARIANCE (FIXED-EFFECTS MODEL) (Cont.)

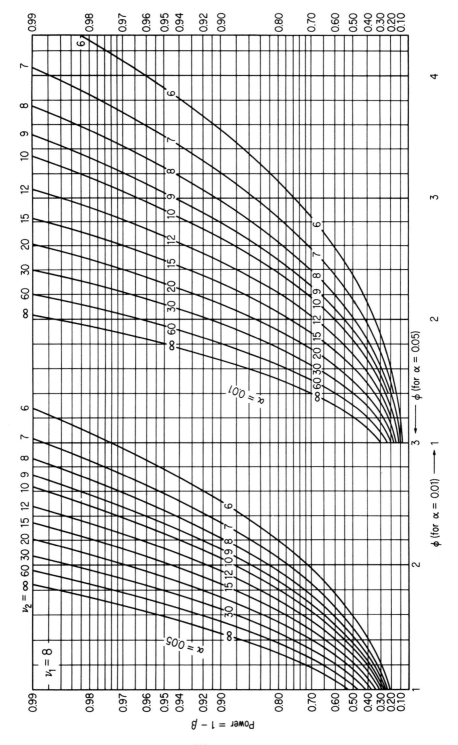

193

$$p = .95$$

Entry $= q_{p;\nu_1,\nu_2}$ where $\Pr[q_{\nu_1,\nu_2} < q_{p;\nu_1,\nu_2}] = p$ $\nu_1 =$ no. treats., $\nu_2 = d.f.$ associated with estimates of variance

ν_2 \ ν_1	2	3	4	5	6	7	8	9	10	11	12	13	14	15	16	17	18	19	20
1	18.0	27.0	32.8	37.1	40.4	43.1	45.4	47.4	49.1	50.6	52.0	53.2	54.3	55.4	56.3	57.2	58.0	58.8	59.6
2	6.09	8.3	9.8	10.9	11.7	12.4	13.0	13.5	14.0	14.4	14.7	15.1	15.4	15.7	15.9	16.1	16.4	16.6	16.8
3	4.50	5.91	6.82	7.50	8.04	8.48	8.85	9.18	9.46	9.72	9.95	10.15	10.35	10.52	10.69	10.84	10.98	11.11	11.24
4	3.93	5.04	5.76	6.29	6.71	7.05	7.35	7.60	7.83	8.03	8.21	8.37	8.52	8.66	8.79	8.91	9.03	9.13	9.23
5	3.64	4.60	5.22	5.67	6.03	6.33	6.58	6.80	6.99	7.17	7.32	7.47	7.60	7.72	7.83	7.93	8.03	8.12	8.21
6	3.46	4.34	4.90	5.31	5.63	5.89	6.12	6.32	6.49	6.65	6.79	6.92	7.03	7.14	7.24	7.34	7.43	7.51	7.59
7	3.34	4.16	4.68	5.06	5.36	5.61	5.82	6.00	6.16	6.30	6.43	6.55	6.66	6.76	6.85	6.94	7.02	7.09	7.17
8	3.26	4.04	4.53	4.89	5.17	5.40	5.60	5.77	5.92	6.05	6.18	6.29	6.39	6.48	6.57	6.65	6.73	6.80	6.87
9	3.20	3.95	4.42	4.76	5.02	5.24	5.43	5.60	5.74	5.87	5.98	6.09	6.19	6.28	6.36	6.44	6.51	6.58	6.64
10	3.15	3.88	4.33	4.65	4.91	5.12	5.30	5.46	5.60	5.72	5.83	5.93	6.03	6.11	6.20	6.27	6.34	6.40	6.47
11	3.11	3.82	4.26	4.57	4.82	5.03	5.20	5.35	5.49	5.61	5.71	5.81	5.90	5.99	6.06	6.14	6.20	6.26	6.33
12	3.08	3.77	4.20	4.51	4.75	4.95	5.12	5.27	5.40	5.51	5.62	5.71	5.80	5.88	5.95	6.03	6.09	6.15	6.21
13	3.06	3.73	4.15	4.45	4.69	4.88	5.05	5.19	5.32	5.43	5.53	5.63	5.71	5.79	5.86	5.93	6.00	6.05	6.11
14	3.03	3.70	4.11	4.41	4.64	4.83	4.99	5.13	5.25	5.36	5.46	5.55	5.64	5.72	5.79	5.85	5.92	5.97	6.03
15	3.01	3.67	4.08	4.37	4.60	4.78	4.94	5.08	5.20	5.31	5.40	5.49	5.58	5.65	5.72	5.79	5.85	5.90	5.96
16	3.00	3.65	4.05	4.33	4.56	4.74	4.90	5.03	5.15	5.26	5.35	5.44	5.52	5.59	5.66	5.72	5.79	5.84	5.90
17	2.98	3.63	4.02	4.30	4.52	4.71	4.86	4.99	5.11	5.21	5.31	5.39	5.47	5.55	5.61	5.68	5.74	5.79	5.84
18	2.97	3.61	4.00	4.28	4.49	4.67	4.82	4.96	5.07	5.17	5.27	5.35	5.43	5.50	5.57	5.63	5.69	5.74	5.79
19	2.96	3.59	3.98	4.25	4.47	4.65	4.79	4.92	5.04	5.14	5.23	5.32	5.39	5.46	5.53	5.59	5.65	5.70	5.75
20	2.95	3.58	3.96	4.23	4.45	4.62	4.77	4.90	5.01	5.11	5.20	5.28	5.36	5.43	5.49	5.55	5.61	5.66	5.71
24	2.92	3.53	3.90	4.17	4.37	4.54	4.68	4.81	4.92	5.01	5.10	5.18	5.25	5.32	5.38	5.44	5.50	5.54	5.59
30	2.89	3.49	3.84	4.10	4.30	4.46	4.60	4.72	4.83	4.92	5.00	5.08	5.15	5.21	5.27	5.33	5.38	5.43	5.48
40	2.86	3.44	3.79	4.04	4.23	4.39	4.52	4.63	4.74	4.82	4.91	4.98	5.05	5.11	5.16	5.22	5.27	5.31	5.36
60	2.83	3.40	3.74	3.98	4.16	4.31	4.44	4.55	4.65	4.73	4.81	4.88	4.94	5.00	5.06	5.11	5.16	5.20	5.24
120	2.80	3.36	3.69	3.92	4.10	4.24	4.36	4.48	4.56	5.64	4.72	4.78	4.84	4.90	4.95	5.00	5.05	5.09	5.13
∞	2.77	3.31	3.63	3.86	4.03	4.17	4.29	4.39	4.47	4.55	4.62	4.68	4.74	4.80	4.85	4.89	4.93	4.97	5.01

APPENDIX TABLE 7 DISTRIBUTION OF THE STUDENTIZED RANGE (Cont.)*

$p = .99$

ν_2 \ ν_1	2	3	4	5	6	7	8	9	10	11	12	13	14	15	16	17	18	19	20
1	90.0	135	164	186	202	216	227	237	246	253	260	266	272	277	282	286	290	294	298
2	14.0	19.0	22.3	24.7	26.6	28.2	29.5	30.7	31.7	32.6	33.4	34.1	34.8	35.4	36.0	36.5	37.0	37.5	37.9
3	8.26	10.6	12.2	13.3	14.2	15.0	15.6	16.2	16.7	17.1	17.5	17.9	18.2	18.5	18.8	19.1	19.3	19.5	19.8
4	6.51	8.12	9.17	9.96	10.6	11.1	11.5	11.9	12.3	12.6	12.8	13.1	13.3	13.5	13.7	13.9	14.1	14.2	14.4
5	5.70	6.97	7.80	8.42	8.91	9.32	9.67	9.97	10.24	10.48	10.70	10.89	11.08	11.24	11.40	11.55	11.68	11.81	11.93
6	5.24	6.33	7.03	7.56	7.97	8.32	8.61	8.87	9.10	9.30	9.49	9.65	9.81	9.95	10.08	10.21	10.32	10.43	10.54
7	4.95	5.92	6.54	7.01	7.37	7.68	7.94	8.17	8.37	8.55	8.71	8.86	9.00	9.12	9.24	9.35	9.46	9.55	9.65
8	4.74	5.63	6.20	6.63	6.96	7.24	7.47	7.68	7.87	8.03	8.18	8.31	8.44	8.55	8.66	8.76	8.85	8.94	9.03
9	4.60	5.43	5.96	6.35	6.66	6.91	7.13	7.32	7.49	7.65	7.78	7.91	8.03	8.13	8.25	8.32	8.41	8.49	8.57
10	4.48	5.27	5.77	6.14	6.43	6.67	6.87	7.05	7.21	7.36	7.48	7.60	7.71	7.81	7.91	7.99	8.07	8.15	8.22
11	4.39	5.14	5.62	5.97	6.25	6.48	6.67	6.84	6.99	7.13	7.25	7.36	7.46	7.56	7.65	7.73	7.81	7.88	7.95
12	4.32	5.04	5.50	5.84	6.10	6.32	6.51	6.67	6.81	6.94	7.06	7.17	7.26	7.36	7.44	7.52	7.59	7.66	7.73
13	4.26	4.96	5.40	5.73	5.98	6.19	6.37	6.53	6.67	6.79	6.90	7.01	7.10	7.19	7.27	7.34	7.42	7.48	7.55
14	4.21	4.89	5.32	5.63	5.88	6.08	6.26	6.41	6.54	6.66	6.77	6.87	6.96	7.05	7.12	7.20	7.27	7.33	7.39
15	4.17	4.83	5.25	5.56	5.80	5.99	6.16	6.31	6.44	6.55	6.66	6.76	6.84	6.93	7.00	7.07	7.14	7.20	7.26
16	4.13	4.78	5.19	5.49	5.72	5.92	6.08	6.22	6.35	6.46	6.56	6.66	6.74	6.82	6.90	6.97	7.03	7.09	7.15
17	4.10	4.74	5.14	5.43	5.66	5.85	6.01	6.15	6.27	6.38	6.48	6.57	6.66	6.73	6.80	6.87	6.94	7.00	7.05
18	4.07	4.70	5.09	5.38	5.60	5.79	5.94	6.08	6.20	6.31	6.41	6.50	6.58	6.65	6.72	6.79	6.85	6.91	6.96
19	4.05	4.67	5.05	5.33	5.55	5.73	5.89	6.02	6.14	6.25	6.34	6.43	6.51	6.58	6.65	6.72	6.78	6.84	6.89
20	4.02	4.64	5.02	5.29	5.51	5.69	5.84	5.97	6.09	6.19	6.29	6.37	6.45	6.52	6.59	6.65	6.71	6.76	6.82
24	3.96	4.54	4.91	5.17	5.37	5.54	5.69	5.81	5.92	6.02	6.11	6.19	6.26	6.33	6.39	6.45	6.51	6.56	6.61
30	3.89	4.45	4.80	5.05	5.24	5.40	5.54	5.65	5.76	5.85	5.93	6.01	6.08	6.14	6.20	6.26	6.31	6.36	6.41
40	3.82	4.37	4.70	4.93	5.11	5.27	5.39	5.50	5.60	5.69	5.77	5.84	5.90	5.96	6.02	6.07	6.12	6.17	6.21
60	3.76	4.28	4.60	4.82	4.99	5.13	5.25	5.36	5.45	5.53	5.60	5.67	5.73	5.79	5.84	5.89	5.93	5.98	6.02
120	3.70	4.20	4.50	4.71	4.87	5.01	5.12	5.21	5.30	5.38	5.44	5.51	5.56	5.61	5.66	5.71	5.75	5.79	5.83
∞	3.64	4.11	4.40	4.60	4.76	4.88	4.99	5.08	5.16	5.23	5.29	5.35	5.40	5.45	5.49	5.54	5.57	5.61	5.65

* Reprinted with permission from E. S. Pearson and H. O. Hartley, *Biometrika Tables for Statisticians* (New York: Cambridge University Press, 1954).

Index